HYPERSTATIC STRUCTURES

Volume II

HYPERSTATIC STRUCTURES

AN INTRODUCTION TO THE THEORY OF STATICALLY INDETERMINATE STRUCTURES

VOLUME II

containing worked examples and examples for solution

J. A. L. MATHESON

M.B.E., M.Sc., Ph.D., M.C.E., M.I.C.E., M.I.Struct.E., M.I.E.Aust.

Vice-Chancellor, Monash University, Victoria

and

A. J. FRANCIS

M.Sc., Ph.D., M.C.E., M.I.C.E., M.I.Struct.E., M.I.E.Aust.

Professor of Civil Engineering, University of Melbourne

With Chapters by

N. W. MURRAY   *and*   R. K. LIVESLEY
B.E., Ph.D.   M.A., Ph.D.

LONDON

BUTTERWORTHS SCIENTIFIC PUBLICATIONS

1960

BUTTERWORTHS PUBLICATIONS LTD
88 KINGSWAY, LONDON, W.C.2

AFRICA: BUTTERWORTH & CO. (AFRICA) LTD
               DURBAN: 33/45 Beach Grove

AUSTRALIA: BUTTERWORTH & CO. (AUSTRALIA) LTD
               SYDNEY: 8 O'Connell Street
               MELBOURNE: 430 Bourke Street
               BRISBANE: 240 Queen Street

CANADA: BUTTERWORTH & CO. (CANADA) LTD
               TORONTO: 1367 Danforth Avenue

NEW ZEALAND: BUTTERWORTH & CO. (AUSTRALIA) LTD
               WELLINGTON: 49/51 Ballance Street
               AUCKLAND: 35 High Street

U.S.A. Edition published by
ACADEMIC PRESS INC., PUBLISHERS
111 FIFTH AVENUE
NEW YORK 3, NEW YORK

©
Butterworth & Co. (Publishers) Ltd.
1960

Set in Monotype Baskerville type
Made and Printed in Great Britain by The Aberdeen University Press

PREFACE

IN Volume I the attempt was made to present the theory of hyperstatic structures in a systematic manner so that the relationship of the various theorems to each other could be clearly seen. Although the number of fundamental theorems is not very large they have been applied to different types of structure in so many ways that the subject is apt to strike the student as being unsystematic or even chaotic. This difficulty can only be resolved by emphasizing that all the methods depend, in the last resort, on the solution, either exactly or by successive approximations, of a sufficient number of equations of equilibrium and compatibility. The *order* in which these equations are set up distinguishes the so-called compatibility methods from the equilibrium methods.

The conceptions of complementary and strain energy can be employed with great effect in formulating the equations in a convenient manner. Engesser and Castigliano, respectively, showed that variations of the complementary and strain energies can be used to find deflexions and so to derive the compatibility equations in a way which, when viewed in isolation, seems to amount to an independent theorem of great power and versatility. Castigliano's Theorem of Least Work, as he called it, has often been so treated in previous text books, but in Volume I, under the title of Castigliano's Theorem of Compatibility, it is given its proper place in the scheme of things. The classification of the various energy theorems is facilitated by discussing their applicability to linear and non-linear structures respectively.

The present volume is supplementary to Volume I in the sense that a large number of examples is presented in order to give the student practice in applying the theorems to suitably chosen problems. The theory has not been expounded again in full but, for the most part, each section is prefaced by one or more examples, usually more complex than their counterparts in Volume I. The order of presentation is much the same in the two volumes although it has been found convenient, here and there, to follow a different sequence in the present volume.

It is sometimes urged, by critics of textbooks consisting mainly of examples, that it is bad for students to spend much time working examination-type problems as this is all too likely to make them good at passing examinations but bad at real life. This view, the authors believe, confuses the study of engineering science with the practice of engineering in which science and art are interwoven. The extent to which the art of engineering should find a place in the curricula of universities and technical colleges is often a matter of hot debate, and different solutions are current. This is no place for further argument on a fascinating and important topic; the authors content themselves with asserting their view that a thorough knowledge of engineering science is essential for the practising engineer. Their aim in the present volume is to help the student to a sound knowledge of the theory of structures; they do not attempt here the more difficult task of relating structural analysis to the creative processes of which the structural engineer must also be master.

PREFACE

The authors wish to express their gratitude to Dr. N. W. Murray and Dr. R. K. Livesley, who have each contributed a chapter; to the Registrars of a number of universities for permission to reproduce examination questions; to Dr. K. G. Moody, Dr. J. G. Nutt, Dr. L. K. Stevens and Dr. K. F. Tse who have helped to check the calculations; and to Mrs. Betty Kemp who typed the manuscript.

It is too much much to expect that errors can be completely eliminated from a book of this nature and the authors would be grateful to have their attention drawn to any that readers detect.

CONTENTS

CONTENTS

LIST OF SYMBOLS

The following list records the symbols used generally in the text. Certain symbols, especially those specific to quoted examination questions, are omitted: they are defined where they appear.

A	Cross-sectional area of member. Elastic weight of arch
A_m	Area of bending moment diagram
C	Complementary energy. Constant of integration. General matrix
D	General displacement vector
E	Young's modulus
F	Axial force in member. General force vector
F_y	Load to cause yield over whole of member section
G	Modulus of rigidity. Transfer matrix
H	Horizontal component of reaction
I	Second moment of area
J	Second polar moment of area
K	I/L. Coefficient. Angular stiffness of spiral spring
L	Length of member
M	Bending moment
M_p	Plastic moment of resistance
M_p'	Plastic moment of resistance modified by axial load
N	Modulus of rigidity. Twisting moment
P	External load
P_E	Euler load
Q	Shearing force
R	Reaction. Radius of curvature. Resultant
S	Sway correction
T	Thrust. Twisting couple. Total stiffness at joint $= \Sigma sk$
	Coordinate transformation matrix
U	Strain energy
V	Potential energy. Vertical component of reaction
W	Elastic 'load' on arch. External load
W_c	Critical load
X	Redundant force
Y	Redundant reaction (arch). Stiffness matrix
Z	Redundant couple (arch). Section modulus
a	Dimension of length. Cross-sectional area of member
b	Dimension of length
c	Dimension of length. Carry-over function
d	Increment (as a prefix). Dimension of length
e	Change of length of member
f	Direct stress. Function
f_y	Yield stress
g	Gusset plate length
h	Vertical dimension. Rise of arch

i	Slope
j	Number of joints in frame
k	Coefficient. Axial stiffness. EI/L
m	Number of members in frame. Coefficient in beam-line method. Sway function
n	Degree of redundancy. Coefficient in beam-line method
p	Stiffness coefficient
q	Shearing stress
r	Number of reactive restraints
s	Dimension of length, especially along arch rib. Model scale. Stiffness function
t	Change of temperature. Tension coefficient
w	Uniformly distributed load per unit length
x	Coordinate. Displacement
y	Coordinate. Distance from central axis of beam. Ordinate to arch axis. Displacement
z	Coordinate
α	Angle. Coefficient
α_i	Coefficient of linear thermal expansion
β	Numerical deflexion coefficient
δ	Displacement. Increment
$\varDelta$	Deflexion
ϵ	Unit change of length. Strain
θ	Angle. Angular rotation
κ	Coefficient of shearing deflexion
λ	Lack of fit. Axial stiffness of helical spring
μ	Moment of elastic 'load'
ρ	L/AE. Extensibility
ϕ	Angular distortion. δ/L. Effective load
ψ	Angle

SUFFIXES AND INDICES

δ_A^B	Displacement of A from the tangent B
$\varDelta_{ab}$	Displacement of point A caused by unit load at point B. Flexibility coefficient
η_i	Value of moment M_i at centroid of M_k diagram
F_a, F_b	Force in member of primary structure caused by force $X_A = 1$, $X_B = 1$
F_o	Force in member of primary structure caused by actual loading
F'	Force in member of framework caused by specified unit load
M_{AB}	Bending moment at end A of member AB
M_{FAB}	Fixing moment at end A of fixed ended beam AB
M_o	Bending moment produced in primary structure by actual loading
M_{SAB}	Sway correction moment
M'	Bending moment produced by specified unit load
$\left.\begin{array}{l} p_{xxA} \\ p_{xyA} \end{array}\right\}$	Stiffness coefficients at joint A

P_i — Imaginary external load

$\overline{P,F}$ — External loads and corresponding bar forces of the force system used in Mohr's equation of virtual work

T_{U_3} — $\sum sk$ for all members connected to joint U_3

T_{ar} — $\sum sk$ for joint adjacent to critical joint

X_a, X_b — Quasi-external forces or moments acting in place of redundants

Numerical Values

The following values of elastic and other constants have been used in numerical examples unless otherwise stated.

Modulus of elasticity E	Steel	30×10^6 lb./in.^{2}
	Brass	16×10^6 lb./in.^{2}
	Concrete	5×10^6 lb./in.^{2}
Coefficient of linear expansion α_t		6×10^{-6} per °F
Density	Steel	490 lb./cub. ft.

References to Volume I

Equations numbers in square brackets are quoted from Volume I.

CHAPTER 1

HYPERSTATIC STRUCTURES:
PRELIMINARY CONSIDERATIONS

1.1. INTRODUCTION

THE first step in the process of determining the behaviour of a hyperstatic or statically indeterminate structure under load or other stress-inducing agency is to decide how many redundant members or reactive restraints it possesses. Often this can be done by removing internal forces or external reactions until the structure is 'cut back' to a recognizably determinate form—the 'primary structure'.

If a cut is made in a member subjected to axial forces and bending moments, as in a plane rigid unbraced frame (FIGURE 1.1(a) and (b)), the degree of redundancy of the structure is reduced by three, since the resultant force at the cut section is equivalent in general to a horizontal and a vertical

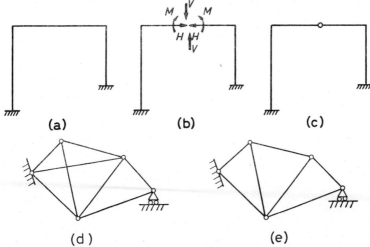

(a) (b) (c)

(d) (e)

FIGURE 1.1. (a) The plane portal frame has three redundants. (b) The degree of redundancy is reduced by three when a cut is made in one member, i.e. the frame is made determinate. (c) The degree of redundancy is reduced by one when a hinge is introduced. (d) This plane pin-jointed frame has one redundant member. (e) Removal of a suitable member makes the frame determinate.

component of force and a couple; if a hinge is inserted in such a position (FIGURE 1.1(c)) only one redundant (a moment) is removed. In a pin-jointed braced framework (FIGURE 1.1(d)), removal of one member (FIGURE 1.1(e)) is normally equivalent to lessening the redundancy by one.

At a point of support of a plane structure (FIGURE 1.2) there may be three, two or one reactive restraints present, depending on whether the support is fixed, pinned or on rollers. The degree of redundancy of the structure may thus be reduced by one by the process of (say) converting a fixed support to a pinned one, or by removing a roller support.

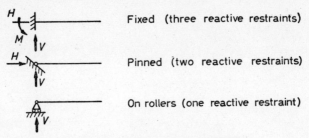

Fixed (three reactive restraints)

Pinned (two reactive restraints)

On rollers (one reactive restraint)

FIGURE 1.2. Supports of plane structures.

Such a process is one of trial and error, yet is often an effective means of investigating degrees of redundancy. Not uncommonly, however, the structure is too complicated for this and a more rigorous approach is required. In Volume I, Chapter 1, rules for investigating the redundancy of various types of structure are derived, and the examples which follow illustrate their use, as well as the process of trial and error.

1.2. PIN-JOINTED STRUCTURES

1.2.1. PLANE FRAMES

The condition for determinacy of any plane pin-jointed framework is expressed in equation [1.3]†

$$m + r = 2j \qquad \qquad \dots \ [1.3]$$

where m = number of members

               r = number of reactive restraints

and j = number of joints including those at which the framework is supported.

Problem 1.1—As our first example we take the framework illustrated. Applying the above equation, we have

$$m = 22, r = 3, j = 12$$

so that

$$m + r = 22 + 3 = 25 = 2j + 1$$

PROBLEM 1.1

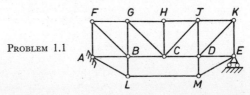

The structure is therefore once indeterminate internally. By inspection, if *LM* were removed the remaining framework would be essentially a Pratt-type truss with

---

† Equation numbers in square brackets are quoted from Volume I.

two triangular appendages *ALB* and *DME*. Alternatively, it could be rendered determinate by removing any other single bar of the bracing system *ALBMDE*. As far as its conditions of support are concerned, however, the structure is determinate.

Problem 1.2—In this case, applying the condition

$$m + r = 2j,$$

we have

$$m = 9, r = 4, j = 6$$

so that

$$m + r = 9 + 4 = 13 = 2j + 1$$

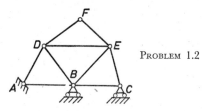

PROBLEM 1.2

The structure is again once indeterminate. In contradistinction to the truss of *Problem 1.1*, however, it could be rendered determinate either by removing one reactive restraint, that at *B* or at *C* for example, or by removing one member, *DE* for example. This framework can therefore be regarded as once indeterminate either internally or externally. The reader should notice that equation [1.3] gives no guidance as to *which* member is redundant and should consider the effect of removing members *AB*, *DB* or *DF*.

Problems *1.1* and *1.2* are both on *simple* frameworks; each joint is located by two bars, the starting point being a single triangle.

Problem 1.3—This is a situation that could arise during the construction of an arch bridge. The part arch *AEJD* is supported by a prop at *J* and by stays at *E* and *G* attaching it to the temporary structure *LMK*.

PROBLEM 1.3

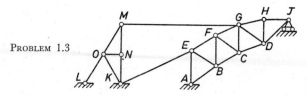

If the two stays *MG* and *KE* were removed the remaining structures would be determinate. The complete framework is therefore twice indeterminate, externally if the part-arch is regarded as the essential structure, or internally if all the bars shown are regarded as part of the structure. In the latter case, we have an example of a *compound* framework, composed of two statically determinate simple frames (*LMK* and *AEJD*) braced together.

Applying the determinacy condition again,

$m = 23, r = 7$ (two reactive restraints at *L*, *K* and *A* and one at *J*)

$j = 14$

$m + r = 30 = 2j + 2$

The structure has therefore two degrees of indeterminacy, as we saw above.

3

Problem 1.4—This is a *complex* framework, i.e. one which is neither *simple* nor *compound* (see preceding examples). In this case,

$$m = 17, r = 3, j = 10$$
$$\therefore\ m + r = 20 = 2j$$

and the structure is statically determinate.

PROBLEM 1.4

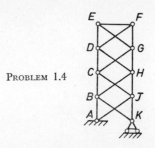

Problems for Solution

1.5. Examine the sufficiency of bracing for the plane frames shown. Where the frame is deficient sketch a suitable arrangement of bars to make good the deficiency and if more bars are used than necessary state which could be removed.

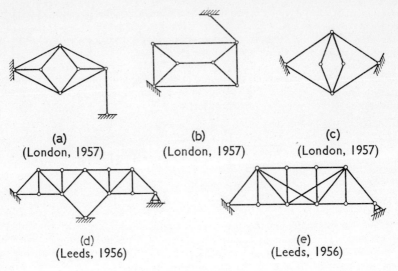

| (a) | (b) | (c) |
| (London, 1957) | (London, 1957) | (London, 1957) |

| (d) | (e) |
| (Leeds, 1956) | (Leeds, 1956) |

PROBLEM 1.5

1.6. Investigate the plane frames shown classifying them as simple, compound or complex. State in each case whether the frame is deficient, statically determinate or hyperstatic. If it is deficient, indicate how it can be made determinate, and if hyperstatic the degree of indeterminacy. Some of the frameworks are simplified versions of actual structures of unusual design: thus 1.6(1) represents the Olympic Swimming Pool at Melbourne, and 1.6(z) Brunel's Saltash Bridge.

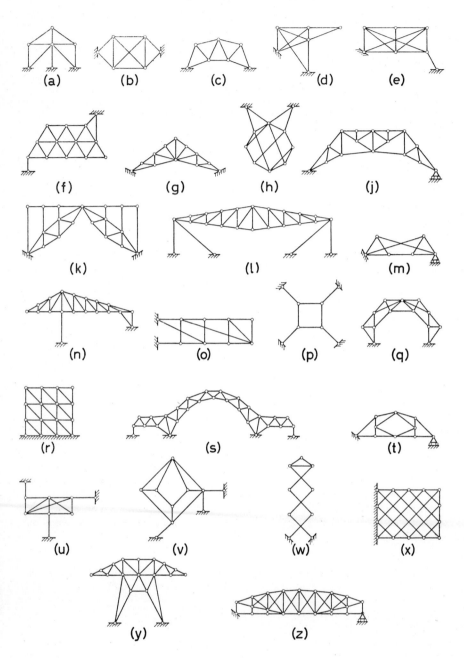

PROBLEM 1.6

1.2.2. SPACE FRAMES

The condition of determinacy for space pin-jointed frames is given by equation [1.5]:

$$m + r = 3j \qquad \qquad \dots \ [1.5]$$

Problem 1.7—This structure is attached to a rigid base at A, D and F by means of universal joints. Applying equation [1.5], we have:

$$m = 10, \ r = 9 \ (3 \text{ at each support}), j = 6,$$

so that

$$m + r = 19 = 3j + 1$$

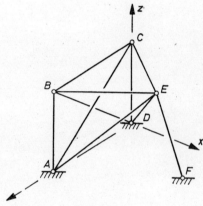

PROBLEM 1.7

This structure is therefore once indeterminate. Various members could be chosen as the redundant, BD or AC for example. Others could not: for example, if BE were removed B could move in the x-direction. One of the reactive restraints at A or D could also be regarded as the redundant quantity.

This framework illustrates one way in which a space frame can be constructed, namely by starting from a rigid base and locating each joint in space by a group of three bars.

Problem 1.8—This framework consists of two tetrahedra $AEFB$ and $ACDB$ having one common side, AB, and braced together by two additional bars, EC, FD. It is simply supported by a universal joint at B, a roller at C constrained to move only in one specified direction, and a roller at D constrained to move in one specified plane.

In this case:

$$m = 13, \ r = 6, j = 6$$

from which

$$m + r = 19 = 3j + 1,$$

so that the structure has one redundant member, which may conveniently be taken as EC or FD.

This example shows one way in which a space frame may be built up by combining tetrahedra, which are the simplest self-contained space structures and are analogous in three dimensions to the triangle in plane frames.

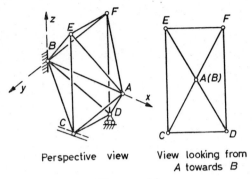

Perspective view   View looking from
                          A towards B

PROBLEM 1.8

Problem 1.9—This illustrates a further way in which tetrahedra can be combined, giving a frame *ABDEHG* which is useful for bridge or roof construction. It is pinned to a rigid base *PQRST* by 7 bars.

We have here: $m = 25, \ r = 5 \times 3 = 15, \ j = 13$

Hence $m + r = 40 = 3j + 1$

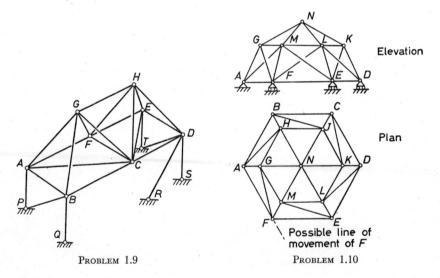

PROBLEM 1.9   PROBLEM 1.10

so that this frame is once redundant. A suitable redundant could be the bar *ET*. Note that the corner *E* thus needs no support.

Problems for Solution

1.10. In the domical framework illustrated, *A* is a universal joint, *F* a roller constrained to move only along the line *AF*, and the other 4 points *B*, *C*, *D* and *E* are freely supported in the horizontal plane through *A*. Show that the frame is statically determinate.

(Leeds, 1953)

1.11. Examine the frames shown, indicating in each case whether it is deficient, determinate or hyperstatic. If deficient state how it could be made determinate, and if hyperstatic the degree of indeterminacy and indicate which restraints or bars could be removed.

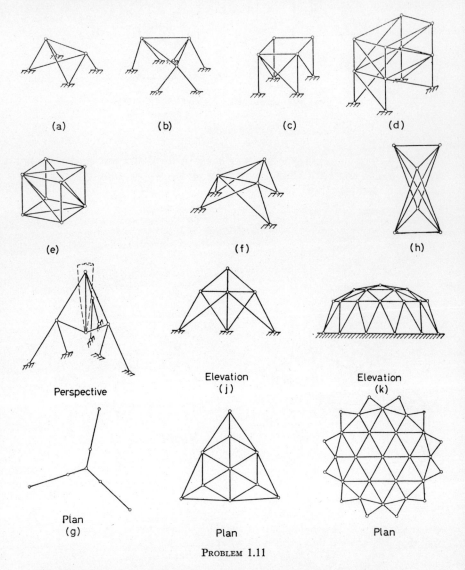

PROBLEM 1.11

Note. Frames (e) and (h) are assumed to be supported in a statically determinate manner. Frame (g) represents schematically the Skylon at the South Bank Exhibition, 1951.

1.3. RIGIDLY JOINTED AND COMPOSITE PIN- AND RIGIDLY JOINTED FRAMES

1.3.1. RIGIDLY JOINTED FRAMES

Equation [1.6] may be used to examine the determinacy of rigidly jointed frames:

$$n = 3m + r - 3j \qquad \ldots [1.6]$$

where n is the number of redundants.

Problem 1.12—For this roof structure,

$$m = 6, \quad r = 6, \quad i = 7$$

so that $\qquad n = 3$

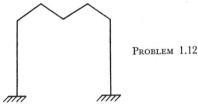

PROBLEM 1.12

The frame could be made determinate by freeing one end for example, or by inserting hinges at three non-collinear points. Any legitimate approach will involve the removal of three reactive restraints or internal forces.

Problem 1.13—In this case: $\quad m = 18, \quad r = 8$ (including 2 at the pin), $\quad j = 14$, giving $\qquad n = 20$

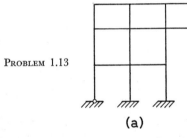

PROBLEM 1.13

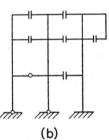

(a)   (b)

The frame could be converted into a cantilever and a three-hinged **arch** by cutting and inserting hinges as shown at (b); this involves the removal of

$$6 \times 3 + 2 \times 1 = 20 \text{ internal forces.}$$

Problem 1.14—Here we have: $\quad m = 10, \quad r = 6, \quad j = 9$

if we regard the curved roof members as single members. Hence $n = 9$

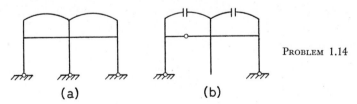

(a)   (b)

PROBLEM 1.14

The reader should satisfy himself that 1.14(b) represents a valid method of 'cutting back' to a statically determinate structure.

Problems for Solution

1.15.—State the degree of redundancy of each of the frames shown, indicating in each case one way in which the frame may be reduced to a statically determinate structure.

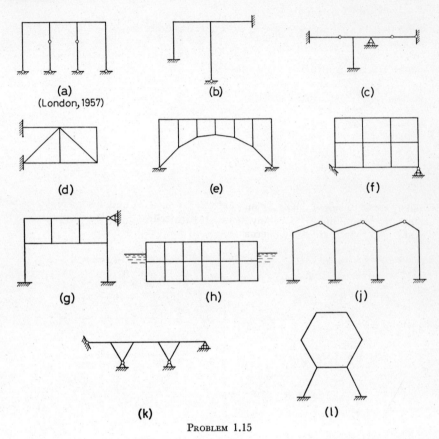

(a)
(London, 1957)

(b)

(c)

(d)

(e)

(f)

(g)

(h)

(j)

(k)

(l)

PROBLEM 1.15

1.3.2. COMPOSITE FRAMES

Composite pin- and rigidly jointed frames may be investigated for determinacy by the general equation [1.7]

$$n = m_1 + 2m_2 + 3m_3 + r_1 + 2r_2 + 3r_3 - j_1 - 2j_2 - 3j_3 \quad \cdots \cdot [1.7]$$

where the various terms have the following connotations.

n = number of redundants

m_1 = number of members with both ends pinned, or number of members with one end fixed and other end sliding

m_2 = number of members with one end fixed and other end pinned

m_3 = number of members with both ends fixed

r_1 = number of roller supports

r_2 = number of hinged supports

r_3 = number of fixed supports

10

j_1 = number of sliding joints
j_2 = number of pinned supports
j_3 = number of rigid supports

Problem 1.16—In this braced beam, the members AB and BC can both be regarded as pinned at one end and fixed at the other.
Thus
$$m_1 = 5, \quad m_2 = 2, \quad m_3 = 0$$
There is one hinged support A and one roller support C, so that
$$r_1 = 1, \quad r_2 = 1, \quad r_3 = 0$$
Four of the joints (A, D, E and C) are pinned, and B is fixed. Hence
$$j_1 = 0, \quad j_2 = 4, \quad j_3 = 1$$
Substitution in the formula then gives $n = 1$.

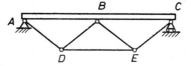

PROBLEM 1.16

Alternatively, we can easily see that the structure could be made determinate either by removing one of the bracing members or by providing a pin in the beam at B. In either case one unknown stress component is removed, so that the structure is once redundant.

Problems for Solution

1.17. Investigate the composite structures shown for determinacy.

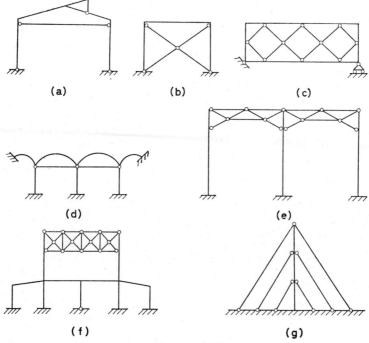

(a)   (b)   (c)

(d)   (e)

(f)   (g)

PROBLEM 1.17

1.4. ANALYSIS OF SIMPLE HYPERSTATIC STRUCTURES FROM CONSIDERATIONS OF GEOMETRICAL COMPATIBILITY

The parts of any hyperstatic structure must fit together both before and after it has been subjected to load. This basic fact can be used to analyse simple structures. The method is explained in Volume I [Chapter 1, Section 1.3] and illustrated by two examples. Four further problems are examined below.

Problem 1.18—In this frame the members AB and BC are elastic and each has a cross-sectional area a, while BD is rigid. Find the force in AB.

Since two bars suffice to locate the joint B in the plane of the frame, and three bars are present, the structure is once redundant. Let X be the force in bar AB.

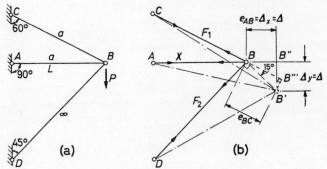

PROBLEM 1.18. (a) It is required to find the forces in the members of this hyperstatic framework. (b) The only joint which is free to move, B, is shown in a displaced position B'. BB' is perpendicular to DB, which is rigid.

There are three unknown bar forces and therefore three independent equations are needed. Two equations may be written from a consideration of the equilibrium of joint B, by resolving horizontally and vertically:

$$F_1 \frac{\sqrt{3}}{2} + \frac{F_2}{\sqrt{2}} + X = 0 \qquad \text{.... (i)}$$

$$\frac{F_1}{2} - \frac{F_2}{\sqrt{2}} - P = 0 \qquad \text{.... (ii)}$$

In deriving these equations we assume that all the bar forces are tensile.

A third equation may be obtained from the fact that the three members must fit together at B in the deformed condition of the frame (1.18(b)). It is helpful to imagine that this deformed state is reached in a series of simple steps.

Since BD is rigid its end B will move perpendicularly to the direction BD to some position B'. The end B of bar AB may be visualized as attaining the position B' by first moving horizontally to B'' and then swinging vertically downwards to B'. Similarly, the end of B of bar BC will fit in with these movements by moving in the direction BC to B''' and then swinging at right angles to BC to reach B'.

These displacements are shown at (b). Evidently,

$$e_{BC} = BB'.\cos 15° = e_{AB} \sqrt{2}.\cos 15° \qquad \text{,.... (iii)}$$

12

But

$$e_{BC} = \frac{F_1}{aE} \frac{2L}{\sqrt{3}}$$

and

$$e_{AB} = \frac{XL}{aE}$$

Substituting in (iii), we have:

$$F_1 = X \frac{\sqrt{3}}{\sqrt{2}} \cos 15° = 1·18\, X \qquad \dots\ (\text{iv})$$

This is the third equation. Equations (i), (ii) and (iv) yield, on solution,

$$X = 0·382P$$

The forces F_1 and F_2 can now be found from equations (ii) and (iv).

Now let us suppose that the bar AB follows a non-linear load–extension law, as follows:

$$e = \frac{L}{aE}\left(F - \frac{F^2}{4aE}\right)$$

while the elastic properties of BC and BD remain as before.

Equations (i) and (ii), being equations of equilibrium of the joint B, still apply. Equation (iii) also holds, since it follows from the geometry of deformation of the structure and was derived without reference to the elastic properties of the members.

Then, as before,

$$e_{BC} = \frac{F_1}{aE} \cdot \frac{2L}{\sqrt{3}}$$

while

$$e_{AB} = \frac{L}{aE}\left(X - \frac{X^2}{4aE}\right)$$

Substituting in (iii), we have:

$$X - \frac{X^2}{4aE} = F_1 \frac{\sqrt{2}}{\sqrt{3}\,\cos 15°} = 0·846\, F_1 \qquad \dots\ (\text{iv}')$$

Equations (i), (ii) and (iv′) lead to the equation

$$\frac{X^2}{4aE} - 1·62X + 0·62P = 0$$

from which

$$X = aE\left(3·24 \pm 2\sqrt{2·62 - \frac{0·62P}{aE}}\right)$$

There are thus two possible values of X for the same value of P. This arises from the fact that AB has a parabolic load–extension law so that each value of its extension corresponds to alternative values of the load in it. This means that when AB and CBD are considered in combination the requirements of compatibility and equilibrium can be satisfied by two different values of the load in AB. It will usually be found, however, that in problems of this kind only one solution is significant.

In the present instance it can be seen that with reasonable values of aE only the negative value of the square root need be considered.

Problem 1.19—As a second example of the use of geometrical compatibility we consider the continuous beam *ABCDE*, of uniform cross-section and supported at *B*, *C* and *D* on unyielding supports.

(a) If it is loaded by two equal loads *P* at *A* and *E*, find the reaction at *C*.

(b) Find also what uniformly distributed load *w* per unit length placed over the span *BCD* would reduce the reaction at *C* to zero.

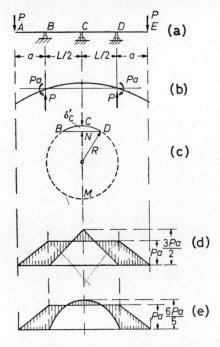

PROBLEM 1.19. (a) This beam has one redundant reaction at *C*. (b) When this support is removed the couples *Pa* bend *BD* into a circular curve. (c) The deflexion of *C* can be found from the geometry of the circle *BCDM*. (d) The resultant bending moment diagram. (e) When a uniformly distributed load of $48Pa/5L^2$ per unit length is applied over *BCD* the reaction at *C* is reduced to zero and the bending moment diagram is as shown.

(a) There are four reactive forces (two at the pin *B* and one each at *C* and *D*) and in general three equations of equilibrium can be written, so that the structure is once redundant. We select R_C, the reaction at *C*, as the unknown quantity. (It is always wise to choose unknowns so that symmetry is maintained, if this is possible; much more work would be entailed in reaching a solution were R_D to be taken instead of R_C.)

Imagine the support *C* to be removed (1.19(b)). The loads *P* are equivalent to couples *Pa*, at *B* and *D*, which bend the span *BCD* in a circular arc (1.19(c) shows this to a reduced scale). The radius of curvature of this arc is $R = \dfrac{EI}{M} = \dfrac{EI}{Pa}$, where *I* is the second moment of area of the section of the beam.

Now
$$CN \times NM = BN \times ND$$

or

$$\delta'_C (2R - \delta'_C) = \left(\frac{L}{2}\right)^2$$

or, if δ'_C is small compared with *R*,

$$\delta'_C = \frac{L^2}{8R} = \frac{PaL^2}{8EI}$$

14

We now introduce R_C. This causes a downward deflexion δ_C'' at C equal to $\dfrac{R_C L^3}{48EI}$, and since no deflexion actually occurs at C we can equate upward and downward deflexions δ_C' and δ_C'', thus:

$$\frac{PaL^2}{8EI} = \frac{R_C L^3}{48EI}$$

giving

$$R_c = \frac{6Pa}{L} \text{ (downwards)},$$

The resultant bending moment diagram is shown in 1.19(d).

(b) Perhaps the simplest way of solving this part of the problem is to remove the support C, apply the loads P and then find what value of the uniformly distributed load would reduce the deflexion at C to zero. If the support C is now restored, no reaction will come into play.

The deflexion δ_C''' due to the U.D. load is $\dfrac{5wL^4}{384EI}$ and equating δ_C''' and δ_C',

we have:

$$\frac{5wL^4}{384EI} = \frac{PaL^2}{8EI}$$

giving

$$w = \frac{48Pa}{5L^2}$$

The bending moment diagram is shown in 1·19 (e).

Problem 1.20—A rigid table top is supported by four legs A, B, C and D ot equal length and cross-section. A vertical load P acts as shown. Find the force in leg D.

Let each leg shorten by an amount $F\rho$, where F is the force in the leg, and ρ is its compressibility (compression per unit load).

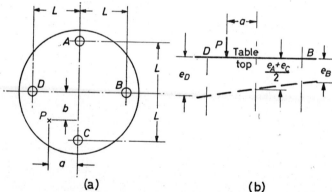

PROBLEM 1.20. (a) The rigid top table shown in plan is supported by four identical legs at A, B, C and D. A load P acts at the point shown. (b) Cross-section along the line DB showing the table top in its displaced position.

There are four unknowns and therefore four independent equations are necessary. Three may be derived from statics, as follows. Let A, B, etc., denote the forces in the several legs.

Resolving vertically for the equilibrium of the table,

$$A + B + C + D - P = 0 \qquad \cdots \text{ (i)}$$

15

Taking moments about the line AC,

$$BL - DL + Pa = 0 \qquad \qquad \dots \text{(ii)}$$

Taking moments about the line BD,

$$AL - CL + Pb = 0 \qquad \qquad \dots \text{(iii)}$$

The final equation is derived from a consideration of the deformation of the various legs. A little study of 1.20(b) will show that along the direction BD

$$e_D = e_A + e_C - e_B$$

i.e.

$$e_D = D\rho = A\rho + C\rho - B\rho$$

or

$$A - B + C - D = 0 \qquad \qquad \dots \text{(iv)}$$

Solving equations (i) to (iv), we have:

$$D = \frac{P}{4}\left(1 + \frac{2a}{L}\right)$$

The forces in the other legs can now be calculated from statics, using equations (i) to (iii).

An Alternative Method of Solution—The load P is equivalent to:

  (a) a central load P
  (b) a moment Pa about AC
  (c) a moment Pb about BD

In (a), each leg is equally loaded with $P/4$.
In (b), taking moments about AC, we have, for the effect of the moment Pa:

$$D \times 2L = Pa$$

or

$$D = \frac{Pa}{2L}$$

In (c) the moment Pb about BD produces no load in D. Hence the resultant load in D is

$$D = \frac{P}{4} + \frac{Pa}{2L}$$

as before.

It will be noted that this solution does not involve a consideration of deformations. The reason for this rather unusual situation is that when the total effect of P is separated out as above, it so happens that the loads in the legs due to the separate effects are statically determinate.

The reader might well consider why this is so, and ask himself if the same situation would arise if the legs were not identical.

Problem 1.21—A mast ABC, of uniform cross-section, is supported by two pairs of steel guy wires in the plane shown, and by similar pairs of guys at right angles to this plane. The guys illustrated are pretensioned so that when a wind force w per unit length acts on the mast the leeward stays BF, CG just remain in tension. Find the required cross-sectional areas of the guys on the following assumptions:

  (a) that sag in the guys is ignored,
  (b) that the mast deflects under wind so that A, B and C remain collinear, and C moves a horizontal distance $L/100$.
  (c) that the mast is regarded as incompressible.

Since the wind may blow from the right or the left, the cross-sectional areas of the two wires in each pair of guys should be equal.

Now consider the behaviour of the mast under the action of the wind. It is supported at A, B and C, the resultant reaction due to the wind at each point being

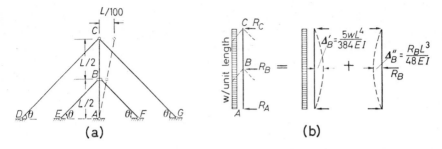

(a)   (b)

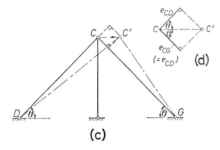

(c)

(d)

PROBLEM 1.21. (a) The mast ABC is to be supported by prestressed guys of such a size that the displacement is linear. (b) The horizontal component of the force in the guys EB and BF is taken as the redundant; the mast is considered under this load and under the wind load separately. (c) and (d) Compatibility relationships at the mast head.

horizontal. Turning to diagram (b) we see that the mast acts as a beam with one redundant reaction, which may be taken as R_B. Since there is no deflexion of the mast at B relative to the line AC, it follows that the deformation Δ'_B due to the wind when R_B is removed is equal to the deformation Δ''_B due to R_B acting alone (1.21(b)).

Hence
$$\frac{5wL^4}{384EI} = \frac{R_B L^3}{48EI}$$

from which
$$R_B = \frac{5}{8}wL$$

By symmetry, also
$$R_A = R_C = \frac{3}{16}wL$$

We now consider the behaviour of the upper pair of guy wires. Since the mast is incompressible, the point C must move in a purely horizontal direction. The extension of DC must therefore equal the shortening of CG, so that the forces in the two wires due to the action of the wind must be equal and opposite. Let these forces be $+ F_1$ and $- F_1$.

Resolving horizontally at C, we have:
$$2F_1 \cos \theta = R_C = \frac{3}{16}wL$$

giving
$$F_1 = \frac{3wL}{32 \cos \theta} \qquad \cdots \text{(i)}$$

From the displacement diagram 1.21(d),

$$e_{CD} = e_{CG} = CC' \cos \theta = \frac{L}{100} \cos \theta$$

But
$$e_{CD} = \frac{F_1 L}{\sin \theta \, AE}$$

where A is the cross-sectional area of each wire.

Hence

$$\frac{F_1 L}{AE \sin \theta} = \frac{L}{100} \cos \theta \qquad \qquad \dots \text{(ii)}$$

and on substituting for F_1 in this equation we find that

$$A = \frac{75wL}{8E \sin \theta \cos^2 \theta}$$

The prestressing of the guys must be enough to prevent either from becoming slack as the wind blows from right or left. The prestressing force in either must therefore be at least equal to F_1. This means that the maximum force developed in either guy is at least $2F_1$. The cross-sectional area A must also be large enough to keep the stresses in the wires within the permissible value.

A similar procedure will yield the required cross-sectional area of the lower pair of guy wires.

The general approach outlined in this example is often adopted in the design of tall masts, but is rather unusual in hyperstatic structural design in general. The more common procedure is to begin by assuming trial cross-sections of members; the structure is then analysed for the effect of the applied loads. The first trial has almost always to be amended, sometimes several times. Such a procedure is quite intractable in mast design since the guy wires are not taut, as in the present idealized example, but sag and therefore have a non-linear response to load.

Problems for Solution

1.22. The two bars *AB*, *BC* are fixed at their ends *A* and *C* and rigidly connected together at *B*. They are both elastic and of the same material. Find the load in the bar *AB*.

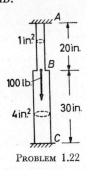

PROBLEM 1.22

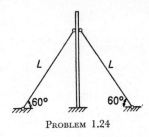

PROBLEM 1.24

1.23. Analyse the structure shown in *Problem 1.18* if member *DB* has the same cross-sectional area as the other bars.

1.24. Find the load in one of the steel wire stays of the steel mast shown when the other stay is tightened until it has a strain of 0·001. The cross-sectional area of each wire is 0·05 in.² and the mast has a flexural rigidity (EI) of 80×10^6 lb./in.². The mast is rigidly fixed to the ground and in the unloaded state the wires are just taut.

(London, 1956)

1.25. A concrete member of square section, 4 in. × 4 in. × 4 ft. long, is pre-compressed axially by a single high-tensile steel wire, 0·2 in. dia., which passes from end to end of the member through a small hole. The wire is tensioned to an initial stress of 130,000 lb./in.².

(a) A tensile load is immediately applied to the wire at its ends. Obtain the relationship between this load and the strain in the wire.

(b) Concrete of the type used has a free shrinkage of 4×10^{-4} in/in. If all the shrinkage occurs after the member has been prestressed, calculate the ultimate reduction in the stresses in the wire and concrete. Neglect the effect of the hole. Take $E = 5 \times 10^6$ lb./in.² for the concrete.

1.26. A steel beam of constant flexural rigidity EI is supported by three steel wires each of cross-sectional area A. The beam carries a uniformly distributed load of w per unit length. Find the force in the central wire, neglecting the weight of the beam.
(Manchester, 1955)

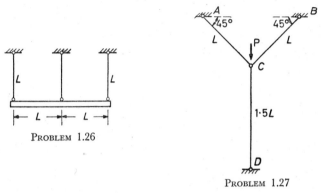

PROBLEM 1.26

PROBLEM 1.27

1.27. In the frame shown the members AC, BC are elastic and of cross-sectional area A. Find the load in strut CD if

(a) CD is also elastic and of cross-section A;

(b) CD shortens an amount e under load F according to the relation $e = KF^2$; Stability effects are to be ignored.

1.28. A beam GHK is supported at the mid-points of three beams AB, CD and EF as shown. The beams are all of the same cross-section. Find the load carried by beam CD if

(a) the beams behave elastically;

(b) the graph of the load against central deflection for each of the beams when centrally loaded over a 40 ft. span is as shown at (b).

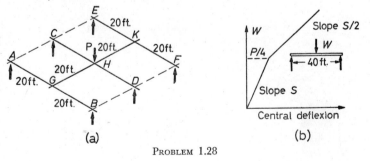

(a)

(b)

PROBLEM 1.28

19

1.29. *ABC* is a steel beam of flexural rigidity *EI*. It is pinned to a wall at *A* and supported by two elastic steel ties *DB*, *CE* of cross-sectional area *A*. A load *P* acts vertically on the beam at *B*. Find the force in *BD*. (Melbourne, 1954)

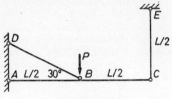

PROBLEM 1.29

1.30. The figure illustrates a steel two-rivet joint connecting two cover plates of combined thickness t_1 and a single plate of thickness t_2. Each rivet when subjected to a load *F* undergoes a shear deformation $\delta = F\rho$, where ρ is the shear flexibility (see diagram (b)). Assuming that the effect of the rivet holes on the flexibility of the plates may be ignored, determine the loads carried by the two rivets when the joint is subjected to an axial tensile load *P*.

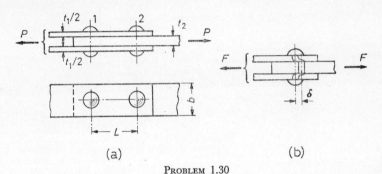

(a)   (b)

PROBLEM 1.30

1.31. A riveted joint similar to that in *Problem 1.30*, but with five rivets in line at a pitch *L*, connects two cover plates each of thickness *t*/2 and a main plate of thickness *t*. It is subjected to an axial tensile load *P*. If the rivets have the same characteristics as those in the preceding example determine an expression for the load on either end rivet. Hence show that when the rivets are infinitely flexible they are all equally loaded, and when they are infinitely stiff the inner three rivets carry no load.

1.32. *ABCDE* is a pontoon bridge of uniform second moment of area I. It is supported on opposite banks of a river at *A* and *E*, and on similar pontoons at *B*, *C* and *D*.

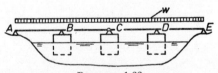

PROBLEM 1.32

Each pontoon sinks an amount *Δ* under unit load. The bridge is hinged at *C* and continuous between *A* and *C* and between *C* and *E*. *AB* = *BC* = *CD* = *DE* = *L*. A uniformly distributed load *w* per unit length is applied to the complete bridge. Calculate the reactions at the supports *C*, *D* and *E*. (Melbourne, 1955)

1.33.   A deck-type girder bridge consists of five equal main girders simply supported at their ends. Load is transmitted to the main girders through seven cross girders whose flexural rigidity is so high compared to that of the main girders that they may be regarded as completely rigid. The connexions between cross girders and main

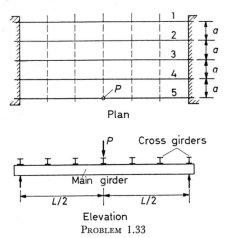

Plan

Elevation

PROBLEM 1.33

girders are incapable of transmitting bending or torsional moments, but they can transmit upward or downward forces. If a load P is applied to the bridge as shown determine the proportion of the load carried by girder No. 1.

CHAPTER 2

ENERGY METHODS

2.1. INTRODUCTION

In Volume I [Chapter 2], certain general methods of analysis of hyperstatic structures are discussed in detail and are here illustrated by further worked examples and problems for solution. The methods discussed include the theorems of minimum potential energy, virtual work, complementary energy and Castigliano. Of these, the first three are applicable both to linear and to non-linear elastic structures; the method of Castigliano is restricted to linear problems.

A few departures have been made from the sequence of Volume I. Problems on the deflexion of structures have been deferred to Chapter 3 of the present volume, and the determination of collapse loads of rigidly jointed structures by virtual work is dealt with in Chapter 6.

2.2. THE THEOREM OF MINIMUM POTENTIAL ENERGY
[Volume I, Chapter 2, Section 2.6.1]

This theorem states that for any structure in a state of equilibrium,

$$\frac{\partial}{\partial \Delta} (U + V) = 0 \qquad \qquad \dots\,[2.4]$$

where Δ is a displacement of some part of the structure in terms of which the strain energy U of the structure itself, and the potential energy V of the applied loads, can be expressed.

Problem 2.1—Problem 1.18 will first be analysed. Only one joint (B) is capable of movement, and it is possible to express U and V in terms of its components of displacement Δ_x and Δ_y. In general these components would be independent variables, but in this particular case, since DB is rigid, B always moves at right angles to the direction DB and therefore

$$\Delta_y = \Delta_x = \Delta$$

From diagram 1.18(b) it can be seen that the elongations of AB and BC are given by

$$\left. \begin{array}{l} e_{AB} = \Delta \\ e_{BC} = \sqrt{2}\,\Delta \cos 15° \end{array} \right\} \qquad \dots\,\text{(i)}$$

This is the compatibility relationship.

Now the strain energy of an elastic prismatic bar is given by

$$U = \frac{AEe^2}{2L} \qquad \qquad \dots\,[2.2(b)]$$

22

$$\qquad\qquad (AB)\qquad\qquad (BC)\qquad\qquad (BD)$$

Then
$$U = \frac{AE\varDelta^2}{2L} + \frac{AE2\varDelta^2 \cos^2 15°}{2L(2 / \sqrt{3})} + 0 \qquad\qquad \cdots \text{ (ii)}$$

We note that the strain energy of BD is zero since it is incompressible.

Also,
$$V = V_0 - P\varDelta \qquad\qquad \cdots \text{ (iii)}$$

where V_0 is the potential energy of the load before the movement of B to B' takes place. Hence

$$U + V = \frac{AE\varDelta^2}{2L} (1 + \sqrt{3} \cos^2 15°) + V_0 - P\varDelta$$

Differentiating the above with respect to $\varDelta$, in order to express the equilibrium condition, we have

$$\frac{\mathrm{d}}{\mathrm{d}\varDelta} (U + V) = \frac{AE\varDelta}{L} (1 + \sqrt{3} \cos^2 15°) - P = 0$$

$$\therefore \quad \varDelta = \frac{PL}{AE(1 + \sqrt{3} \cos^2 15°)}$$

and since $\varDelta$ is also equal to $\dfrac{F_{AB}L}{AE}$

$$F_{AB} = \frac{P}{1 + \sqrt{3} \cos^2 15°} = 0\cdot382P$$

The forces in BC and BD can now be obtained by resolving at the joint B.

It will be seen that the solution agrees with that previously obtained in Chapter 1.

Problem 2.2—As a simple example of a non-linear problem let us take the structure of *Problem 2.1* and assume that the bars AB and BC, instead of having linear behaviour, obey the load–extension law:

$$F = Ke - 2Ke^2$$

BD is rigid, as before.

What is the force in AB when $P = \dfrac{K}{10}$?

The compatibility relation between $\varDelta$, the horizontal movement of B, and the extensions of AB and BC is independent of the elastic properties of the members and therefore remains as in equation (i).

The strain energy of bar AB or BC now becomes

$$\int F \, \mathrm{d}e = \int (Ke - 2Ke^2)\mathrm{d}e = \frac{Ke^2}{6} (3 - 4e).$$

Substituting for e_{AB} and e_{BC} from (i), the total strain energy of the system is therefore given by

$$U = \frac{K\varDelta^2}{6} (3 - 4\varDelta) + \frac{2K \cos^2 15° \, \varDelta^2}{6} (3 - 4\sqrt{2} \cos 15° \, \varDelta)$$

$$= K\varDelta^2 (1\cdot433 - 2\cdot362\varDelta)$$

As before,

$$V = V_0 - P\varDelta$$

23

Hence

$$\frac{d}{d\Delta}(U - V) = 2.866\,K\Delta - 7.086\,K\Delta^2 - P = 0$$

Solving for Δ, we have

$$\Delta = 0.202 - \sqrt{0.0408 - \frac{0.1412P}{K}}$$

taking the negative sign as relevant because it gives the lower value of Δ;

when
$$P = \frac{K}{10}$$

we have
$$\Delta = 0.0385$$

Then since $e_{AB} = \Delta$, we have, on substituting in the expression for F,

$$F_{AB} = K\,0.0385 - 2K\,(0.0385)^2$$
$$= 0.0355K = 0.355P$$
$$e_{BC} = \sqrt{2}\cos 15°\Delta = 0.0526$$

Hence

$$F_{BC} = K\,0.0526 - 2K\,(0.0526)^2$$
$$= 0.0471K = 0.471P$$

We can readily check this solution by verifying that it satisfies the requirements of equilibrium and compatibility of deformations. The latter has in fact been ensured in the course of the solution. To check equilibrium we resolve forces at B horizontally and vertically:

$$F_{CB}\frac{\sqrt{3}}{2} + F_{AB} + \frac{F_{BD}}{\sqrt{2}} = 0$$

$$\frac{F_{CB}}{2} - P - \frac{F_{BD}}{\sqrt{2}} = 0$$

Adding these two equations, we find that

$$F_{CB} = \frac{P - F_{AB}}{1.366}$$

Substituting for $F_{AB} = 0.355P$,

we have
$$F_{AB} = 0.471P, \text{ as above.}$$

Thus the requirement of equilibrium at the point B has been satisfied.

In the preceding two examples the potential energy of the system was expressible in terms of a single variable Δ. Had the member DB not been rigid, there would have been two independent variables Δ_x and Δ_y. In general, for every joint of a plane pin-jointed structure there are two such variables, and it can be seen that where there are several joints the number of simultaneous equations, one for every independent variable, becomes unwieldy.

On the other hand, the method is valuable where there are many members but few joints—as in the spoked wheel in *Problem 2.5* below. It is also convenient where the deformed shape of the structure can be expressed in terms of a few parameters: these can then be treated as the independent variables, as in *Problem 2.3* below.

Problem 2.3—The cantilever shown is of uniform flexural rigidity EI. Four equal ties are attached to it as shown and each tie extends an amount ρ under unit load, where $\rho = \dfrac{50L^3}{EI}$. Find the tensions in the ties.

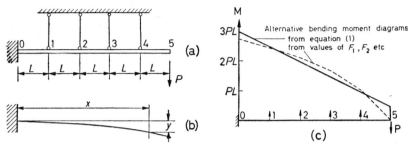

PROBLEM 2.3. (a) Uniform cantilever supported by four ties. (b) A suitable polynomial expression is used for the deflected shape. (c) Alternative bending moment diagrams obtained from the equation obtained for the beam and from the forces in the ties. The better the approximation the closer these lie together.

We assume† that the deflected form of the beam may be approximately represented by the polynomial

$$y = ax^2 + bx^3 + cx^4 + \ldots$$

The deflexion at each tie can be calculated from this expression so that the total strain energy of beam and ties can be obtained; when this is added to the potential energy of the load the total potential energy of the system is obtained and this will be stationary if the terms $a, b, \ldots$ have been correctly chosen.

Thus we may differentiate $U + V$ with respect to $a, b, \ldots$ and so obtain the correct values of these terms.

In simple problems the expression for y may in fact be a polynomial, and the accuracy of the solution depends on the number of terms assumed, in relation to the number of terms in the correct expression. We will assume that only two terms are involved, giving the expression

$$y = ax^2 + bx^3$$

in order to demonstrate the method without too much complication. Now

$$\frac{d^2y}{dx^2} = 2a + 6bx = \frac{M}{EI}$$

or

$$M = EI(2a + 6bx) \qquad \ldots \text{(i)}$$

The strain energy U_B of the beam $= \displaystyle\int_0^{5L} \frac{M^2 dx}{2EI}$

It is convenient to perform the partial differentiation of U_B at this stage. Thus:

$$\frac{\partial U_B}{\partial a} = \frac{1}{EI}\int_0^{5L} M\frac{\partial M}{\partial a}\,dx = EI\int_0^{5L}(2a + 6bx)2\,dx$$

$$= EI\,(20aL + 150\,bL^2)$$

Similarly,

$$\frac{\partial U_B}{\partial b} = EI(150\,aL^2 + 1500\,bL^3)$$

---

† A procedure suggested by D. Williams. See discussion on a paper by Pippard, A. J. S., entitled 'Stresses by Analysis and Experiment', *Proc. Inst. Mech. Engrs.*, 1947.

The strain energy U_T of a tie is $e\dfrac{F}{2}$ where e is the extension of the tie and, since
$$e = \frac{50L^3F}{EI},$$

$$U_T = \frac{e^2EI}{100L^3}$$

In this expression $e = y_1$ for tie 1, y_2 for tie 2, etc. Then for any one tie

$$\frac{\partial U_T}{\partial a} = \frac{EI}{50L^3} y \frac{\partial y}{\partial a} = \frac{EI}{50L^3}(ax^2 + bx^3)x^2$$

$$= \frac{EI}{50L^3}(ax^4 + bx^5)$$

and similarly $\qquad\qquad \dfrac{\partial U_T}{\partial b} = \dfrac{EI}{50L^3}(ax^5 + bx^6)$

Also, $\qquad\qquad V = V_0 - Py_5$

$$= V_0 - P(25aL^2 + 125bL^3)$$

$$\therefore\qquad\qquad \frac{\partial V}{\partial a} = -25PL^2$$

and $\qquad\qquad \dfrac{\partial V}{\partial b} = -125PL^3$

Now $\qquad\qquad \dfrac{\partial}{\partial a}(U + V) = \dfrac{\partial}{\partial a}(U_B + \textstyle\sum U_T + V) = 0.$

$$\therefore\qquad 0 = EI(20aL + 150bL^2) + \frac{EI}{50L^3}[aL^4(1 + 2^4 + 3^4 + 4^4)$$

$$+ bL^5(1 + 2^5 + 3^5 + 4^5)] - 25PL^2$$

or $\qquad\qquad 0 = 27{\cdot}08a + 176bL - 25\dfrac{PL}{EI} \qquad\qquad \dots\text{(ii)}$

In the same way, we find that

$$\frac{\partial}{\partial b}(U + V) = 0 = 176a + 1597{\cdot}8\,bL - \frac{125PL}{EI} \qquad\qquad \dots\text{(iii)}$$

The solution to equations (ii) and (iii) is:

$$a = \frac{1{\cdot}457PL}{EI} \qquad b = -\frac{0{\cdot}0825P}{EI}$$

so that

$$y = \frac{P}{EI}(1{\cdot}457Lx^2 - 0{\cdot}0825x^3) \qquad\qquad \dots\text{(iv)}$$

We can now verify the accuracy of the solution by calculating the forces F_1, F_2, etc., using equation (iv), and comparing the values of the bending moments at $0, 1, 2, \dots$ given by these forces together with P, with the values given by equation (i).

We find that

$$F_1 = 0{\cdot}0275P, \quad F_2 = 0{\cdot}103P, \quad F_3 = 0{\cdot}218P, \quad F_4 = 0{\cdot}363P$$

and hence

$$M_0 = 2.66PL \quad (2.91PL)$$

$$M_1 = 2.37PL \quad (2.42PL)$$

$$M_2 = 2.06PL \quad (1.92PL)$$

$$M_3 = 1.64PL \quad (1.43PL)$$

$$M_4 = PL \quad (0.93PL)$$

$$M_5 = 0 \quad (0.44PL)$$

In the above the figures in brackets in each line represent the values of moments derived from equation (i). At first sight these may seem to differ unduly from those obtained from the forces in the ties but when the two sets of figures are plotted, as at (c), an explanation at once suggests itself. This is that the straight line diagram given by (i) cannot possibly coincide with the polygonal diagram which the nature of the problem requires. The straight line is, however, a sort of average of the polygon.

In *Problem 2.8*, below, a 3-term polynomial is used for the same beam. It is interesting to note that the values of the tie forces are hardly changed by this refinement but that the bending moment diagrams are now very close to one another.

It is to be observed that a simple check on the accuracy of working is obtained by calculating alternative versions of the bending moments in this way. Similarly, in *Problem 2.9*, the moments obtained in two ways can be compared; the total reaction can also be checked against the load.

Another important point about this method of solution is that little more work would have been involved if there had been, say, 10 ties instead of 4. The number of 'unknowns' would still have been 2, and not 10 (the number of redundant forces).

Problems for Solution

2.4. Solve *Problems 1.22* to *1.33*, Chapter 1.

2.5. The circular wheel shown has a rigid rim and n identical equally spaced spokes, which are equally prestressed so that they remain in tension when the load P is applied to the hub. Find the change in tension in the ith spoke. Use the result to obtain the change in tension in one of the inclined spokes when $n = 3$, and check by another method.

(Manchester, 1957)

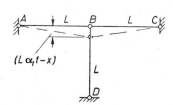

PROBLEMS 2.5   PROBLEM 2.6

2.6. The three rods shown are identical and are pinned together at B and to unyielding supports at A, C and D. The rods are initially unstressed, but following a fall in temperature of $t°$ they take up the position indicated by the dotted line. Find the extension x of BD caused by the resulting stress.

(Manchester, 1957)

2.7. Three bars 1, 2 and 3 are carried by a rigid beam and attached to a rigid cross bar. $AB = BC = L$. The deflexions per unit force are ρ_1, ρ_2 and ρ_3 respectively, where $\rho_1 = a_1 F_1$ and ρ_2 and ρ_3 are constant. Obtain an expression for the force in bar 1.

(Manchester, 1956)

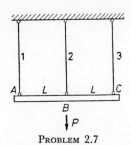

PROBLEM 2.7

2.8. Solve *Problem 2.3* using as the equation for the deflected form of the cantilever the polynomial

$$y = ax^2 + bx^3 + cx^4$$

2.9. A beam AB of flexural rigidity EI and length $8L$ is simply supported at its ends A and B, and also rests on 7 intermediate supports equally spaced along the beam. Each support deflects an amount $\dfrac{40L^3}{EI}$ per unit load. Using a three-term polynomial of the form $y = a + bx^2 + cx^3$ find approximate values for the reactions at A and B and at the intermediate supports when a uniformly distributed load w per unit length covers the whole length of the beam.

2.3. THE METHOD OF VIRTUAL WORK APPLIED TO STATICALLY DETERMINATE PROBLEMS

[Volume I, Chapter 2, Section 2.6.2]

This general principle in structural theory may be employed with advantage in the solution of statically determinate problems, as an alternative to the straightforward application of the equations of statical equilibrium. *Problems 2.10* and *2.11* illustrate its application in such cases.

Problem 2.10—The beam shown carries various loads, and it is required to find V_D, M_D and V_G.

The course adopted is to give the structure one degree of freedom by imposing a small displacement corresponding to the force or moment which is required. Then for the structure to be in equilibrium the virtual work corresponding to the displacements must be zero.

(a) *For V_D*

The appropriate displacement is a movement Δ vertically upwards at D. This brings the beam into the position shown to an enlarged vertical scale at (b). Then

$$\sum F . \delta = 0$$

where δ is the displacement of the point of application of any load or reaction.

28

Hence, working from A to G, we have

$$10\varDelta/3 + V_B.\theta + 20.(-\varDelta/2) + V_D.\varDelta + 2.10.\left(\frac{-5\varDelta}{6}\right) + V_G.\theta + M_G.\theta = 0$$

from which $V_D = + 23\cdot33$ tons.

It should be noted that the virtual work associated with the 20 ton point load and the distributed load is negative; this is because the displacements are in the opposite sense to the loads. The work associated with the distributed load is equal to the total value of the load times the distance through which its centroid is displaced.

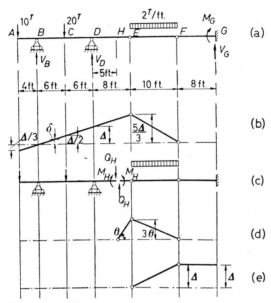

PROBLEM 2.10. (a) The reactions and bending moments at various points on this beam are to be found by virtual work. (b) V_D is found by giving a corresponding virtual displacement $\varDelta$. (c) To find M_H a cut is made at H. (d) A virtual rotation imposed at H. (e) A virtual displacement $\varDelta$ imposed at G gives V_G.

It may further be noted that the unwanted unknowns—V_B, V_G and M_G—are neatly excluded from the equation.

(b) *For M_H*

It is often convenient in investigating an internal force in structures to visualize the structure as having a cut in it at the point where the internal force acts, and to regard the internal force as a *quasi-external* force applied at the cut section. To determine M_H we may imagine a cut made at H; the bending moment M_H and the shearing force Q_H then act on both sides of the cut so as to preserve the equilibrium of the system.

Evidently the displacement corresponding to M_H is a rotation θ at the cut. In order to eliminate the unwanted term Q_H from the equation we must arrange matters so that there is no nett displacement corresponding to Q_H. This is accomplished by making the cut a hinge, so that if a vertical movement occurs, both sides displace vertically by the same amount (see (d)). Then, by imposing a rotation θ at the hinge, we have

$$M_H \cdot \theta + 2.10 \left(\frac{-3\theta}{2} \right) = 0$$

i.e.
$$M_H = + 30 \text{ ton ft.}$$

Again the unwanted unknowns do not appear.

(c) *For V_G*

Here the appropriate displacement is a vertical movement Δ of G *without rotation* (diagram (e)) (any rotation at G would mean that there would be virtual work associated with M_G). Then the virtual work done is

$$V_G \Delta + 2.10 \left(\frac{-\Delta}{2} \right) = 0$$

so that
$$V_G = + 10 \text{ tons.}$$

In each of the above calculations the answer was positive, indicating that the assumed direction of the unknown was correct. A negative sign would have indicated that the force actually acted in the opposite sense.

The principle of virtual work may also be used to determine the forces in the members of braced frameworks, as outlined in Volume I, Chapter 2, Section 2.6.2.1 (b). In simple trusses the deformation pattern may be derived by inspection. In more complicated problems, especially those on complex frameworks, the deformed shape is not easily visualized, and it is preferable to draw a Williot diagram, if necessary with a Mohr correction diagram [see Volume I, Chapter 3].

Problem 2.11—In Volume I, FIGURE 2.13 illustrates a common type of compound framework where the direct application of statics breaks down, and where the principle of virtual work is valuable. In *complex* frameworks the principle shows to even greater advantage. Suppose it is required to find the forces in the members of the truss of diagram 2.11 under the loading shown.

Once the force in one member of this framework is known, the other member forces follow quickly by resolution at the various joints. Taking BE as an obvious choice, we shorten or increase the length of this member by any arbitrary amount Δ. We may conveniently imagine the consequent distortion of the truss to occur initially about the direction BE as a base (2.11(b)). Since the diagonals AE, DC and the verticals AD, CF do not change in length, the only way in which they can displace in a symmetrical fashion is as shown in diagram (b), the verticals rotating about their mid-points and the diagonals displacing parallel to themselves. Denoting the lateral movement of A or D by δ, the vertical downward movement of B is $\delta/\tan 30°$; this follows from the fact that the instantaneous centre of rotation of AB is at X where AX is $10/\tan 30°$. Similarly the vertical upward movement of E is δ.

Hence

$$\Delta = \delta \left(1 + \frac{1}{\tan 30°} \right) = 2.732\delta.$$

Since, however, the joint A is pinned, we must shift the whole framework a distance δ to the right, giving the displacement pattern shown in 2.11(c).

The total virtual work performed during the displacement is

$$10(2\delta) + 10(-\delta) + F(-2.732\delta) = 0$$

from which
$$F = + 3.66 \text{ tons.}$$

It is now possible to obtain the forces in all the other members by resolution at the joints; the force in *FC*, for example, will be found to be — 13·66 tons.

The alternative analytical approach, known as Henneberg's method, will be found to be much more laborious. Furthermore, by the use of virtual work it is possible quickly to find the effect of any other system of loads once the displaced form of the truss is known.

When the deformation is unsymmetrical it will not be possible, as it was in the above example, to take advantage of symmetry, but the displaced form can always be obtained by a Williot-Mohr diagram [see Volume I, Chapter 3]. For example, suppose we select *FC* as the member whose force we wish to determine. We begin by

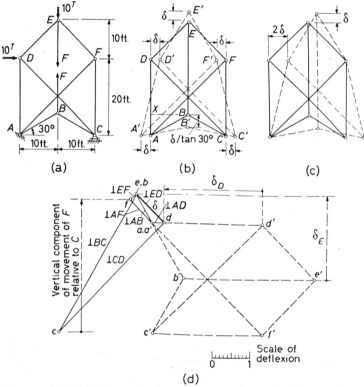

PROBLEM 2.11. (a) This complex framework cannot be analysed directly either by the method of sections or by the method of joints. (b) A cut is made in *BE* and a virtual displacement of *B* relative to *A* shifts the joints to the position shown. (c) Since the joint *A* is pinned the final displaced position is obtained as shown. (d) If a member is cut which results in an unsymmetrical distortion a Williot-Mohr diagram can be used to obtain the displaced position; that shown here corresponds to a displacement of *F* relative to *C*.

choosing any quadrilateral system of bars in the truss, none of which undergoes a change in length, and give the quadrilateral an arbitrary deformation, assuming one of its members to remain fixed in direction. The displacements of the remaining joints of the truss are then located in the usual way. It may be necessary to draw a Mohr correction diagram. Finally the vertical component of the movement of *F* relative to *C*, Δ_{FC}, is obtained.

In the present example, *EB* is assumed to be fixed in direction, and *D* is given an initial displacement δ downwards and to the right (2.11(d)). This locates *d*, the displaced position of D on the Williot diagram; a is then fixed in the usual way by drawing lines through d and b perpendicular respectively to AD and AB. Point f, the displaced position of joint F, is then found from a and e, and c by working from b and d. Since a and c are not at the same level, a Mohr diagram is necessary. This is shown dotted.

The absolute movement of any joint is obtained, in the usual way, by measuring from the Mohr to the Williot diagram; thus $d'd = \delta_D$ gives the displacement of D. For the present purpose the vertical component of the displacement of E is required and this is shown on diagram (d) as δ_E. In the same way F moves from f' to f and C from c' to c; the relative movement of these two joints could be obtained by compounding $f'f$ and $c'c$ vectorially but it is clear that Δ_{FC}, which is all that is required for the present purpose, can be obtained as shown.

If we assume that F_{FC} is tensile the virtual work equation becomes

$$F_{FC}(\Delta_{FC}) + 10\delta_D + 10\delta_E = 0$$

Inserting the measured values with the proper signs, we have

$$F_{FC}(-3\cdot50) + 10(-2\cdot54) + 10(-2\cdot21) = 0$$

$$\text{i.e.} \quad F_{FC} = -13\cdot60 \text{ tons.}$$

The slight discrepancy between this value and that previously obtained is an indication of the accuracy obtainable when a graphical construction is used. In this instance the triangle edc is rather ill-conditioned and the accuracy correspondingly less than would otherwise have been the case.

Problems for Solution

2.12. Determine R_C, M_A, V_A and M_D.

PROBLEM 2.12

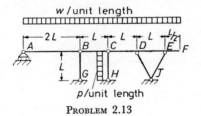

2.13. Determine V_A, V_G, V_J, H_J and M_D.

PROBLEM 2.13

2.14. Determine V_D, V_F, M_D, M_F, M_J and Q_J (shearing force at J).

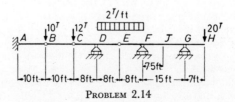

PROBLEM 2.14

2.15.   The beam *A-H* is loaded through stringers and cross girders with a uniformly distributed load *w* per unit length extending from *A* to *H*.
   Find V_A, V_F, M_C, M_J and Q_J.

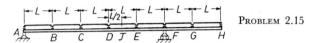

PROBLEM 2.15

2.16.   The Pratt truss *A-G* is loaded at the lower chord joints.
   Find V_A and the forces in members *JK*, *JC*, *JD*, *HB*, *KD* and *AB*.

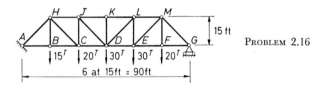

PROBLEM 2.16

2.17.   Find V_A, H_A and the forces in members *GH*, *GC* and *FG*.

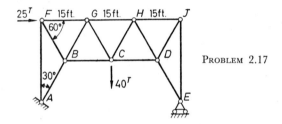

PROBLEM 2.17

2.18.   Find the forces in members *DE*, *BD*, *AD*, *AF* and *CD*.

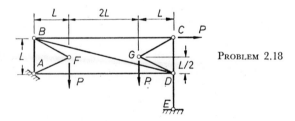

PROBLEM 2.18

2.19.   Find the force in member *DK*.

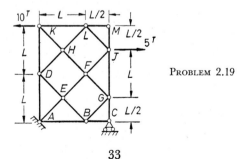

PROBLEM 2.19

33

2.4. THE EQUATION OF VIRTUAL WORK AND THE
ANALYSIS OF HYPERSTATIC STRUCTURES
[see Volume I, Chapter, 2, Section 2.6.2.2]

Mohr's Equation of Virtual Work provides a powerful and general means of analysis of hyperstatic structures. In its finite form the equation is:

$$\Sigma \bar{P}\{\Delta\} = \Sigma \bar{F}\{e\} \qquad \dots \text{[2.6]}$$

$\bar{P}$ and $\bar{F}$ are any mutually consistent set of external and internal forces, respectively, and are called the *force system;* in a pin-jointed framework, for example, $\bar{P}$ might represent a set of applied loads and $\bar{F}$ the bar forces caused thereby.

Δ and e are a mutually consistent set of joint displacements and member extensions, not necessarily due to the loads $\bar{P}$; they are called the *displacement system.* In a pin-jointed framework Δ might, for example, be the movement of a joint in a specified direction, and e the change in length of any member.

It is essential to adhere strictly to the sign convention in equation [2.6]. Δ is positive when it is in the same direction as $\bar{P}$, $\bar{F}$ is positive when tensile and e when it is an extension.

Problem 2.20—The members of the framework *ABCD* are of the same material and obey Hooke's Law; their cross-sectional areas are indicated in circles. Find the force in the member *BD*.

Let the members *AD*, *BD* and *CD* be denoted by 1, 2 and 3 respectively. $\bar{P}$ and $\bar{F}$ are conveniently chosen as the actual applied load and bar forces. As the displacement system we first select an imaginary or virtual displacement Δx of the joint *D* in the *x*-direction (diagram (b)). Then the corresponding extensions of the three bars are:

$$e_1 = \Delta x \cos 30°, \quad e_2 = \Delta x, \quad e_3 = 0.$$

Assuming that all the bar forces $\bar{F}$ are tensile, the equation of virtual work is:

$$P \cos 60° \, \Delta x = F_1 \Delta x . \frac{\sqrt{3}}{2} + F_2 \Delta x + F_3 . 0$$

or
$$\frac{P}{2} - F_1 \frac{\sqrt{3}}{2} - F_2 = 0 \qquad \dots \text{(i)}$$

Next we select as the displacement system a displacement of *D* in the *y*-direction (diagram (c)). The corresponding values of *e* are:

$$e_1 = \Delta y \sin 30°, \quad e_2 = 0, \quad e_3 = -\Delta y$$

The equation for this case is:

$$P \sin 60° \, (-\Delta y) = F_1 \Delta y \sin 30° + F_2 . 0 + F_3 (-\Delta y)$$

or
$$P \frac{\sqrt{3}}{2} + \frac{F_1}{2} - F_3 = 0 \qquad \dots \text{(ii)}$$

Equations (i) and (ii) it will be observed, are the equations of equilibrium for the joint *D*.

We now turn our attention to the actual movement δx, δy of the joint D due to the load P (diagram (d)), and express the bar forces in terms of these displacements. Thus:

$$e_1 = \delta x \cos 30° + \delta y \sin 30° = \frac{1}{2} (\sqrt{3}\, \delta x + \delta y), \quad e_2 = \delta x, \quad e_3 = -\delta y$$

These are the compatibility relationships.

The bar force F in each case equals $\dfrac{AEe}{L}$ where A is the cross-sectional area of the member.

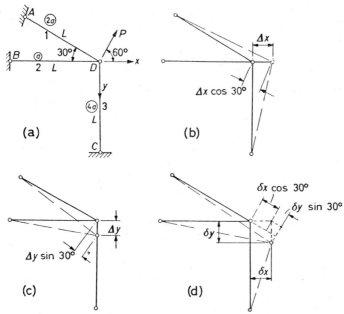

(a)

(b)

(c)

(d)

PROBLEM 2.20. (a) The cross-sectional areas of the members of this linear hyperstatic framework are shown in the figure. (b) Virtual displacement of D in the x-direction. (c) Virtual displacement of D in the y-direction. (d) The compatibility relationship is obtained by considering the final position of D.

We now substitute for the F's in equations (i) and (ii). From equation (i), we have:

$$\frac{P}{2} - \frac{\sqrt{3}}{2} \cdot \frac{2aE}{2L} (\sqrt{3}\, \delta x + \delta y) - \frac{aE\delta x}{L} = 0$$

i.e.
$$\frac{PL}{2aE} - 2.5\, \delta x - 0.866\, \delta y = 0 \qquad \dots \text{(iii)}$$

From equation (ii), we have:

$$P\frac{\sqrt{3}}{2} + \frac{2aE}{2.2L} (\sqrt{3}\, \delta x + \delta y) - \frac{4aE}{L} (-\delta y) = 0$$

i.e.
$$\frac{0.866PL}{aE} + 0.866\, \delta x + 4.5\, \delta y = 0 \qquad \dots \text{(iv)}$$

35

The solution to equations (iii) and (iv) is:

$$\delta x = 0 \cdot 286 \frac{PL}{aE}$$

$$\delta y = -0 \cdot 247 \frac{PL}{aE}$$

The bar forces can now be found from the extensions: for example

$$F_2 = \frac{aEe_2}{L} = +0 \cdot 286P$$

The positive sign indicates that F_2 is tensile.

Problem 2.21—We now consider the previous problem when member 2 extends under load according to the following law (see also diagram 2.21):

$$F = \frac{aEe}{L} - \frac{aEe^2}{2L} \quad (e \leqslant 1)$$

$$F = \frac{aE}{2L} \quad (e > 1)$$

for positive values of e.

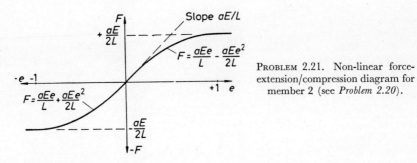

PROBLEM 2.21. Non-linear force-extension/compression diagram for member 2 (see *Problem 2.20*).

(a) Find F_2 when $P = \frac{aE}{L}$;

(b) Determine at what value of P member 2 becomes completely plastic.

(a) Equations (i) and (ii) and the expressions for the e's in terms of δx and δy, derived in *Problem 2.20* still hold: for the elastic properties of the members were not invoked in obtaining these expressions. We assume that $e_2 \leqslant 1$ and use the quadratic relation between F and e for member 2. Substituting in equation (i) we have:

$$\frac{P}{2a} - \frac{\sqrt{3}}{2} \cdot \frac{2E}{2L} (\sqrt{3}\, \delta x + \delta y) - \left(\frac{E\delta x}{L} - \frac{E\delta x^2}{2L} \right) = 0$$

or

$$\frac{PL}{2aE} - 2 \cdot 5\, \delta x + 0 \cdot 5\, \delta x^2 - 0 \cdot 866\, \delta y = 0 \qquad \dots \text{(v)}$$

Equation (ii) does not involve F_2 and remains as before:

i.e.

$$\frac{0 \cdot 866PL}{aE} + 0 \cdot 866\, \delta x + 4 \cdot 5\, \delta y = 0 \qquad \dots \text{(iv)}$$

36

Eliminating δy, we obtain:

$$\delta x^2 - 4 \cdot 667 \, \delta x + 1 \cdot 333 \frac{PL}{aE} = 0 \qquad \dots \dots \text{(vi)}$$

from which

$$\delta x = 2 \cdot 333 \left(1 \pm \sqrt{1 - \frac{0 \cdot 245 PL}{aE}} \right)$$

When $P = \dfrac{aE}{L}$, $\delta x = e_2 = 0 \cdot 305$ or $4 \cdot 361$.

We discard the second value of δx as inadmissible since it makes $e_2 > 1$. Hence

$$F_2 = \frac{aE e_2}{L} \left(1 - \frac{e_2}{2} \right) = \frac{aE}{L} 0 \cdot 305 \left(1 - \frac{0 \cdot 305}{2} \right) = 0 \cdot 259 P$$

(b) Member 2 becomes completely plastic when

$$e_2 = \delta x = 1$$

i.e. $\qquad\qquad 1 = 2 \cdot 333 \, (1 \pm \sqrt{1 - 0 \cdot 245 PL/aE})$

$$- 0 \cdot 571 = \sqrt{1 - 0 \cdot 245 PL/aE}$$

Squaring both sides

$$0 \cdot 326 = 1 - 0 \cdot 245 PL/aE$$

giving $\qquad\qquad P = 2 \cdot 75 aE/L$

In this problem it is evident that F_2 is tensile. However, if the load P were applied downwards and to the right at 60° to the horizontal we could not be certain of the sign of F_2. Suppose we assumed F_2 to be tensile and then found, on solving the problem using the quadratic relationship between F and e, that it was compressive. It would not then be sufficient to accept the solution with this alteration in sign, as would be the case in a linear problem, because the relationship between F and e is valid only for positive values of the latter. If the member behaves similarly in tension and compression, as indicated in the diagram, the equation to the compressive part of the curve is

$$F = \frac{aE e}{L} + \frac{aE e^2}{2L}$$

The working should therefore be repeated using this revised relationship.†

Problem 2.22—A rigid bar is supported by three wires 1, 2 and 3. The load–extension relations for the three wires are shown in diagram (b); wire 2 is linear and wires 1 and 3 non-linear in behaviour. Diagram (b) also shows how wires 1 and 3 behave if the load in them is reduced. Find the forces in the wires when a load $3\frac{1}{2}P$ is applied at A, followed by a load $3\frac{1}{2}P$ at B, and compare the final situation with that resulting from the simultaneous application of these loads.

The system has two degrees of freedom: its deformation can always be specified by an equal extension Δ of each wire and a rotation of the rigid bar about wire 2, causing a change of length δ of wires 1 and 3 (diagrams (c) and (d)).

We first apply $3\frac{1}{2}P$ at A.

---

† See Matheson, J. A. L.: 'Virtual Work and Complementary Energy applied to non-linear braced frameworks'. *Engineering*, May 1, 1959, p. 581.

Treating Δ and δ as the independent variables, we need two equations which can be obtained by treating (c) and (d) in turn as displacement systems in the virtual work equation.

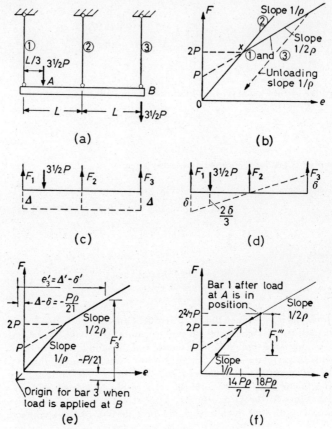

(a)

(b)

(c)

(d)

(e)

(f)

PROBLEM 2.22. (a) A rigid bar is supported by three wires. (b) Load-extension diagram for wires 1, 2 and 3. (c) and (d) Virtual displacements. (e) The load of $3\frac{1}{2}P$ at A is applied first, producing a force of $-P/21$ in wire 3. This gives a new origin for the load-extension diagram for that wire. (f) If the wires are now supposed to follow the same laws for unloading as for loading, bar 1 behaves as shown after the $3\frac{1}{2}P$ load is in position at A.

Thus from (c) we have

$$3\tfrac{1}{2}P\Delta = (F_1 + F_2 + F_3)\Delta \qquad \dots \text{(i)}$$

and from (d)

$$3\tfrac{1}{2}P \cdot \frac{2\delta}{3} = (F_1 - F_3)\delta \qquad \dots \text{(ii)}$$

Regarding Δ and δ as the actual deformations of the structure we can express the forces F in terms of them:

thus

$$F_1 = P + \frac{\Delta + \delta}{2\rho}; \quad F_2 = \frac{\Delta}{\rho}; \quad F_3 = \frac{\Delta - \delta}{\rho}$$

38

(Here we have assumed that $F_1 \geqslant 2P$, $F_3 < 2P$. This must be verified when the solution is reached).

Substituting in (i), we have

$$5P\rho = 5\varDelta - \delta \qquad \dots \text{(iii)}$$

and in (ii)

$$8P\rho = -3\varDelta + 9\delta \qquad \dots \text{(iv)}$$

Solving (iii) and (iv) simultaneously, we have

$$\delta = \frac{55P\rho}{42} \text{ and } \varDelta = \frac{53P\rho}{42}$$

giving

$$\left. \begin{array}{l} F_1 = \ \ 2\frac{2}{7}P \\ F_2 = \ \ 1\frac{11}{42}P \\ F_3 = -\frac{1}{21}P \end{array} \right\} \qquad \dots \text{(v)}$$

These total $3\frac{1}{2}P$, which is a check on the working, and they also satisfy the assumptions made about the magnitudes of F_1 and F_3. Now with the system in this state we add $3\frac{1}{2}P$ at B. We assume that $F_3 \geqslant 2P$. The forces F now to be discussed are the *additional* forces caused by the extra load of $3\frac{1}{2}P$ at B and the relationship between these forces and the corresponding changes of length of the members must be considered. Bars 1 and 2 cause no difficulty, since they simply obey the law $F = e/\rho$. The effect of the load of $-P/21$ in bar 3, however, is to alter its 'elastic limit'. Thus from diagram (e) we can see that

$$F_3' - P/21 = \frac{(\varDelta' - \delta') - P\rho/21}{2\rho} + P$$

i.e.

$$F_3' = \frac{43P}{42} + \frac{(\varDelta' - \delta')}{2\rho}$$

The virtual work equations, with the load of $3\frac{1}{2}P$ acting at B instead of at A, are

$$3\frac{1}{2}P\varDelta' = (F_1 + F_2 + F_3)\varDelta' \qquad \dots \text{(vi)}$$

$$3\frac{1}{2}P\delta' = (F_3 - F_1)\delta' \qquad \dots \text{(vii)}$$

Now

$$F_1' = \frac{\varDelta' + \delta'}{\rho}; \quad F_2' = \frac{\varDelta'}{\rho}; \quad F_3' = \frac{43P}{42} + \frac{\varDelta' - \delta'}{2\rho}$$

Substituting in (vi) and (vii) and solving for δ' and $\varDelta'$ we have

$$\delta' = -\frac{104P\rho}{49} \text{ and } \varDelta' = \frac{208P\rho}{147} \text{ from which}$$

$$\left. \begin{array}{l} F_1' = -\frac{104P}{147} \qquad F_2' = +\frac{208P}{147} \\ \\ F_3' = +\frac{821P}{294} \quad [\text{N.B. } F_3' \geqslant 2P] \end{array} \right\} \qquad \dots \text{(viii)}$$

These again total $3\frac{1}{2}P$.

The final forces in the three bars are therefore obtained by adding (v) and (viii), thus

$$\left. \begin{array}{l} F_1 + F_1' = \dfrac{232P}{147} \\ \\ F_2 + F_2' = \dfrac{787P}{294} \\ \\ F_3 + F_3' = \dfrac{807P}{294} \end{array} \right\} \qquad \dots \text{(ix)}$$

We now examine the effect of applying the loads at A and B simultaneously, assuming that $F_1 < 2P$ and $F_3 > 2P$.

The virtual work equations for this situation, again using the displacement systems (c) and (d), are

$$7P\Delta'' = (F_1'' + F_2'' + F_3'')\Delta'' \qquad \dots \text{(x)}$$

$$\frac{7P}{6}\delta'' = (F_3'' - F_1'')\delta'' \qquad \dots \text{(xi)}$$

The forces in the bars are given by

$$F_1'' = \frac{\Delta'' + \delta''}{\rho}; \quad F_2'' = \frac{\Delta''}{\rho}; \quad F_3'' = P + \frac{\Delta'' - \delta''}{2\rho}$$

Substituting in (x) and (xi) and solving for Δ'' and δ'' we have

$$\Delta'' = \frac{109P\rho}{42} \text{ and } \delta'' = \frac{-41P\rho}{42}$$

from which

$$F_1'' = \frac{68P}{42} \quad \text{[N.B. } F_1 < 2P\text{]}$$

$$F_2'' = \frac{109P}{42} \qquad \left.\begin{array}{c} \\ \\ \\ \end{array}\right\} \qquad \dots \text{(xii)}$$

$$F_3'' = \frac{117P}{42} \quad \text{[N.B. } F_3 > 2P\text{]}$$

Comparing (ix) and (xii) we see that the result of applying the two loads together is not the same as when they are applied in succession. This may well be because bar 1 follows different laws when loading and unloading and we now examine this suggestion.

Diagram (f) shows the situation in bar 1 after the $3\frac{1}{2}$-ton load at A is in position. As F_1''' increases the law is $F_1''' = \frac{e}{2\rho}$ until $F_1''' = 2P/7$ and thereafter it is $F_1''' = \frac{e}{\rho}$

i.e.

$$F_1''' - \frac{2P}{7} = \frac{1}{\rho}\left(e - \frac{4P\rho}{7}\right)$$

i.e.

$$F_1''' = \frac{e}{\rho} - \frac{2P}{7}$$

We therefore have

$$F_1''' = +\frac{2P}{7} + \frac{\Delta''' + \delta'''}{\rho}$$

$$F_2''' = \frac{\Delta'''}{\rho}$$

$$F_3''' = \frac{43P}{42} + \frac{\Delta''' - \delta'''}{2\rho}$$

assuming that $F_3''' > 2P$.

40

The virtual work equations (vi) and (vii) are still relevant, so we have

$$3\tfrac{1}{2}P = +\frac{2P}{7} + \frac{\Delta''' + \delta'''}{\rho} + \frac{\Delta'''}{\rho} + \frac{43P}{42} + \frac{\Delta''' - \delta'''}{2\rho} \qquad \dots \text{(vi')}$$

and

$$3\tfrac{1}{2}P = \frac{43P}{42} + \frac{\Delta''' - \delta'''}{2\rho} - \left\{\frac{2P}{7} + \frac{\Delta''' + \delta'''}{\rho}\right\} \qquad \dots \text{(vii')}$$

Solving (vi') and (vii') for Δ''' and δ''' we have

$$\delta''' = -\frac{16P\rho}{7} \;;\quad \Delta''' = \frac{4P\rho}{3} \text{ from which}$$

$$\left.\begin{array}{l} F_1''' = -\dfrac{2}{3}P \\[2mm] F_2''' = +\dfrac{4}{3}P \\[2mm] F_3''' = +\dfrac{17P}{6} \quad [\text{N.B. } F_3''' > 2P] \end{array}\right\} \qquad \dots \text{(xiii)}$$

When these are added to (v), we have

$$\left.\begin{array}{l} F_1'''' = F_1 + F_1''' = \dfrac{34P}{21} \\[2mm] F_2'''' = F_2 + F_2''' = \dfrac{109P}{42} \\[2mm] F_3'''' = F_3 + F_3''' = \dfrac{117P}{42} \quad [\text{N.B. } F_3'''' > 2P] \end{array}\right\} \qquad \dots \text{(xiv)}$$

These results coincide with (xii) from which we conclude that the anomalous results (ix) emerged because bar 1 was then following different loading and unloading laws; there was not, in fact, a single-valued relationship between load and deflexion.

On the other hand we have been able to superimpose the results of the second load on those of the first in spite of the fact that this is a non-linear problem. It might at first be thought that this has demonstrated that the remarks on the Principle of Superposition, in Volume I, Chapter 2, Section 2.5, were incorrect. It will be noticed, however, that in the present example we have been careful to calculate the *additional* effect of the second load with the first already in position. To this end diagrams (e) and (f) were prepared so as to give the starting points for the new calculations. The Principle of Superposition, however, contemplates quite independent calculations, made without regard to the existence, or otherwise, of any initial loads. Such a procedure certainly leads to incorrect results in non-linear problems.

A further application of virtual work, discussed in detail in Volume I [Chapter 2, Section 2.6.2.5(b)], is the analysis of non-linear frameworks with a number of redundants. The method is essentially one of successive approximations. It will not be dealt with further in the present book, but *Problem 2.26* is intended to be solved by this method.

Problems for Solution

2.23. Solve *Problems 1.22* to *1.33*, Chapter 1.

2.24. Solve *Problems 2.5, 2.6* and *2.7*.

2.25. The cross-sectional areas of the members (in circles) and the signs of the bar forces are indicated on the figure (a). The stress-strain relation for each member is shown at (b). All members are of length L and are under stresses that exceed the 'elastic limit' of 10/3 tons/in.² Find the force in the central vertical member.

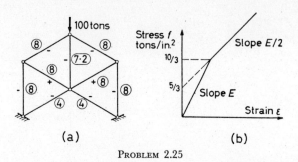

(a)   (b)

PROBLEM 2.25

2.26. The cross-sectional areas of the members (in circles) and the signs of the bar forces are indicated on the figure. The stress-strain relations for the members are:

$$f = 1 \cdot 34\epsilon \times 10^4 \text{ (tension)}$$

$$f = 1 \cdot 34\epsilon \times 10^4 + 4\epsilon^2 \times 10^6 \text{ (compression)} \quad (|\epsilon| < 1 \cdot 67 \times 10^{-3})$$

where f is the stress in tons/in.²
Find the forces in *DE* and *EF*.

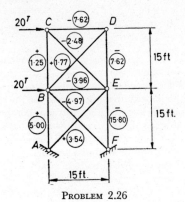

PROBLEM 2.26

2.5. ENGESSER'S THEOREM OF COMPATIBILITY
(COMPLEMENTARY ENERGY)
[Volume I, Chapter 2, Section 2.6.7]

The two methods already illustrated by worked examples—minimum potential energy and virtual work—have one rather serious drawback: the independent variables (the 'unknowns') are displacements. Hyperstatic structures usually have more independent displacements than redundant forces, often very many more; these methods then lead to an unmanageable number of simultaneous equations even in simple problems. This difficulty is avoided in the remaining methods to be discussed in this chapter.

Engesser's Theorem states that in a structure in which the members fit properly in the unloaded state

$$\frac{\partial C}{\partial X} = 0 \qquad\qquad \dots. [2.13(a)]$$

where X is the force in any redundant member or reaction and C is the complementary energy of the structure. If an axially loaded member extends under load as shown in FIGURE 2.1 then the complementary energy

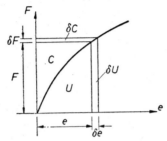

FIGURE 2.1. Load-extension diagram for a non-linear member. C is the complementary energy and U the strain energy.

C is indicated in the figure, and if a small increase δF in the force F in the member takes place, the increment of complementary energy is

$$\delta C = e.\delta F$$

Evidently by differentiating the expression for the total complementary energy with respect to each redundant force in turn, enough equations of compatibility to solve any problem are obtained. The method is applicable to non-linear as well as linear structures, and is often much simpler in application than the minimum potential energy or virtual work methods.

Problem 2.27—Our first example of the application of Engesser's Theorem is *Problem 2.20*, which has already been solved by virtual work.

Let the tensile force in member 2 be X. By resolving horizontally and vertically at D we obtain the following equations:

$$F_1 = \frac{P}{\sqrt{3}} - \frac{2X}{\sqrt{3}}$$

$$F_3 = \frac{2P}{\sqrt{3}} - \frac{X}{\sqrt{3}}$$

Now for any member in the frame,

$$C = \int e.dF = \int \frac{FL}{AE}\,dF = \frac{F^2L}{2AE}$$

43

Where A is the cross sectional area of the member and L its length. Then, for the complete structure, taking members 1, 2 and 3 in turn,

$$C = \left(\frac{P}{\sqrt{3}} - \frac{2X}{\sqrt{3}}\right)^2 \frac{L}{4aE} + \frac{X^2L}{2aE} + \left(\frac{2P}{\sqrt{3}} - \frac{X}{\sqrt{3}}\right)^2 \frac{L}{8aE}$$

$$\frac{dC}{dX} = 0 = \left(\frac{2X}{\sqrt{3}} - \frac{P}{\sqrt{3}}\right)\frac{L}{\sqrt{3}aE} + \frac{XL}{aE} + \left(\frac{X}{\sqrt{3}} - \frac{2P}{\sqrt{3}}\right)\frac{L}{4\sqrt{3}aE}$$

or

$$0 = -\frac{P}{2} + \frac{7X}{4}$$

giving

$$X = + 2P/7 = + 0{\cdot}286P \text{ as before.}$$

Problem 2.28—Our first example of the solution of a non-linear problem by Engesser's Theorem is *Problem 2.21*. Members 1 and 3 remain as in the previous *Problem*, but member 2 is non-linear, with the following load–extension relation:

$$F = \frac{aEe}{L} - \frac{aEe^2}{2L} \quad (e \leqslant 1) \left.\vphantom{\frac{aEe}{L}}\right\}$$
$$F = \frac{aE}{2L} \quad (e > 1) \left.\vphantom{\frac{aE}{2L}}\right\} \text{ for positive values of } e.$$

What is F_2 when $P = \dfrac{aE}{L}$?

The complementary energy of members 1 and 3 is as before. That of member 2 is

$$C_2 = \int e.dX$$

Then

$$C = \frac{F_1{}^2 L_1}{2A_1 E} + \int_0^X e.dX + \frac{F_3{}^2 L_3}{2A_3 E}$$

It is convenient to perform the differentiation immediately, thus

$$0 = \frac{\partial C}{\partial X} = F_1 \frac{\partial F_1}{\partial X}\frac{L_1}{A_1 E} + e_2 + F_3 \frac{\partial F_3}{\partial X}\frac{L_3}{A_3 E}$$

On solving the quadratic load-extension equation for member 2, assuming that $e \leqslant 1$, we have

$$e_2 = 1 - \sqrt{1 - \frac{2LX}{aE}}$$

Hence

$$\frac{dC}{dX} = 0 = \left(\frac{2X}{\sqrt{3}} - \frac{P}{\sqrt{3}}\right)\frac{L}{\sqrt{3}aE} + \left(1 - \sqrt{1 - \frac{2LX}{aE}}\right) + \left(\frac{X}{\sqrt{3}} - \frac{2P}{\sqrt{3}}\right)\frac{L}{4\sqrt{3}aE}$$

or

$$0 = \left(\frac{3X}{4} - \frac{P}{2}\right)\frac{L}{aE} + \left(1 - \sqrt{1 - \frac{2LX}{aE}}\right)$$

44

On putting $P = \dfrac{aE}{L}$, this equation reduces to:

$$X^2 + \frac{44aE}{9L}X - \frac{4a^2E^2}{3L^2} = 0$$

the solution to which is

$$X = +\,0{\cdot}259\,\frac{aE}{L} = +\,0{\cdot}259P, \text{ as before.}$$

It is to be observed that the remarks about the correctness or otherwise of the sign of the solution, which followed *Problem 2.21*, apply equally to Engesser's method. If the sign of the solution is different from that assumed when evaluating the complementary energy the working *must* be repeated with the sign changed.

Problem 2.29—The members 2, 4 and 10 of the framework shown are non-linear in behaviour, and follow the stress-strain relation shown at (b); the other members obey Hooke's law and have a modulus of elasticity of E. The members are designated by the numbers on diagram (a) and their cross-sectional areas in square inches are shown in circles at (c). Find the force in the bar 4 and the horizontal force at A or B.

Since the structure is twice redundant we may conveniently choose X, the force in bar 4, and Y, the horizontal force at A or B as the redundant forces.

We shall assume that members 2, 4 and 10 are all stressed beyond 4 tons/in.². The equation to the stress-strain curve above this stress is:

or

$$\left. \begin{aligned} f &= 2 + \frac{eE}{2} \\[2mm] e &= 2f/E - 4/E \end{aligned} \right\} \qquad \dots \text{(i)}$$

The complementary energy of a bar loaded into this regime is

$$C = \int_0^F e\,\mathrm{d}F = \int_0^{4A} e\,\mathrm{d}F + \int_{4A}^F e\,\mathrm{d}F$$

$4A$ being the load in tons at which the change in slope occurs.

$$\therefore\quad C = \int_0^{4A} \frac{FL}{AE}\,\mathrm{d}F + \frac{1}{E}\int_{4A}^F (2f-4)L\,\mathrm{d}F$$

$$= \left[\frac{F^2L}{2AE}\right]_0^{4A} + \frac{2}{E}\int_{4A}^F \left(\frac{F}{A}-2\right)L\,\mathrm{d}F$$

or

$$C = \frac{8AL}{E} + \frac{2L}{E}\left(\frac{F^2}{2A} - 2F\right)$$

Hence

and

$$\left. \begin{aligned} \frac{\partial C}{\partial X} &= \frac{2L}{E}\left(\frac{F}{A}-2\right)\frac{\partial F}{\partial X} \\[2mm] \frac{\partial C}{\partial Y} &= \frac{2L}{E}\left(\frac{F}{A}-2\right)\frac{\partial F}{\partial Y} \end{aligned} \right| \qquad \dots \text{(ii)}$$

For the linear members

$$C = \frac{F^2L}{2AE} \quad \text{so that} \quad \frac{\partial C}{\partial X} = \frac{FL}{AE}\cdot\frac{\partial F}{\partial X} \quad \text{and} \quad \frac{\partial C}{\partial Y} = \frac{FL}{AE}\cdot\frac{\partial F}{\partial Y} \qquad \dots \text{(iii)}$$

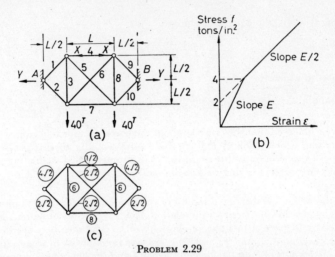

(a)

(b)

(c)

PROBLEM 2.29

TABLE 2.29

ANALYSIS BY ENGESSER'S THEOREM OF COMPATIBILITY

1	2	3	4	5	6
Member	Length	Area in.²	F	$\dfrac{\partial F}{\partial X}$	$\dfrac{\partial F}{\partial Y}$
1, 9	$L/\sqrt{2}$	$4\sqrt{2}$	$\sqrt{2}(Y/2 - 20)$	0	$1/\sqrt{2}$
2, 10	$L/\sqrt{2}$	$2\sqrt{2}$	$\sqrt{2}(Y/2 + 20)$	0	$1/\sqrt{2}$
3, 8	L	6	$40 - X - Y$	-1	-1
5, 6	$L\sqrt{2}$	$2\sqrt{2}$	$\sqrt{2}(Y/2 + X - 20)$	$\sqrt{2}$	$1/\sqrt{2}$
4	L	1/2	X	1	0
7	L	8	$40 - X$	-1	0

Assuming that X is compressive and that Y acts outwards at A and B, the forces in the members are given in column (4) of TABLE 2.29. The partial differentials $\dfrac{\partial F}{\partial X}$, $\dfrac{\partial F}{\partial Y}$ are also given in columns (5) and (6). Then

$$\frac{\partial C}{\partial X} = 0 = 2(40 - X - Y) \cdot \frac{L}{6E}(-1) + 2\sqrt{2}\left(\frac{Y}{2} + X - 20\right)\frac{\sqrt{2}L}{2\sqrt{2}E}(\sqrt{2})$$

$$\text{(bars 3, 8)} \qquad\qquad\qquad \text{(bars 5, 6)}$$

$$+ \frac{2L}{E}(2X - 2)(1) + \frac{(40 - X)L}{8E}(-1)$$

$$\text{(bar 4)} \qquad\quad \text{(bar 7)}$$

from which

$$0 = -62 \cdot 333 + 6 \cdot 458X + 1 \cdot 333Y \qquad\qquad \dots\text{(iv)}$$

In the above calculation, expressions (iii) were used for bars 3, 8, 5, 6 and 7, and expression (ii) for bar 4, which is non-linear.

Similarly,

$$\frac{\partial C}{\partial Y} = 0 = 2\sqrt{2}\left(\frac{Y}{2} - 20\right)\frac{L}{\sqrt{2}.4\sqrt{2E}}\left(\frac{1}{\sqrt{2}}\right) + \frac{2.2.L}{\sqrt{2E}}\left\{\frac{\sqrt{2}\left(\frac{Y}{2} + 20\right)}{2\sqrt{2}} - 2\right\}\frac{1}{\sqrt{2}}$$

(bars 1, 9)   (bars 2, 10)

$$+ 2\,(40 - X - Y)\frac{L}{6E}\,(-1) + 2\sqrt{2}\left(\frac{Y}{2} + X - 20\right)\frac{\sqrt{2}L}{2\sqrt{2E}}\left(\frac{1}{\sqrt{2}}\right)$$

(bars 3, 8)   (bars 5, 6)

from which

$$0 = -\,22{\cdot}333 + 1{\cdot}333X + 1{\cdot}458Y \qquad \dots\text{ (v)}$$

The solution to equations (iv) and (v) is:

$$X = Y = 8{\cdot}00 \text{ tons.}$$

As both X and Y are found to be positive, that is in the assumed direction, the solution is correct.

It is worth remarking that if the method of minimum potential energy or of virtual work had been used in this problem, there would have been 4 unknown displacements instead of 2 unknown forces, and if the structure had been unsymmetrical there would have been 8 unknown displacements.

Finally it may be remarked that if in a hyperstatic pin-jointed framework a redundant member is inserted an amount λ too short when the frame is put together, then

$$\frac{\partial C}{\partial X} = +\,\lambda \qquad \dots\text{ [2.13]}$$

where X is the force in this member, assumed tensile.

Problem 2.31, below, is an exercise dealing with this point.

Problems for Solution

2.30.   Solve *Problems 1.27* and *1.28*, Chapter 1 and *Problems 2.6, 2.7, 2.22* and *2.25*.

2.31.   If in *Problem 2.25* the central vertical member has an area of 12 in.², the other members being as before, and is an amount $\dfrac{20L}{3E}$ too short when the frame is constructed, find the force in this member when the structure carries the load shown.

2.6. CASTIGLIANO'S THEOREM OF COMPATIBILITY (MINIMUM STRAIN ENERGY)
[Volume I, Chapter 2, Section 2.6.8]

Referring to FIGURE 2.1, which was used in the discussion of Engesser's Theorem of Compatibility, the area U under the load–extension curve for a member of a framework is known as the strain energy of the member. Evidently,

$$U = \int_0^e F.\,\mathrm{d}e \qquad \dots\text{ [2.1(a)]}$$

while for an assemblage of n bars we can write

$$U = \sum \int_0^{e_n} F_n \cdot de \qquad \dots \ [2.1(b)]$$

The conditions of compatibility relevant to a redundant X of a hyperstatic structure can be written in the form

$$\frac{\partial U}{\partial X} = 0 \qquad \dots \ [2.14(a)]$$

provided the structure is linear in behaviour. Since this equation implies that the strain energy of the structure is stationary for variations in X it was called the equation of minimum strain energy or 'least work' by its originator Castigliano.

Since for linear structures $U = C$, the theorem is evidently a special case of the more general theorem of Engesser. If the redundant member has an initial lack of fit λ, then:

$$\frac{\partial U}{\partial X} = \lambda \qquad \dots \ [2.14]$$

λ being positive if the member is too short and tensile forces being taken as positive.

Castigliano's Theorem is dealt with fully in Chapter 4, and it will be sufficient here to illustrate its application by a few simple examples.

Problem 2.32—Reverting to *Problem 2.20* again we know that the strain energy U of a bar under axial load is $\dfrac{F^2 L}{2AE}$.

Hence

$$\frac{dU}{dX} = \frac{FL}{AE} \cdot \frac{\partial F}{\partial X}$$

and for the complete structure,

$$\frac{dU}{dX} = \sum \frac{FL}{AE} \cdot \frac{\partial F}{\partial X} = 0 \qquad \dots \ (i)$$

Resolving at D, we obtain as before (Example 2.27),

$$\left. \begin{aligned} F_1 &= \frac{P}{\sqrt{3}} - \frac{2X}{\sqrt{3}} \\[2mm] F_3 &= \frac{2P}{\sqrt{3}} - \frac{X}{\sqrt{3}} \end{aligned} \right\} \qquad \dots \ (ii)$$

The working is most conveniently done in tabular form (TABLE 2.32). From this table, which is self-explanatory,

$$\sum \frac{FL}{AE} \frac{\partial F}{\partial X} = \frac{(21X - 6P)L}{12aE} = 0$$

from which $X - \dfrac{2P}{7}$, as before.

If this solution is compared with that given in *Problem 2.27* it will be seen that the calculation is essentially the same. This illustrates the comment above that Castigliano's

TABLE 2.32

ANALYSIS BY CASTIGLIANO'S THEOREM OF COMPATIBILITY

1	2	3	4	5	6
Member	Length	Area	F	$\dfrac{\partial F}{\partial X}$	$\dfrac{FL}{AE}\dfrac{\partial F}{\partial X}$
1	L	$2a$	$\dfrac{1}{\sqrt{3}}(P-2X)$	$-\dfrac{2}{\sqrt{3}}$	$\dfrac{(2X-P)L}{3aE}$
2	L	a	X	1	$\dfrac{XL}{aE}$
3	L	$4a$	$\dfrac{1}{\sqrt{3}}(2P-X)$	$-\dfrac{1}{\sqrt{3}}$	$\dfrac{(X-2P)L}{12aE}$
				$\sum$	$\dfrac{(7X-2P)L}{4aE}$

Theorem is merely a special case of Engesser's Theorem. It should particularly be noted that careful attention must be paid to signs throughout. It is advisable to adhere to one convention such as that tensile forces are positive.

Problem 2.33—All the members of the framework shown have the same value of $\dfrac{L}{AE} = \rho$ except 8, for which it is ρ_1. Bar 8 is inserted last in making the framework.

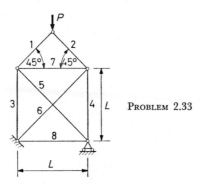

PROBLEM 2.33

(a) If it is of the correct length when inserted find the force in it due to the load P;
(b) How much shorter should it be if the force in bar 3 is to be reduced to one-half of its value in the frame without the member 8?

(a) This frame has one redundant which we take to be the force X, assumed tensile, in member 8 (in symmetrical structures some time is usually saved in calculation if the redundant forces are symmetrical with respect to the structure: rather more work would be involved if member 6, say, had been selected instead). We obtain the bar forces in terms of X and the load P, and again tabulate the values obtained (TABLE 2.33). The working is self explanatory.

From the Table,

$$\sum \frac{FL}{AE}\frac{\partial F}{\partial X} = X(7\rho + \rho_1) - P\frac{\rho}{2} = 0$$

from which

$$X = \frac{P\rho}{2(7\rho + \rho_1)}$$

TABLE 2.33

ANALYSIS BY CASTIGLIANO'S THEOREM OF COMPATIBILITY

1	*2*	*3*	*4*	*5*
Member	$\dfrac{L}{AE}$	F	$\dfrac{\partial F}{\partial X}$	$\dfrac{FL}{AE}\dfrac{\partial F}{\partial X}$
1, 2	ρ	$-P/\sqrt{2}$	0	0
3, 4	ρ	$-\dfrac{P}{2} + X$	1	$(X - P/2)2\rho$
5, 6	ρ	$-\sqrt{2}X$	$-\sqrt{2}$	$4X\rho$
7	ρ	$P/2 + X$	1	$(X + P/2)\rho$
8	ρ_1	X	1	XP_1
			$\sum$	$X(7\rho + \rho_1) - \dfrac{P\rho}{2}$

(b) If member 8 were inserted an amount λ too short, we would have

$$\sum \frac{FL}{AE}\frac{\partial F}{\partial X} = + \lambda$$

Hence

$$X(7\rho + \rho_1) - \frac{P\rho}{2} = \lambda$$

from which

$$X = \frac{2\lambda + P\rho}{2(7\rho + \rho_1)}$$

The force in $3 = X - \dfrac{P}{2} = \dfrac{2\lambda - 6P\rho - P\rho_1}{2(7\rho + \rho_1)}$

Without the member 8 the force in member 3 is $-\dfrac{P}{2}$

Hence

$$-\frac{P}{2} = 2\left(\frac{2\lambda - 6P\rho - P\rho_1}{2(7\rho + \rho_1)}\right)$$

from which

$$\lambda = \frac{P(5\rho + \rho_1)}{4}$$

50

Problem 2.34—As a final example of the use of Castigliano's Theorem in simple problems we take the table previously analysed in Chapter 1 (*Problem 1.20*). For any leg $\dfrac{L}{AE} = \rho$.

The table top is rigid, so that it has no strain energy.

Resolving vertically and taking moments about the lines AC and BD in turn, we obtain the equations previously derived:

$$A + B + C + D = P \qquad \qquad \dots \text{(i)}$$

$$BL - DL = -Pa \qquad \qquad \dots \text{(ii)}$$

$$AL - CL = -Pb \qquad \qquad \dots \text{(iii)}$$

from which we find that

$$
\left.
\begin{aligned}
A &= \frac{P}{2}\left(1 + \frac{a}{L} - \frac{b}{L}\right) - D \\
B &= D - \frac{Pa}{L} \\
C &= \frac{P}{2}\left(1 + \frac{a}{L} + \frac{b}{L}\right) - D
\end{aligned}
\right\} \qquad \dots \text{(iv)}
$$

We derive the fourth equation which we need from the relationship:

$$\sum \frac{FL}{AE} \cdot \frac{\partial F}{\partial D} = \sum F\rho \cdot \frac{\partial F}{\partial D} = 0$$

Substituting the above values of the forces, we find that

$$
0 = -\rho\left\{\frac{P}{2}\left(1 + \frac{a}{L} - \frac{b}{L}\right) - D\right\} + \rho\left(D - \frac{Pa}{L}\right)
$$
$$
-\rho\left\{\frac{P}{2}\left(1 + \frac{a}{L} + \frac{b}{L}\right) - D\right\} + \rho D
$$

from which

$$D = \frac{P}{4}\left(1 + \frac{2a}{L}\right)$$

Problems for Solution

2.35. Solve *Problems 1.22–1.26* inclusive and *1.29–1.33* inclusive.

2.36. Solve *Problem 2.22* using a step-by-step procedure (a separate calculation is necessary for each increment of applied load within which the change in load in each wire is proportional to the change in applied load).

CHAPTER 3

DEFLEXION OF STRUCTURES
[Volume 1, Chapters 2 and 3]

3.1. INTRODUCTION

It is very often necessary to calculate the deflexions of various joints in a structure. Not infrequently deflexion rather than stress is the criterion by which the sizes of the members are determined; during the erection of structures careful calculation of deflexions at various stages is often essential, while in hyperstatic structures the distribution of the internal forces depends on the relative flexibility of the various components; deflexion calculations therefore play an important part in hyperstatic analysis.

In this chapter examples are first given of deflexion calculations by the methods of virtual work and complementary energy [Volume 1, Chapter 2] which apply to non-linear as well as to linear structures. The remainder of the chapter is devoted to the more powerful procedures which have been devised for linear problems: Castigliano's Theorem, Part II, the dummy unit load method, the special procedures for beams based on integration of the equation,

$$EI\frac{d^2y}{dx^2} = M \qquad \qquad \dots [3.14]$$

and the graphical methods of Williot-Mohr and Hoadley [see Volume 1, Chapter 3]

3.2. GENERAL METHODS FOR CALCULATING DEFLEXIONS OF LINEAR AND NON-LINEAR STRUCTURES

3.2.1. Virtual Work [Volume 1, Chapter 2, Section 2.6.2.5]

Let us suppose that it is required to find the deflexion ΔE of a certain joint E in a pin-jointed structure the lengths of whose members change by amounts e owing to the action of some agency.

In Mohr's Equation of Virtual Work

$$\sum \bar{P}\{\Delta_E\} = \sum \bar{F}\{e\} \qquad \qquad \dots [2.6]$$

we choose as the force system $\bar{P}$ a unit load applied at the joint in question, in the direction in which the deflexion is required. The equation then becomes:

$$\Delta_E = \sum F'\{e\}$$

where

$$F' = (\bar{F})_{\bar{P}=1}$$

52

Problem 3.1—In the framework shown, the load-deformation relation for members *EF* and *FG* is

$$F = 600e \pm 1200e^2 \quad (|e| < 0.25 \text{ in.}, |F| < 75 \text{ tons})$$

(In this equation the negative sign is relevant if the member is in tension and the positive sign if it is in compression)

$$F = \pm 75 \text{ tons} \quad (|e| > 0.25 \text{ in.})$$

The other members are linear in behaviour and have the cross-sectional areas (in in.²) shown in circles. Find the vertical deflexion of *B* due to (a) the loading shown, (b) a slip of 0·03 in. in each end connexion of all members which carry force when the loading is applied.

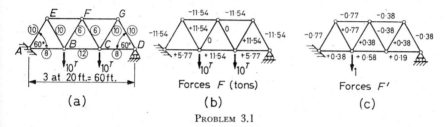

Forces *F* (tons)

(a)   (b)   Forces *F'* (c)

PROBLEM 3.1

(a) The forces *F* due to the 10 ton loads are shown at (b) and in TABLE 3.1, column 3. For the elastic members the change in length *e* equals $\dfrac{FL}{AE}$; using the areas

TABLE 3.1

CALCULATIONS OF DEFLEXION BY VIRTUAL WORK

1	2	3	4	5	6	7	8
Member	Area in.²	F tons	e × 10⁻² in.	F'	F'e × 10⁻²	e in.	F'e
AB	8	5·77	1·29	0·38	0·49	0·06	0·023
BC	12	11·54	1·72	0·58	1·00	0·06	0·035
CD	8	5·77	1·29	0·19	0·24	0·06	0·011
EF	—	− 11·54	− 2·00	− 0·77	1·54	− 0·06	0·046
FG	—	− 11·54	− 2·00	− 0·38	0·76	− 0·06	0·023
AE	10	− 11·54	− 2·06	− 0·77	1·59	− 0·06	0·046
EB	10	11·54	2·06	0·77	1·59	0·06	0·046
BF	6	0	0	0·38	0	0	0
FC	6	0	0	− 0·38	0	0	0
CG	10	11·54	2·06	0·38	0·78	0·06	0·023
GD	10	− 11·54	− 2·06	− 0·38	0·78	− 0·06	0·023
				Σ	8·77	Σ	0·276

given, $L = 240$ in. for each member and $E = 13{,}400$ tons/in.², we find that the *e*'s for these members are as recorded in column 4. As the members *EF* and *FG* are in

E   53

compression we use the load-deformation equation

$$F = -11 \cdot 54 = 600e + 1200e^2$$

the solution to which is $e = -0 \cdot 02$ in. or $-0 \cdot 48$ in.
Since $|F| < 75$ tons we take $e = -0 \cdot 02$ in.
The appropriate force system $\bar{P}$ is chosen as a unit load acting vertically downwards at B. This gives the virtual bar forces F' shown in (c) and TABLE 3.1, column 5. The product $F'e$ is then calculated for each member (column 6) and summed for the complete truss, giving

$$\Delta_B = + 8 \cdot 77 \times 10^{-2} \text{ in.}$$

The positive sign means that B moves in the same sense as $\bar{P} = 1$, i.e. downwards. In this particular problem the sign of $F'e$ is positive for all loaded members but this is quite fortuitous and in general the product $F'e$ may be either positive or negative for a particular member. Proper regard must always be paid to signs in such calculations.

(b) In the second part of the problem every member loaded in tension will extend a further amount $0 \cdot 06$ in. owing to slip, and every compression member will shorten by the same amount. These movements are now the e's (column 7).

Then
$$\Delta_B = \sum F'e$$

The products $F'e$ are tabulated in column 8. On summing these we find that the additional vertical movement of B due to the yield of the connexions is

$$\Delta_B = 0 \cdot 276 \text{ in. (downwards)}$$

3.2.2. FIRST THEOREM OF COMPLEMENTARY ENERGY [Volume 1, Chapter 2, Section 2.6.5]

The theorem states that

$$\frac{\partial C}{\partial P_j} = \Delta_j \qquad \qquad \dots \text{ [2.10]}$$

where C is the complementary energy of the structure, P_j is one of the applied loads and Δ_j is the displacement, in the direction of P_j, of the joint j at which P_j acts.

Here

$$C = \sum_n \int_0^{F_n} e \, \mathrm{d}F_n \qquad \qquad \dots \text{ [2.9]}$$

where F_n is the force in the nth member of the frame and e_n is its change of length.

Problem 3.2—Solve *Problem 3.1(a)* by Complementary Energy.

In the present problem the load at B is stated numerically. In order to use equation [2.10], however, it is necessary for P_j, the load at the point at which the deflexion is required, to be in algebraic form.

This difficulty may be overcome by the device of adding a further imaginary load P_i at B, differentiating C with respect to this load, and then equating P_i to zero. The forces F with this additional load acting are first tabulated (TABLE 3.2, column 3).

Now for each of the linear elastic members,

$$C = \int e \, \mathrm{d}F = \int_0^F \frac{FL}{AE} \, \mathrm{d}F = \frac{F^2 L}{2AE}$$

and
$$\left(\frac{\partial C}{\partial P_i}\right)_{P_i=0} = \left(\frac{FL}{AE}\cdot\frac{\partial F}{\partial P_i}\right)_{P_i=0}$$

Thus for member AB, for example, we have

$$\left(\frac{\partial C}{\partial P_i}\right)_{P_i=0} = (+\,5{\cdot}77 + 0{\cdot}38P_i)\frac{240\times0{\cdot}38}{8\times13400} = +\,0{\cdot}49\times10^{-2}\text{ in. when }P_i = 0.$$

$\partial F/\partial P_i$ is tabulated for each member in column 4 and it will be noticed that in each case it is equal to F' (TABLE 3.1, column 5) as was to be expected from the definition

TABLE 3.2

CALCULATION OF DEFLEXIONS BY COMPLEMENTARY ENERGY

1	2	3	4	5
Member	Area A in.^{2}	F tons	$\dfrac{dF}{dP_i}$	$\left(\dfrac{dC}{dP_i}\right)P_i = 0$
AB	8	$5{\cdot}77 + 0{\cdot}38P_t$	$0{\cdot}38$	$0{\cdot}49$
BC	12	$11{\cdot}54 + 0{\cdot}58P_t$	$0{\cdot}58$	$1{\cdot}00$
CD	8	$5{\cdot}77 + 0{\cdot}19P_t$	$0{\cdot}19$	$0{\cdot}24$
EF	—	$-\,11{\cdot}54 - 0{\cdot}77P_t$	$-\,0{\cdot}77$	$1{\cdot}54$
FG	—	$-\,11{\cdot}54 - 0{\cdot}38P_t$	$-\,0{\cdot}38$	$0{\cdot}76$
AE	10	$-\,11{\cdot}54 - 0{\cdot}77P_t$	$-\,0{\cdot}77$	$1{\cdot}59$
EB	10	$11{\cdot}54 + 0{\cdot}77P_t$	$0{\cdot}77$	$1{\cdot}59$
BF	6	$0{\cdot}38P_t$	$0{\cdot}38$	0
FC	6	$-\,0{\cdot}38P_t$	$-\,0{\cdot}38$	0
CG	10	$11{\cdot}54 + 0{\cdot}38P_t$	$0{\cdot}38$	$0{\cdot}78$
GD	10	$-\,11{\cdot}54 - 0{\cdot}38P_t$	$-\,0{\cdot}38$	$0{\cdot}78$
			Σ	$8{\cdot}77$

of a partial differential coefficient. It is particularly to be observed that $\partial F/\partial P_i$ has a real value even though $P_i=0$. $\dfrac{\partial C}{\partial P_i}$ for each member is tabulated in column 5. For either of the non-linear members EF or FG,

$$F = 600e + 1200e^2$$

from which

$e = -\tfrac{1}{4}(1 - \sqrt{1 + F/75})$, taking the negative sign as relevant, so that for either member

$$C = \int e.dF = -\tfrac{1}{4}\int_0^F (1 - \sqrt{1 + F/75})\,dF = -\tfrac{1}{4}[F - 50(1 + F/75)^{\,l\text{-}}]$$

Now
$$\left(\frac{\partial C}{\partial P_i}\right)_{P_i=0} = \frac{\partial C}{\partial F}\cdot\frac{\partial F}{\partial P_i} = \left[-\tfrac{1}{4}\left\{1 - \sqrt{1 + F/75}\right\}\frac{\partial F}{\partial P_i}\right]_{P_i=0}$$

Member EF: $F = -\,11{\cdot}54 - 0{\cdot}77P_i$

$$\frac{\partial F}{\partial P_i} = -\,0{\cdot}77$$

DEFLEXION OF STRUCTURES

$$\therefore \left(\frac{\partial C}{\partial P_i}_{P_i=}\right)_0 = -\tfrac{1}{4}\left(1 - \sqrt{1 - \frac{11\cdot54}{75}}\right)(-0\cdot77) = +1\cdot54 \times 10^{-2}\,\text{in.}$$

Member FG:

$$F = -11\cdot54 - 0\cdot38P_i$$

$$\frac{\partial F}{\partial P_i} = -0\cdot38$$

$$\therefore \left(\frac{\partial C}{\partial P_i}\right)_{P_i=0} = -\tfrac{1}{4}\left(1 - \sqrt{1 - \frac{11\cdot54}{75}}\right)(-0\cdot38) = +0\cdot76 \times 10^{-2}\,\text{in.}$$

Summing for all the members, we find again that

$$\Delta_B = 8\cdot77 \times 10^{-2}\,\text{in.}$$

As is pointed out in Volume I [Chapter 2, Section 2.6.5.2] the calculations of deflexions by virtual work and by complementary energy are basically identical: a comparison of TABLES 3.1 and 3.2 will further illustrate this.

Problems for Solution

3.3. Find the vertical deflexion of B if all the members of the truss are (a) linearly elastic and have cross-sectional areas A; (b) obey the load-deformation law:

$$e = 0 \quad (\text{for } |F| \leqslant P/4)$$

$$F = \pm P/4 + Ke \quad (\text{for } |F| > P/4), \text{ where the } + \text{ sign is}$$

relevant for tension members and the $-$ sign for compression members.

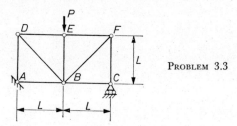

PROBLEM 3.3

3.4. The members of the truss shown obey the same law as in *3.3* (b) above. Find the vertical deflexion of B and the rotation (See *Problem 3.6*) of the member FG.

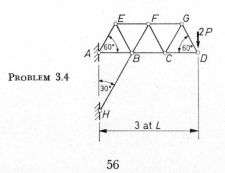

PROBLEM 3.4

56

3.5.   In the steel truss shown, find the vertical deflexion of C if the members ED and DC follow the load-deformation law:

$$F = 3P(2e + e^2) \quad (e \leqslant 1)$$
$$F = 3P \qquad\qquad (e > 1)$$

while the other members are linear and have cross-sectional area A, where $L/AE = 1$.

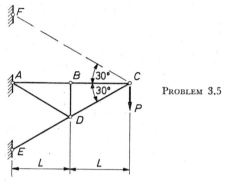

PROBLEM 3.5

It is proposed to stiffen the structure by adding the tie FC (area $A/2$) before the load P is applied. Find the force in FC and the change in the vertical deflexion of C if $P = 1/3$ ton.

3.3. DEFLEXION OF LINEAR PIN-JOINTED FRAMEWORKS

3.3.1. THE DUMMY UNIT LOAD METHOD [Volume 1, Chapter 3, Section 3.6]

This is the most convenient analytical method of determining the deflexion in a specified direction of a point on a pin-jointed framework. Suppose the members of the truss illustrated in FIGURE 3.1(a) change in length by amounts e because of some agency such as loading or temperature variation and that, as a result, joint j moves to j'. We wish to find the component of movement Δ_j in the specified oblique direction shown.

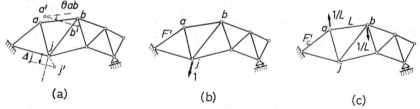

(a)   (b)   (c)

FIGURE 3.1 (a) As a result of changes of length e of the members the joints of this truss move to new positions: a to a', b to b', etc.; (b) To find the displacement Δ_j of j in the given direction a unit load is applied at j, in this direction, and forces F' are produced in the members; (c) To find the rotation of ab a unit couple is applied to the member.

To do this we apply a dummy unit load to the truss at j in the specified direction. Then if F' is the force thus induced in any member of the framework,

$$\Delta_j = \sum F'e \qquad\qquad \dots \text{[3.12]}$$

To find a rotation we apply the appropriate dummy unit couple. Thus θ_{ab}, the clockwise rotation of the member ab, is given by

$$\theta_{ab} = \sum F'_c e$$

where F'_c is the force due to a unit clockwise couple applied to ab (FIGURE 3.1(c).

Equation [3.12] is applicable to both linear and non-linear frameworks. In the special case of linear frameworks in which the changes in length e are caused by applied loads, we have

$$\Delta_j = \sum F'F\rho \qquad \dots [3.13]$$

where F is the actual force in a member due to the applied loads and $\rho = \dfrac{L}{AE}$

Problem 3.6—The cross-sectional areas of the members of the truss shown are tabulated in TABLE 3.6, column 2. It is required to find (a) the vertical displacement of D and the angular rotation of HJ due to the loads shown; (b) the vertical displacement of D if the top chord members and FM increase in temperature by 20°, the coefficient of linear expansion of the material being α_t; (c) the force in DN due to the loads shown if DN is an additional vertical member supporting D and of length L and area 10 in.². (*DN* is shown dotted at (a) in the diagram.)

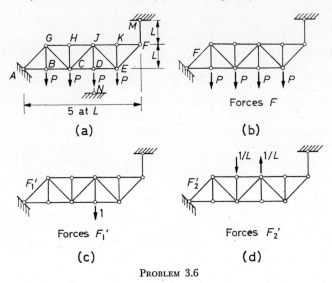

PROBLEM 3.6

(a) We determine the vertical displacement of D due to the loads P from the formula

$$\Delta_D = \sum \frac{F'_1 FL}{AE}$$

where F is the force in any member due to these loads, and F'_1 is the force due to a unit vertical load at D, acting downwards (3.6(c)). These forces are calculated by statics and are tabulated in columns 4 and 5 of TABLE 3.6. We then calculate the terms $\dfrac{F'_1 FL}{AE}$ (column 6) and add them up.

58

TABLE 3.6

CALCULATION OF DEFLEXIONS

1	2	3	4	5	6	7	8	9	10	11	12
Member	Area A in.²	Length	F	F_1'	$\dfrac{F_1'FL}{AE}$ $\times PL/E$	F_2'	$\dfrac{F_2'FL}{AE}$ $\times P/E$	e (temp.) $\times L\alpha_t$	$F_1'e$ $\times L\alpha_t$	$\dfrac{(F_1')^2 L}{AE}$ $\times L/E$	$\dfrac{FL}{AE}$ $\times PL/E$
AB	3	L	$+2P$	$+2/5$	$+0\cdot267$	$+1/5L$	$+0\cdot133$	0	0	$0\cdot053$	$2/3$
BC	6	L	$+2P$	$+2/5$	$+0\cdot133$	$+1/5L$	$+0\cdot067$	0	0	$0\cdot027$	$1/3$
CD	6	L	$+3P$	$+6/5$	$+0\cdot600$	$-2/5L$	$-0\cdot200$	0	0	$0\cdot240$	$1/2$
DE	3	L	$+3P$	$+6/5$	$+1\cdot200$	$-2/5L$	$-0\cdot400$	0	0	$0\cdot480$	1
EF	4	$L\sqrt{2}$	$+2\sqrt{2}P$	$+3\sqrt{2}/5$	$+0\cdot850$	$-\sqrt{2}/5L$	$-0\cdot283$	$+20$	$+12\cdot0$	$0\cdot254$	1
FM	10	L	$+2P$	$+3/5$	$+0\cdot120$	$-1/5L$	$-0\cdot040$	$+20$	$-12\cdot0$	$0\cdot036$	$1/5$
FK	6	L	$-2P$	$-3/5$	$+0\cdot200$	$+1/5L$	$-0\cdot067$	$+20$	$-12\cdot0$	$0\cdot060$	$-1/3$
KJ	8	L	$-2P$	$-3/5$	$+0\cdot150$	$+1/5L$	$-0\cdot050$	$+20$	$-16\cdot0$	$0\cdot045$	$-1/4$
JH	8	L	$-3P$	$-4/5$	$+0\cdot300$	$-2/5L$	$-0\cdot150$	$+20$	$-16\cdot0$	$0\cdot080$	$-3/8$
HG	6	L	$-3P$	$-4/5$	$+0\cdot400$	$-2/5L$	$-0\cdot200$	$+28\cdot3$	$-16\cdot0$	$0\cdot107$	$-1/2$
GA	4	$L\sqrt{2}$	$-2\sqrt{2}P$	$-2\sqrt{2}/5$	$+0\cdot556$	$-\sqrt{2}/5L$	$+0\cdot283$	0	0	$0\cdot113$	-1
GB	2	L	$+P$	0	0	0	0	0	0	0	$1/2$
GC	2	$L\sqrt{2}$	$+\sqrt{2}P$	$+2\sqrt{2}/5$	$+0\cdot566$	$+\sqrt{2}/5L$	$+0\cdot283$	0	0	$0\cdot226$	1
CH	1	L	0	0	0	$-1/L$	0	0	0	0	0
CJ	2	$L\sqrt{2}$	0	$-2\sqrt{2}/5$	0	$+4\sqrt{2}/5L$	0	0	0	$0\cdot226$	0
JD	2	L	$+P$	$+1$	$+0\cdot500$	0	0	0	0	$0\cdot500$	$1/2$
JE	2	$L\sqrt{2}$	$-\sqrt{2}P$	$-3\sqrt{2}/5$	$+0\cdot848$	$+\sqrt{2}/5L$	$-0\cdot283$	0	0	$0\cdot508$	-1
KE	1	L	0	0	0	0	0	0	0	0	0
				Σ	$+6\cdot700$	Σ	$-0\cdot207$	Σ	$-60\cdot0$	$2\cdot955$	

Thus

$$\Delta_D = + \frac{6 \cdot 700 PL}{E}$$

the positive sign indicating that the movement is downwards (i.e. in the direction of the dummy unit load) and not upwards.

The rotation of HJ is given by the formula

$$\theta_{HJ} = \sum \frac{F_2' FL}{AE}$$

where F_2' is the force in any member due to a unit couple applied to HJ (diagram 3.6(d)). In the diagram the loads $\frac{1}{L}$ at H and J produce a unit couple in an anticlockwise direction. The choice of direction is quite arbitrary.

The forces F_2' appear in column 7 and the terms $\frac{F_2' FL}{AE}$ in column 8 of TABLE 3.6. Summing, we find that

$$\theta_{HJ} = - \frac{0 \cdot 207 P}{E}$$

The negative sign indicates that the rotation is in fact clockwise, i.e. opposite in direction to the dummy unit couple.

(b) The vertical displacement of D when the top chord members and FM rise in temperature by $20°$ is given by the formula

$$\Delta_D = \sum F_1' e$$

where $e = $ length $\times \alpha_t \times 20°$ for each member which changes in length. The e's, which are all positive, being extensions, are shown in column 9 and the products $F_1' e$ in column 10. Then from the summation at the bottom of the column we have

$$\Delta_D = - 60 \cdot 0 L \alpha_t$$

Thus D moves upwards in this case.

(c) If R is the compressive force in DN when the loads P are applied, DN will shorten by an amount $\frac{RL}{10E}$. This is equal to the vertical movement of D in the original framework, i.e. without DN. Now the latter is subjected to the loads P and also to the load R acting vertically upwards at D. We already know Δ_D due to the loads P_1 and it is necessary to calculate the vertical movement of D due to R. If we call this movement Δ_D' then

$$\Delta_D' = \frac{F_R F_3' L}{AE}$$

where F_R is the force in any member due to R, and F_3' is the force due to a dummy unit load acting vertically upwards at D. We already know the forces due to a unit load at D acting downwards: these are the forces F_1'. Hence

$$\Delta_D' = \frac{- F_1' R(- F_1') L}{AE} = \frac{(F_1')^2 LR}{AE}$$

The quantities $(F_1')^2 L$ are given in TABLE 3.6, column 11. Thus we find that the downward movement of D due to the deformation of the framework is

$$\Delta_D'' = \frac{6 \cdot 70 PL}{E} - \frac{2 \cdot 955 RL}{E} = \frac{RL}{10E}$$

from which

$$R = + 2 \cdot 19P$$

It cannot be too often stressed that in all deflexion calculations in pin-jointed frames the correct signs for forces and deformations must be used, tensile forces and elongations being positive and compressive forces and shortenings negative.

In finding displacements in pin-jointed space frames we follow the same procedure as above and *Problem 3.7* illustrates this. The calculation of the forces in the bars is performed by the method of tension coefficients (Volume 1, Chapter 4, Section 4.5.6.1).

Problem 3.7—All the members of the frame, shown numbered for convenience, have the same ratio of cross-sectional area to length and are of the same material. The load P acts parallel to the x-axis. Find the movement of C parallel to the x-axis.

(Birmingham, 1949)

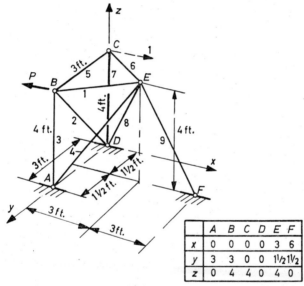

	A	B	C	D	E	F
x	0	0	0	0	3	6
y	3	3	0	0	$1\frac{1}{2}$	$1\frac{1}{2}$
z	0	4	4	0	4	0

PROBLEM 3.7

The displacement of C parallel to the x-axis is given by

$$\Delta_{Cx} = \sum F'F\rho$$

where F is the force in any member due to the load P and F' is the force due to a dummy unit load at C in the direction of the x-axis.

Forces F—We first observe that there can be no forces in the members meeting at C. If we resolve vertically we have only one bar force, F_7, and this must therefore be zero; we are then left with two bars 5 and 6 in the same plane but not in the same direction, and the forces in these must also be zero, i.e. $t_5 = t_6 = t_7 = 0$. It is very common for some of the bars in a space frame to be without load, and inspection should always precede the systematic use of the method of tension coefficients.

Now at joint B, if we resolve in the x-direction, the equation of equilibrium in tension coefficient form will be

$$t_1(x_E - x_B) - P = 0$$

or

$$t_1(3 - 0) - P = 0$$

$$\therefore t_1 = + P/3$$

In the y-direction we have

$$t_1(y_E - y_B) + t_2(y_D - y_B) + t_5(y_C - y_B) = 0$$

or

$$t_1(1 \cdot 5 - 3) + t_2(0 - 3) = 0$$

giving

$$t_2 = -\frac{t_1}{2} = - P/6$$

and in the z-direction,

$$t_2(0 - 4) + t_3(0 - 4) = 0$$

$$\therefore t_3 = - t_2 = + P/6$$

At joint E, in the x-direction, omitting the term in t_6 which is known to be zero,

$$t_1(0 - 3) + t_4(0 - 3) + t_8(0 - 3) + t_9(6 - 3) = 0$$

or

$$t_1 + t_4 + t_8 - t_9 = 0 \qquad \dots \text{(i)}$$

In the y-direction,

$$t_1(3 - 1 \cdot 5) + t_4(3 - 1 \cdot 5) + t_8(0 - 1 \cdot 5) = 0$$

or

$$t_1 + t_4 - t_8 = 0 \qquad \dots \text{(ii)}$$

Finally in the z-direction,

$$t_4(0 - 4) + t_8(0 - 4) + t_9(0 - 4) = 0$$

or

$$t_4 + t_8 + t_9 = 0 \qquad \dots \text{(iii)}$$

Solving equations (i) to (iii) we find that

$$t_4 = - P/4, \qquad t_8 = +\frac{P}{12}, \qquad t_9 = +\frac{P}{6}$$

Now the force F in any member $= tL$.

The lengths of the members are given in TABLE 3.7, column 2 and the forces F in column 3.

Forces F'—We apply a dummy unit horizontal load at C acting in the positive direction of x, i.e. to the right (see the dotted arrow in the figure) and determine the bar forces thus induced.

Then at the joint C, resolving vertically, we see that $t_7' = 0$.

In the x-direction, we have:

$$t_6'(3 - 0) + 1 = 0$$

or

$$t_6' = -\frac{1}{3}$$

In the y-direction,

$$t_5'(3 - 0) + t_6'(1\cdot5 - 0) = 0$$

or

$$t_5' = -\frac{t_6'}{2} = +\frac{1}{6}$$

Turning to joint B, we first observe that there is only one component of force in the x-direction, that in bar 1, so that $t_1' = 0$.

TABLE 3.7

CALCULATION OF DEFLEXIONS

1	2	3	4	5
Member	Length : ft.	F	F'	F'F
1	3·36	+ 1·12P	0	0
2	5·00	− 0·83P	− 0·83	+ 0·69P
3	4·00	+ 0·67P	+ 0·67	+ 0·44P
4	5·22	− 1·31P	− 0·44	+ 0·57P
5	3·00	0	+ 0·50	0
6	3·36	0	− 1·12	0
7	4·00	0	0	0
8	5·22	+ 0·44P	+ 1·31	+ 0·57P
9	5·00	+ 0·83P	− 0·83	− 0·69P
			Σ	+ 1·58P

In the y-direction, we have:

$$t_5'(0 - 3) + t_2'(0 - 3) = 0$$

$$\therefore t_2' = -t_5' = -\frac{1}{6}$$

In the z-direction,

$$t_2'(0 - 4) + t_3'(0 - 4) = 0$$

or

$$t_3' = -t_2' = +\frac{1}{6}$$

We now consider joint E.
In the x-direction,

$$t_6'(0 - 3) + t_4'(0 - 3) + t_8'(0 - 3) + t_9'(3 - 0) = 0$$

or

$$\frac{1}{3} - t_4' - t_8' + t_9' = 0 \qquad \dots\text{(iv)}$$

In the y-direction, we have:

$$t_6'(0 - 1\cdot5) + t_4'(3 - 1\cdot5) + t_8'(0 - 1\cdot5) + t_9'(1\cdot5 - 1\cdot5) = 0$$

or

$$\frac{1}{3} + t_4' - t_8' = 0 \qquad \dots\text{(v)}$$

And finally in the z-direction,

$$t'_4(0-4) + t'_8(0-4) + t'_9(0-4) = 0$$

or $$t'_4 + t'_8 + t'_9 = 0 \qquad \dots \text{(vi)}$$

Solving these three equations, we find that

$$t'_4 = -\frac{1}{12}, \quad t'_8 = +\frac{1}{4}, \quad t'_9 = -\frac{1}{6}$$

The forces F', obtained by multiplying the tension coefficients by the lengths of the members, are given in column 4.

The products $F'F$ are now worked out (see column 5).

Finally,

$$\Delta_{C_x} = \sum F'F\rho = + 1 \cdot 58\rho$$

the positive sign indicating that the movement of C is in the positive direction of x.

When using tension coefficients, one can save some work by expressing the formula for deflexion in terms of the coefficients. Thus in the general case

$$\Delta = \sum F'F\rho = \sum t'tL^3/AE$$

and it is not necessary to evaluate the forces F' and F.

Problems for Solution

3.8. The cross-sectional area of the diagonals of the truss shown is $A/2$; that of all other members is A. Find θ_{DE} and the horizontal movement of F.

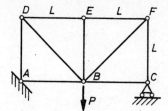

PROBLEM 3.8

3.9. All members are of steel and have a cross-sectional area of 1 in.² A vertical load at F causes the joint G to deflect $\frac{1}{4}$ in. downwards. Find the load at F.

(Leeds, 1952)

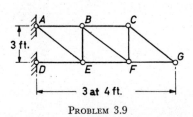

PROBLEM 3.9

PROBLEM 3.10

3.10. When equal loads act at the lower panel points of the steel truss shown, the stress in all tension members is f tons/in.² and in all compression members $0 \cdot 8f$ tons/in.² Find f if the ratio of maximum deflexion to span is 1/900.

(London, 1951)

64

3.11. The truss shown is pinned at *A*, the other support being free to move. Under a given application of load the alteration in the lengths of members is

$$AC, CD, DB, CE, FD, GD: + 0.12 \text{ in.}$$

$$AE, EF, FG, BG, FC: \quad - 0.08 \text{ in.}$$

If the movement of *G* is horizontal find the horizontal and vertical movements of *C*.

(Glasgow, 1957)

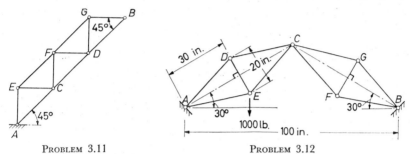

PROBLEM 3.11   PROBLEM 3.12

3.12. In this symmetrical frame members *DE* and *FG* are bisected at right angles by lines *AC* and *BC* respectively. *AE*, *AD*, *BF* and *BG* are all of the same length. *DC*, *CE*, *GC* and *FC* are also all of the same length which is not the same as that of *AE* etc. All bars have a cross-sectional area of 1 in.² and are of steel.

If *AB* is horizontal find the true movement of *C* due to the 1000 lb. load acting at *E*. (The forces in the members are best found graphically.)

(Birmingham, 1952)

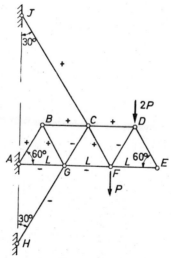

PROBLEM 3.13

3.13. The truss shown is so designed that under the loads shown the stress in all members is $\pm f$. Find the horizontal movement of *B* if the signs of the stresses are as indicated in the figure.

(Melbourne, 1957)

3.14. In this truss the cross-sectional area of the chord members is 2*A* and of the web members is *A*. Find the vertical deflexion of *E* and the relative movement of *A* and *G* caused (a) by the vertical load *P* at *E*, and (b) by a rise *t*° in the temperature of the lower chord members.

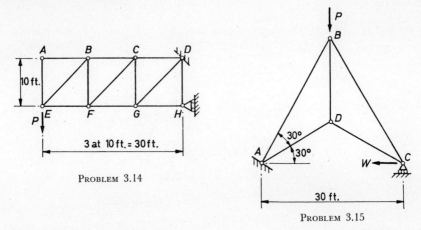

PROBLEM 3.14

PROBLEM 3.15

3.15. All the members have the same value of ρ. Find the vertical deflexion of *B* and the horizontal movement of *C*.

3.16. The cross-sectional area of each member is *A*. Find the relative movement of *H* and *E* caused by the loads shown. Find also what uniform change of temperature of the whole truss would reduce this movement to zero if the members are of steel and *A* = 10 in.²

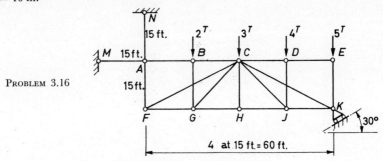

PROBLEM 3.16

3.17. All the members of this symmetrical three-pinned arch have the same value of ρ. Find the horizontal and vertical components of the movement of *D*.

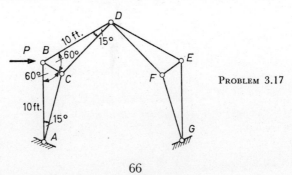

PROBLEM 3.17

66

3.18.   The framework shown is loaded in a certain way and the reaction at E due to this loading is $4P$, upwards. The frame is then hoisted up at H by a sling HJ which is tied to a point J vertically above A. Find by how much H must move in the direction HJ for the roller support at E to leave the bearing surface XX and move unit distance perpendicular to this surface. The cross-sectional area of each member is A.

(Melbourne, 1956)

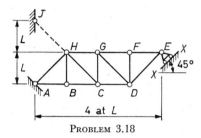

PROBLEM 3.18

3.19.   The top chord members of the steel truss shown are made 24 ft. 0·3 in. long. Find the elevation of the lower chord joint K above AG when the truss is assembled if the weight of the truss is ignored.

If all the members have the same cross-sectional area, find the deflexion of K due to the dead weight of the truss.

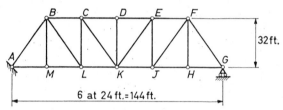

PROBLEM 3.19

3.20.   Find the vertical deflexion of C in the framework shown in the diagram if the cross-sectional area of the tension members is A and that of the compression members $2A$. It is proposed to stiffen the structure by adding the tie shown dotted (area A). Find the change in the vertical deflexion of C.

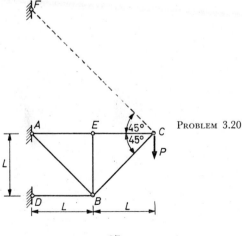

PROBLEM 3.20

67

3.21. If all the bars have the same extensibility aE, calculate the vertical deflexion of A.

(St. Andrews, 1949)

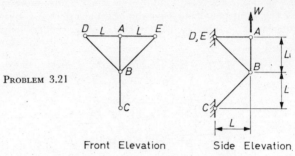

PROBLEM 3.21

Front Elevation   Side Elevation

3.22. In the steel derrick shown the rope OFH is attached to a winch fixed to the ground in the plane BCD, and is applying a pull of 2000 lb. at a point H. The areas

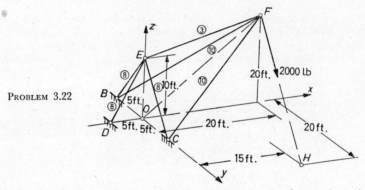

PROBLEM 3.22

of the members, in square inches, are shown in circles in the figure. Assuming that the rope wheel bearings at F are frictionless, find the movements of F in the y- and z-directions when the pull is being taken.

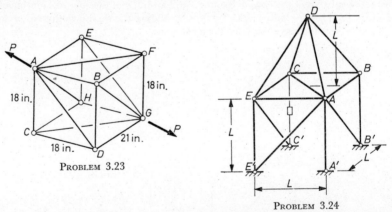

PROBLEM 3.23

PROBLEM 3.24

3.23. All the members of the frame shown have the same value of ρ. If two opposite corners A and G are pulled apart with a force P, find the relative movement of A and G and compare this with the relative movement of B and H.

(After London, 1957)

68

3.24. The members of the truss shown have the same cross-sectional area A. In plan, D is centrally located in the square $ECBA$, which is parallel to the base $E'C'B'A'$ and at a height L above it. By means of a turnbuckle in CC' a tensile force P is induced in bar CC'. By how much does the turnbuckle shorten the member CC'?

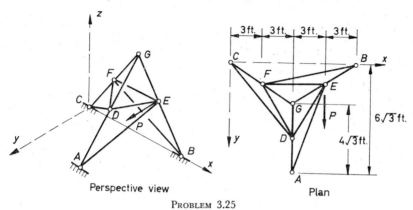

Perspective view   Plan

PROBLEM 3.25

3.25. In the space frame shown, the z-coordinate of G is $+6$ ft. and that of D, E and $F+3$ ft. GEB, GDA and GFC are all straight lines. The cross-sectional areas are all A. Find the movement of G in the y-direction when a load P parallel to the y-axis is applied at E as shown. Show that this equals the movement of E in the y-direction when the load P is transferred to G.

(After Melbourne, 1956)

3.26. A horizontal rigid triangular plate ABC is supported as shown by six bars, each of cross-sectional area A, pinned to a horizontal base DEF at a distance L below the plate. The plate is subjected to a couple M in its plane and to a horizontal force P perpendicular to the plane EBF. Find the movement of B in the horizontal and vertical directions and the rotation of the plate in its own plane.

(After Melbourne, 1957)

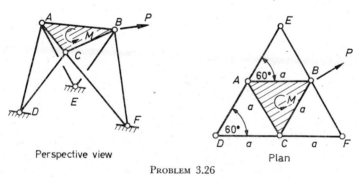

Perspective view   Plan

PROBLEM 3.26

3.3.2. THE WILLIOT-MOHR METHOD [Volume I, Chapter 3, Section 3.6.2]

The dummy unit load method gives the deflexion of a certain joint in a specified direction so that if the absolute movement of the joint is required a second calculation must be made to find the deflexion in the direction at right angles to the first. In this case it may be better to use a graphical method and this is especially so if the deflexion of several joints is required.

Problem 3.27—Problem 3.6, part (a) will be solved by the Williot-Mohr method.

It is first necessary to calculate the change in length of each member of the truss under the loads shown in diagram 3.6(a). These values of FL/AE were tabulated in column 12 of TABLE 3.6 and are shown again at (a) on diagram 3.27.

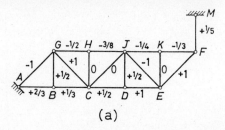

(a)

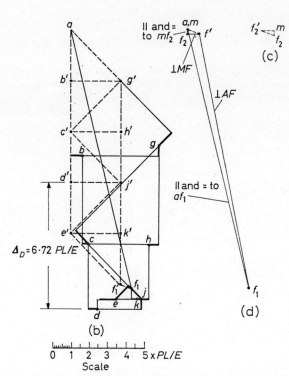

(b)

PROBLEM 3.27 (a). It is required to find the deflexion of the truss caused by the changes of length of the members shown; (b) Williot-Mohr diagram for the truss *AGFE*; (c) Williot-Mohr diagram for the bar *MF*; (d) Williot diagram for the triangle *AFM*.

We now draw the displacements of the joint of the truss *AGFEA* on the assumption that *J* is fixed and that *JK* does not rotate. The Williot diagram 3.27(b) is therefore drawn by starting at *j* and proceeding in the order *j-k-e-f, e-d-c-h-g-b-a*. The line af_1 gives the movement of *F* relative to *A*. A second Williot diagram is now drawn for the

70

single member MF; this is shown at (c) and consists only of the line mf_2. (The construction now being described is that used for three-hinged braced arches in which the first step is to draw separate Williot diagrams for each half of the arch.) A third Williot diagram, shown at (d), is now drawn for the triangle AFM. In this diagram A and M, being fixed points, are represented by the single point a,m; the movement of F relative to A, af_1, is transferred from diagram (b) while its movement relative to G, mf_2, is transferred from diagram (c). The final position of F, namely f', is then obtained in the usual way by drawing lines perpendicular to MF and AF respectively. Thus the absolute movement of F is represented on this diagram by $a,m - f'$ and this vector must now be transferred to the two Williot diagrams (b) and (c) so that Mohr rotation diagrams can be drawn.

Remembering that the absolute movement of a joint is given by the vector joining the point on the Mohr diagram to the corresponding point on the Williot diagram, we obtain the points f_1' and f_2' on diagrams (b) and (c) respectively.

Thus $f_1' - f_1 = f_2' - f_2 = a,m - f' =$ absolute movement of F.

It is now possible to draw the Mohr diagram for the truss $A - F$ by superimposing on (b) a diagram of the truss rotated through 90°; the point f_1' on this diagram has already been located so that the scale of the diagram is known.

Thus $a - b' - g' \ldots f_1'$ is the Mohr diagram for the truss $A - F$.

The Mohr diagram for MF is the single dotted line mf_2' on diagram (c). (If MF had also been a truss the advantage of separating the diagrams, in the manner just described, would have become apparent.)

It is now possible to obtain the absolute movement of any joint; thus:

The vertical displacement of D is equal to the vertical component of $d'd$ on the complete displacement diagram and is $6\ 72 \dfrac{PL}{E}$ $\left(6{\cdot}70\dfrac{PL}{E}\right)$ H moves downwards a distance $5{\cdot}99\dfrac{PL}{E}$, and J a distance $6{\cdot}21\dfrac{PL}{E}$. The rotation of HJ is therefore clockwise and equal to $0{\cdot}22\dfrac{P}{E}$. $\left(0{\cdot}207\dfrac{P}{E}\right)$.

The values obtained previously by calculation are given in parentheses for comparison.

Problems for Solution

3.28.   Problem *3.6* part (b) and *Problems 3.8* to *3.20* inclusive.

3.4. DEFLEXION OF BEAMS AND RIGIDLY JOINTED STRUCTURES [Volume I, Chapter 3, Section 3.7]

3.4.1. Beams

Various methods are available for the calculation of the deflexions of simply supported beams. Those discussed in Volume I are the method of integration, the dummy unit load method and the moment area method. A number of examples are given in Volume I and it will be sufficient here to solve one rather more involved problem by the various methods.

3.4.1.1. *Method of Integration* [Volume I, Chapter 3, Section 3.7.2]

Problem 3.29—The beam $ABDC$ illustrated in diagram (a) is of uniform EI and is loaded by a couple Z acting at A and a uniformly distributed load of w/unit length over DC. Find the deflexion and angular discontinuity at B.

We deal first with the part BC, and take the origin of coordinates at B.

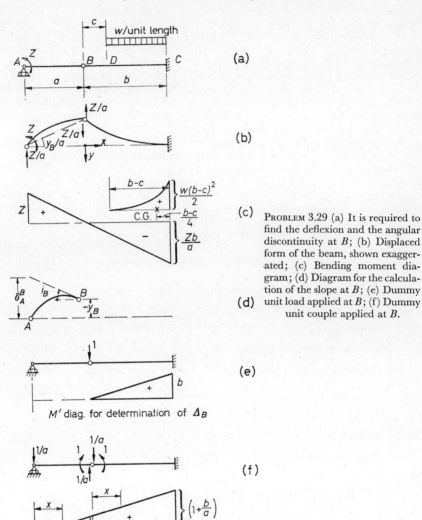

(a)

(b)

(c)

(d)

(e)

PROBLEM 3.29 (a) It is required to find the deflexion and the angular discontinuity at B; (b) Displaced form of the beam, shown exaggerated; (c) Bending moment diagram; (d) Diagram for the calculation of the slope at B; (e) Dummy unit load applied at B; (f) Dummy unit couple applied at B.

M' diag. for determination of Δ_B

(f)

M' diag. for determination of θ_B

Then we have

$$M = EI \frac{d^2y}{dx^2} = -\frac{Zx}{a} + \frac{w}{2}[x - c]^2 \qquad \dots \text{(i)}$$

Using the convention of signs given in Volume I and making use of Macaulay's device in the term involving w (the square brackets indicate that the term enclosed by them is to be ignored when $x < c$), we have, on integration

$$EI \frac{dy}{dx} = -\frac{Zx^2}{2a} + \frac{w[x - c]^3}{6} + C_1 \qquad \dots \text{(ii)}$$

and

$$EIy = -\frac{Zx^3}{6a} + \frac{w[x-c]^4}{24} + C_1 x + C_2 \qquad \dots \text{(iii)}$$

We obtain the values of the constants C_1 and C_2 as follows:

At C, when $x = b$, $\dfrac{dy}{dx} = 0$;

hence on substituting for $x = b$ in (ii),

$$C_1 = \frac{Zb^2}{2a} - \frac{w}{6}(b-c)^3$$

Also at C when $x = b$, $y = 0$;

in (iii), therefore,

$$0 = -\frac{Zb^3}{6a} + \frac{w(b-c)^4}{24} + \left\{\frac{Zb^2}{2a} - \frac{w(b-c)^3}{6}\right\}b + C_2$$

from which

$$C_2 = -\frac{Zb^3}{3a} + \frac{w}{24}(b-c)^3(3b+c)$$

Hence

$$EI\frac{dy}{dx} = \frac{Z}{2a}(b^2 - x^2) + \frac{w}{6}\{[x-c]^3 - (b-c)^3\} \qquad \dots \text{(iv)}$$

and

$$EIy = -\frac{Z}{a}\left(\frac{x^3}{6} - \frac{b^2x}{2} + \frac{b^3}{3}\right)$$

$$+ \frac{w}{24}\{[x-c]^4 + (b-c)^3(3b+c-4x)\} \qquad \dots \text{(v)}$$

At B when $x = 0$, we have from (iv),

$$EI\left(\frac{dy}{dx}\right)_{BC} = \frac{Zb^2}{2a} - \frac{w}{6}(b-c)^3 \qquad \dots \text{(iva)}$$

(Note that the term in square brackets is ignored since $x < c$.) and from (v),

$$EIy_B = -\frac{Zb^3}{3a} + \frac{w}{24}(b-c)^3(3b+c) \qquad \dots \text{(va)}$$

We now turn our attention to the length AB.

Here, taking A as the new origin,

$$M = EI\frac{d^2y}{dx^2} = Z - \frac{Zx}{a}$$

from which integration leads to

$$EI\frac{dy}{dx} = Z\left(x - \frac{x^2}{2a}\right) + C_3 \qquad \dots \text{(vi)}$$

and

$$EIy = Z\left(\frac{x^2}{2} - \frac{x^3}{6a}\right) + C_3 x + C_4 \qquad \dots \text{(vii)}$$

At A, $x = 0$ and $y = 0$ so that on substitution in (vii) $C_4 = 0$.

At B, $x = a$ and $y = (y)_B$.

Thus in (vi) we have, on substituting and collecting terms,

$$C_3 = -\frac{Z}{3a^2}(a^3 + b^3) + \frac{w}{24a}(b - c)^3(3b + c)$$

so that from (vi) and (vii) we find that

$$EI\frac{dy}{dx} = Zx\left(1 - \frac{x}{2a}\right) - \frac{Z}{3a^2}(a^3 + b^3) + \frac{w}{24a}(b - c)^3(3b + c)$$

and

$$EIy = \frac{Zx^2}{2}\left(1 - \frac{x}{3a}\right) - \frac{Zx}{3a^2}(a^3 + b^3) + \frac{wx}{24a}(b - c)^3(3b + c)$$

At B, when $x = a$,

$$EI\left(\frac{dy}{dx}\right)_{BA} = \frac{Z}{6a^2}(a^3 - 2b^3) + \frac{w}{24a}(b - c)^3(3b + c) \quad \dots \text{ (viii)}$$

The angular discontinuity at B, θ_B, is given by deducting $\left(\frac{dy}{dx}\right)_{BA}$ from $\left(\frac{dy}{dx}\right)_{BC}$

Hence

$$EI\theta_B = \frac{Z}{6a^2}(3ab^2 - a^3 + 2b^3) + \frac{w}{24a}(b - c)^3(4a + 3b + c).$$

3.4.1.2. *The Moment-Area Method* [Volume I, Chapter 3, Section 3.7.4]

Problem 3.29—The bending moment diagram is shown in diagram (c). Considering first the length BC, we recall that the area of the parabolic diagram equals

$$\frac{\text{base} \times \text{height}}{3}$$

and that its centroid is at a distance $\dfrac{\text{base}}{4}$ from C.

Then $\quad EI\left(\dfrac{dy}{dx}\right)_{BC} = -(i_C - i_B)$, for $i_C = 0$

$$= -\int_B^C \frac{M dx}{EI} = \text{minus the nett area of the bending moment diagram for } BC$$

$$= -\frac{w(b - c)^2}{2}\left(\frac{b - c}{3}\right) + \frac{Zb}{a} \times \frac{b}{2}$$

$$= -\frac{w(b - c)^3}{6} + \frac{Zb^2}{2a}$$

Also, $EIy_B = \delta_B^C =$ the moment of area of the bending moment diagram for BC about B.

Hence

$$EIy_B = \frac{w(b - c)^3}{6}\left(b - \frac{b - c}{4}\right) - \frac{Zb^2}{2a} \times \frac{2b}{3}$$

$$= -\frac{Zb^3}{3a} + \frac{w}{24}(b - c)^3(3b + c)$$

Now considering AB, if we draw the tangent to the deflected form of the beam at B (diagram (d)) we have

$$\delta_A^B = \left[\frac{A\bar{x}}{EI}\right]_A^B = \frac{Za}{2EI} \times \frac{a}{3} = \frac{Za^2}{6EI}$$

and hence

$$EI \left(\frac{dy}{dx} \right)_{BA} = EIi_B = \frac{EI}{a} (\delta_A^B - (-y_B))$$

$$= \frac{Za}{6} - \frac{Zb^3}{3a^2} + \frac{w}{24a} (b - c)^3 (3b + c) \text{ as before}$$

In using the moment-area method little difficulty with signs is usually experienced since the signs of deflexions and slopes can be seen by inspection in most cases.

3.4.1.3. *The Dummy Unit Load Method* [Volume 1, Chapter 3, Section 3.7.3]

Problem 3.29—The deflexion due to bending effects at any point j on a structure is given by

$$\Delta_j = \int \frac{M'M dx}{EI} \qquad \qquad \dots \text{ [3.9(a)]}$$

where M is the bending moment due to the applied loads or other agency causing distortion of the structure, and M' is the bending moment due to a dummy unit load applied at j in the direction in which the deflexion is required.

To find the vertical deflexion of B using the dummy unit load method we apply an imaginary unit vertical load at B. The downward direction of this unit load indicates that we regard a downward deflexion as positive.

Diagram 3.29(e) gives the M' bending moment diagram for this dummy load. There is no moment M' in AB and the integration is therefore confined to BC.

Diagram (c) shows the M diagram. It is convenient to split up the bending moment in BC into that produced by Z/a acting at B, and that due to the distributed load on BC. Then, taking B as the origin of coordinates, and using Macaulay's convention, we have

$$M = -\frac{Z}{a}x + \frac{w[x - c]^2}{2}$$

and

$$M' = x$$

Hence

$$EIy_B = \int_0^b x \left(-\frac{Z}{a}x \right) dx + \int_c^b x \frac{w(x - c)^2}{2} dx$$

$$= -\frac{Z}{a} \left[\frac{x^3}{3} \right]_0^b + \frac{w}{2} \int_c^b (x^3 - 2x^2c + xc^2) dx$$

$$= -\frac{Zb^3}{3a} + \frac{w}{2} \left[\frac{x^4}{4} - \frac{2x^3c}{3} + \frac{x^2c^2}{2} \right]_c^b$$

which reduces to

$$EIy_B = -\frac{Zb^3}{3a} + \frac{w}{24} (b - c)^3 (3b + c) \quad \text{as before.}$$

To obtain the angular discontinuity at B we apply dummy unit couples to the two sides of the beam at B (diagram (f)). These produce vertical reactions $1/a$ on the two parts of the beam and the M' diagram shown at (f). The origin for AB is chosen at A; that for BC is at B as before.

Then, for AB

$$M' = \frac{x}{a}$$

$$M = Z\left(1 - \frac{x}{a}\right)$$

and for BC

$$M' = \left(1 + \frac{x}{a}\right)$$

and

$$M = -\frac{Z}{a}x + \frac{w[x - c]^2}{2} \quad \text{as before.}$$

Then

$$EI\theta_b = \int_0^a \frac{x}{a}\left\{Z\left(1 - \frac{x}{a}\right)\right\}dx + \int_0^b \left(1 + \frac{x}{a}\right)\left(-\frac{Zx}{a}\right)dx$$

$$+ \int_c^b \left(1 + \frac{x}{a}\right)\frac{w}{2}(x - c)^2 dx$$

$$= \frac{Z}{a}\left[\frac{x^2}{2} - \frac{x^3}{3a}\right]_0^a - \frac{Z}{a}\left[\frac{x^2}{2} + \frac{x^3}{3a}\right]_0^b$$

$$+ \frac{w}{2}\left[\frac{(x - c)^3}{3} + \frac{x^4}{4a} - \frac{2x^3c}{3a} + \frac{c^2x^2}{2a}\right]_c^b$$

On further reduction we find finally that

$$EI\theta_b = \frac{Z}{6a^2}(a^3 - 2b^3 - 3ab^2) + \frac{w}{24a}(b - c)^3(4a + 3b + c) \quad \text{as before.}$$

3.4.2. RIGIDLY JOINTED FRAMES

The horizontal movement of D in *Problem 3.30* is to be determined. This problem will be solved by the dummy unit load method and by the graphical method of Hoadley (Volume I, Chapter 3, Section 3.7.5).

3.4.2.1. *Dummy Unit Load Method*

Problem 3.30—

$$\Delta_D = \int \frac{M'M ds}{EI}$$

where M' is the moment at any point in the frame due to a unit horizontal load at D (see diagram (b)) and M is the bending moment due to the applied loads (see diagram (c)).

Separate integrations are necessary for each member, and the origins will be selected as shown at (c). We will denote as positive a moment which produces tension on the outside fibres of any member.

M' and M vary along the members as follows:

$$AB: \quad M' = +12 \cdot 5\frac{s}{10\sqrt{2}} = +0 \cdot 886s \left.\vphantom{\frac{s}{10\sqrt2}}\right\}$$

$$M = (1\tfrac{1}{2} - 2\tfrac{1}{8})s/\sqrt{2} = -0 \cdot 443s$$

$$BC: \quad M' = 12 \cdot 5 + 0 \cdot 25s$$

$$M = \frac{s^2}{2} - 2 \cdot 125s - 6 \cdot 25$$

$$CD: \quad M' = s$$

$$M = 1 \cdot 5s$$

Then in the above formula for Δ_D we have

$$EI\Delta_D = -\int_0^{10\sqrt{2}} 0 \cdot 886s.0 \cdot 443s \, ds + \int_0^{10} (12 \cdot 5 + 0 \cdot 25s)\left(\frac{s^2}{2} - 2 \cdot 125s - 6 \cdot 25\right)\frac{ds}{3} + \int_0^{15} 1 \cdot 5s^2 \frac{ds}{2}$$

$$= -368 + 10 + 844$$
$$(AB) \quad (BC) \quad (CD)$$

$$= +486 \text{ i.e. to the left.}$$

3.4.2.2. *Hoadley's Method*

Problem 3.30—The principle of the method, which is analogous to the Williot-Mohr method for pin-jointed frameworks, is explained fully in Volume 1, and the symbols used here are the same.

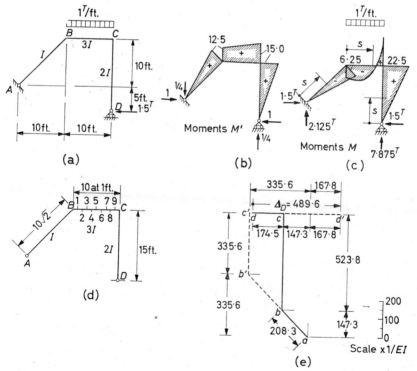

PROBLEM 3.30 (a) It is required to find the horizontal deflexion of D; (b) Moments M' produced by dummy unit horizontal load at D; (c) Moments M produced by the actual loading; (d) Frame divided into suitable lengths for the application of Hoadley's method; (e) Williot-Mohr diagram.

In using the method the structure is first subdivided into elements in which the variation of bending moment can be taken as linear. This is actually true of AB and CD, which have therefore not been subdivided, while BC has been divided into ten equal parts. The working is best arranged in tabular form. In TABLE 3.30, column 2 records the moment at each section, and column 4 the change of slope di between successive sections, di being calculated from the formula

$$di = \frac{l}{EI}\left[\frac{M_p + M_q}{2}\right]$$

where M_p and M_q are the bending moments at the two adjacent sections.

TABLE 3.30

CALCULATION OF DATA FOR HOADLEY'S METHOD

1	2	3	4	5	6	7	8
Point	M	l	di $\times 1/EI$	i $\times 1/EI$	li $\times 1/EI$	δ_q^p $\times 1/EI$	$\varDelta$ $\times 1/EI$
A	0						
B	$-6\cdot25$	$10\sqrt{2}$	$-44\cdot19$	$-44\cdot19$		$-208\cdot33$	$-208\cdot33$
1	$-7\cdot875$	1	$-2\cdot35$	$-46\cdot54$	$-44\cdot19$	$-1\cdot14$	$-45\cdot33$
2	$-8\cdot50$	1	$-2\cdot73$	$-49\cdot27$	$-46\cdot54$	$-1\cdot35$	$-47\cdot89$
3	$-8\cdot125$	1	$-2\cdot77$	$-52\cdot04$	$-49\cdot27$	$-1\cdot40$	$-50\cdot67$
4	$-6\cdot75$	1	$-2\cdot48$	$-54\cdot52$	$-52\cdot04$	$-1\cdot28$	$-53\cdot32$
5	$-4\cdot375$	1	$-1\cdot85$	$-56\cdot37$	$-54\cdot52$	$-0\cdot99$	$-55\cdot51$
6	$-1\cdot00$	1	$-0\cdot90$	$-57\cdot27$	$-56\cdot37$	$-0\cdot54$	$-56\cdot91$
7	$+3\cdot375$	1	$+0\cdot40$	$-56\cdot87$	$-57\cdot27$	$+0\cdot08$	$-57\cdot19$
8	$+8\cdot75$	1	$+2\cdot02$	$-54\cdot85$	$-56\cdot87$	$+0\cdot86$	$-56\cdot01$
9	$+15\cdot125$	1	$+3\cdot98$	$-50\cdot87$	$-54\cdot85$	$+1\cdot81$	$-53\cdot04$
C	$+22\cdot50$	1	$+6\cdot27$	$-44\cdot60$	$-50\cdot87$	$+2\cdot93$	$-47\cdot94$
D	0	15	$+84\cdot37$	$+39\cdot77$	$-669\cdot00$	$+843\cdot75$	$+174\cdot45$

(column 8 bracketed total for points 1–C: $-523\cdot81$)

Thus for the change of slope between sections B and 1 we have

$$di = \frac{1}{3EI}\left[\frac{-6\cdot25 - 7\cdot875}{2}\right] = -\frac{2\cdot35}{EI}$$

By adding the successive di's we obtain the actual change of slope at each section (column 5), and on multiplying this by the length l of the element we obtain the deflexion at each section due to the change of slope between this section and section A, which is assumed not to rotate (column 6).

We have also to calculate the deflexion caused by flexure within each element. This is given by the formula

$$\delta_q^p = \frac{l^2}{EI}\left[\frac{2M_p + M_q}{6}\right]$$

and the values for this particular problem are given in column 7. Finally we add corresponding terms in columns 6 and 7 to obtain the additional deflexion which occurs from one section to the next throughout the frame. This deflexion is at right angles to the direction of the member at all sections.

78

The Williot diagram (diagram 3.30(e)), which is drawn on the assumption that A is fixed, does not require any explanation. On this assumption point D moves upwards and to the left relative to A. D, however, can only move horizontally, and a Mohr correction diagram is required. This is shown in broken lines.

From the combined diagram we find that

$$\Delta_D = 489 \cdot 6/EI$$

which agrees reasonably well with the calculated value $(486/EI)$.

Problems for Solution

By the integration, dummy unit load and moment area methods:

3.31.   A uniform beam $ABCD$ is supported at A and C and carries a load of 5 tons at B. $AB = CD = 4$ ft.; $BC = 6$ ft. Find the slope at C and the deflexion of D above the horizontal through A and C.

What load applied at D would restore D to the level of A and C?

3.32.   A flagstaff ABC, of length $4L$ and weighing w lb. per unit length, is lying on level ground with the end A hinged to a base at ground level. If the flagstaff is lifted by a vertical force applied at B, distant L from the hinge, until the end C is just clear of the ground find the slope at B and its height above the ground.

3.33.   A uniform beam ABC of length L weighs w per unit length. It is simply supported at A and B at the same level and BC overhangs. $AB = L - a$; $BC = a$.

Find the deflexion of C from the horizontal through A and B.

3.34.   A uniform beam ABC is simply supported at A and C. $AB = a$; $BC = b$.

Find the deflexion of B from the line AC if a couple M is applied to the beam (a) at C and (b) at B.

3.35.   Find Δ_B, Δ_E, i_C and the change of slope at B.

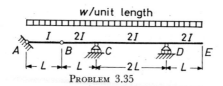

PROBLEM 3.35

3.36.   Find Δ_E and Δ_D.

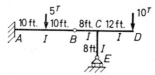

PROBLEM 3.36

3.37.   Find Δ_E and i_E.

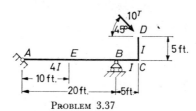

PROBLEM 3.37

79

DEFLEXION OF STRUCTURES

By the dummy unit load and graphical methods:

3.38. The second moment of area I of the cross-section of this parabolic arched rib varies as follows: $I = I_0 \sec \alpha$. Find Δ_C.

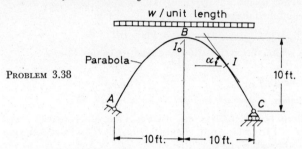

PROBLEM 3.38

3.39. *ACB* is a semi-circular arched rib of uniform second moment of area I. Find Δ_B and the vertical deflexion at C.

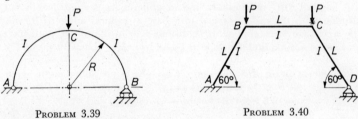

PROBLEM 3.39

PROBLEM 3.40

3.40. The frame *ABCD* is subjected to
  (a) the loads P as shown.
  (b) a unit horizontal load at D.
  Find the horizontal movement of D in each case. Hence find the horizontal thrust at D if D is pinned instead of being on rollers.   (Melbourne, 1955)

3.41. (a) The arched rib shown at (a) is loaded by
    (i) a horizontal load H applied at C;
    (ii) a vertical load W uniformly distributed along BC.
  Find Δ_C in each case.

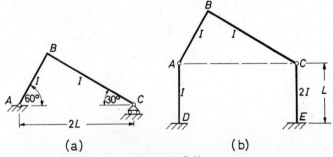

(a)   (b)

PROBLEM 3.41

(b) The rib is pinned to two columns as shown at (b).
    Find the horizontal thrust in the structure if the vertical load W referred to above acts on BC.   (Melbourne, 1951)

3.42. During modifications a rectangular steel portal frame *ABCD* is supported at *D* by a steel pin-jointed frame. The portal frame is of uniform section with a relevant second moment of area = 842 in.[4]. The members of the supporting frame each have a cross-sectional area of 3·6 in.[2]. Find the horizontal thrust caused at *D* by a total vertical load of 24 tons uniformly distributed along *BC* by comparing the deflexions at *D* of the portal and the pin-jointed frame.

(London, 1956)

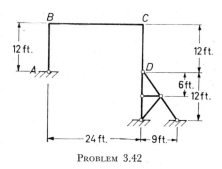

PROBLEM 3.42

3.5. RECIPROCAL RELATIONSHIPS

[Volume I, Chapter 3, Section 3.5]

The Reciprocal Theorems of Maxwell and Betti can be used to explain many important facts in structural theory. In Volume I it is shown how the identity of the 'flexural centre' and the 'centre of twist' of an unsymmetrical section may be demonstrated by Maxwell's theorem. The following examples further illustrate the use of reciprocal relationships.

Problem 3.43—Prove the following statements in relation to the rigidly jointed structures shown if it is assumed that axial deformations may be ignored in comparison with flexural deformations.

(a) Diagram (a). *C* does not move when a force or moment is applied at *B*.

(d) Diagram (d). For any inclination α of the force *P* the rotations at *A* and *D* are numerically equal.

(Melbourne, 1957)

(a) We consider the structure subjected to the two load groups shown in diagrams (b) and (c). Since axial deformations are to be ignored, the load *Q* at *C* will produce purely axial forces in *AC* and *CE*, which together form a 'linear arch' [see Volume I, Chapter 7]: *B* therefore does not move or rotate. We now write down the reciprocal relationship between the two groups:

$$P.0 = Q.\Delta_C$$

so that $\Delta_C = 0$

The same conclusion is reached if instead of a force *P* we apply a moment at *B*.

(b) Let the rotations at *A* and *D* due to *P* be θ_A and θ_D in a clockwise direction (diagram (e)). This is Group 1. For Group 2 we consider equal and opposite

81

couples M applied at A and D respectively, as at (f). Under these couples the frame must take up a position as indicated by the dotted lines and it is clear, from symmetry, that no translation of B will occur.

Hence

$$P \cdot 0 = M.\theta_A - M.\theta_D$$

i.e.

$$\theta_A = \theta_D$$

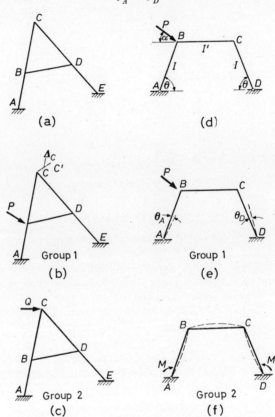

PROBLEM 3.43 (a) It is required to show that C does not move when a force or moment is applied at B; (b) The actual force P and the presumed deflexion of C constitute Group 1; (c) Group 2 consists of a force applied at C; (d) It is required to show that the force P produces equal rotations of A and D; (e) The actual force at B and the rotations at A and D constitute Group 1; (f) Group 2 comprises equal and opposite couples applied at A and D and the resulting deflexions.

Problems for Solution

3.44. This structure is acted upon in turn by three forces:

(1) a unit downward load at E;

(2) a unit clockwise moment at A;

(3) a unit clockwise moment at B.

Indicate which of the following relations are correct:

(a) $\theta_{b2} = \theta_{a3}$ (e) $\theta_{e2} = \theta_{a1}$

(b) $\Delta_{a1} = \theta_{e2}$ (f) $\theta_{b1} = \Delta_{e3}$

(c) $\theta_{a2} = \theta_{b3}$ (g) $\Delta_{e1} = \theta_{a3}$

(d) $\Delta_{e2} = \Delta_{a3}$ (h) $\Delta_{e2} = \theta_{a1}$

(The second suffix in each case denotes the force applied: thus θ_{b2} denotes the rotation of B under loading (2).) Clockwise rotations and downward deflexions are to be considered positive.

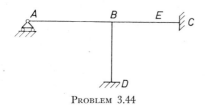 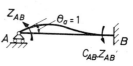

PROBLEM 3.44   PROBLEM 3.45

3.45. A non-uniform beam is fixed at B and supported on rollers at A and a moment Z_{AB}, sufficient to produce unit rotation at A, is applied at A; the moment produced at B is $C_{AB} \cdot Z_{AB}$.

If, alternatively, A is fixed and B is supported on rollers and rotated through unit angle by a moment Z_{BA}, a moment $C_{BA} \cdot Z_{BA}$ is produced at A.

Show that

$$C_{AB} \cdot Z_{AB} = C_{BA} \cdot Z_{BA}$$

3.46. The diagram shows a rectangular grid of elastic girders. A and E are simply supported, and LM is clamped. A 1-ton load at G causes the following deflexions: 0·005 in. (B and D), 0·006 in. (F, C and K), 0·010 in. (G and J) and 0·012 in. (H). What will be the deflexion of G due to a 10-ton load divided equally between the 15 joints?

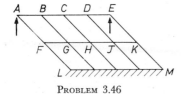 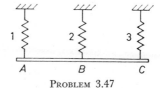

PROBLEM 3.46   PROBLEM 3.47

3.47. Three spring balances 1, 2 and 3, each of which deflects 0·2 in. under a load of 1 lb., are equally spaced as shown and support an elastic beam ABC. The balances are adjusted to read zero when only the weight of the beam is carried.

When a load of 10 lb. is applied at B the balance readings are:

     No. 1 .... 1 lb.   No. 2 .... 8 lb.   No. 3 .... 1 lb.

Find the readings when an additional load of 10 lb. is applied at A.

Also find the values of the deflexions Δ_{ab}, Δ_{ac}, Δ_{bc}, Δ_{aa}, Δ_{bb} and Δ_{cc} for the combined system of beam and balances.

(After Oxford, 1936)

GENERAL METHODS FOR
LINEAR ELASTIC STRUCTURES

4.1. INTRODUCTION

THE problems in this chapter have been selected to illustrate further the general methods for the analysis of linear hyperstatic structures discussed in Volume I, Chapter 4.

4.2. THE STIFFNESS COEFFICIENT EQUATIONS (Equilibrium Method) [Volume I, Chapter 4, Section 4.2]

This method is illustrated in Volume I by a simple problem involving three bars and one pinned joint capable of displacement. This problem should be studied again before the reader proceeds to the following rather more complicated example involving two joints capable of movement.

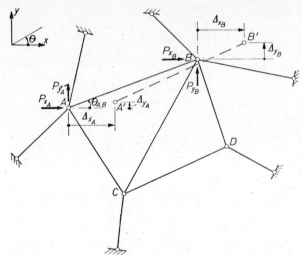

FIGURE 4.1. Pin-jointed framework for solution by means of stiffness coefficients. The four joints A, B, C and D each have two degrees of freedom.

It was shown in Volume I that when displacements Δ_{x_A}, Δ_{y_A}, Δ_{x_B} and Δ_{y_B} are imposed at the ends of a member AB in a pin-jointed framework (see FIGURE 4.1), the force in it is

$$F_{AB} = e_{AB}/\rho_{AB} = \frac{1}{\rho_{AB}}[(\Delta_{x_B} - \Delta_{x_A})\cos\theta_{AB} + (\Delta_{y_B} - \Delta_{y_A})\sin\theta_{AB}] \quad \dots \quad [4.4]$$

Applying the conditions of equilibrium to the complete framework at joint A we have, in the x-direction,

$$P_{x_A} + \sum F_{AB} \cos \theta_{AB} = 0$$

On substituting for F_{AB} in terms of e_{AB}, we find that this equation of equilibrium becomes

$$
\left.
\begin{aligned}
P_{x_A} + p_{xx_A} \cdot \varDelta_{x_A} + p_{xy_A} \cdot \varDelta_{y_A} &+ \sum \frac{\cos^2 \theta_{AB} \varDelta_{x_B}}{\rho_{AB}} \\
&+ \sum \frac{\sin \theta_{AB} \cos \theta_{AB} \varDelta_{y_B}}{\rho_{AB}} = 0 \\
\text{While in the y-direction at } A \qquad \\
P_{y_A} + p_{yx_A} \varDelta_{x_A} + p_{yy_A} \varDelta_{y_A} &+ \sum \frac{\sin \theta_{AB} \cos \theta_{AB} \varDelta_{x_B}}{\rho_{AB}} \\
&+ \sum \frac{\sin^2 \theta_{AB} \varDelta_{y_B}}{\rho_{AB}} = 0
\end{aligned}
\right\} \quad \cdots \text{(i)}
$$

p_{xx_A}, p_{xy_A} and p_{yy_A} are defined as stiffness coefficients and have the same meanings as in equations [4.5].

$$p_{xx_A} = - \sum \cos^2 \theta_{AB}/\rho_{AB}$$
$$p_{xy_A} = p_{yx_A} = - \sum \cos \theta_{AB} \sin \theta_{AB}/\rho_{AB}$$
$$p_{yy_A} = - \sum \sin^2 \theta_{AB}/\rho_{AB}$$

If the above equations (i) are compared with equations [4.1] it will be noticed that each contains two additional summation terms. It is necessary to include these terms when the structure contains more than one movable joint. It should be noted that the summations in these terms cover only those members connected at *both* ends to movable joints. Thus in the framework shown in the figure we consider only members AB and AC in these terms when writing down the equations of equilibrium for joint A.

Problem 4.1—Determine the forces in the bars of the frame shown due to the load P acting at D if all bars have the same value of ρ.

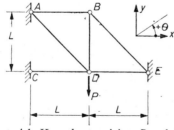

PROBLEM 4.1. Here the two joints B and D each have two degrees of freedom.

In this frame joints B and D can each move in the x- and y-directions, and the frame therefore has four degrees of freedom. In the present method of attack we

G

take as the unknown quantities the components of displacement of these two joints, Δ_{x_B}, Δ_{y_B}, Δ_{x_D} and Δ_{y_D}.

It is first necessary to evaluate the stiffness coefficients and the other terms in equations (i). This is done in TABLE 4.1. For each member θ is measured in an anticlockwise direction from the positive direction of x. ρ is conveniently taken as unity.

TABLE 4.1

CALCULATION OF STIFFNESS COEFFICIENTS

1	2	3	4	5	6	7
Member	$\sin \theta$	$\cos \theta$	$\sin^2 \theta$	$\cos^2 \theta$	$\cos \theta . \sin \theta$	F
BE	$-1/\sqrt{2}$	$1/\sqrt{2}$	$1/2$	$1/2$	$-1/2$	$-\dfrac{5\sqrt{2}P}{13}$
BD	-1	0	1	0	0	$\dfrac{5P}{13}$
BA	0	-1	0	1	0	$-\dfrac{5P}{13}$
	$\sum$		$p_{yy_B} = -1\frac{1}{2}$	$p_{xx_C} = -1\frac{1}{2}$	$p_{xy_B} = 1/2$	
DE	0	1	0	1	0	$\dfrac{4P}{13}$
DC	0	-1	0	1	0	$-\dfrac{4P}{13}$
DA	$1/\sqrt{2}$	$-1/\sqrt{2}$	$1/2$	$1/2$	$-1/2$	$\dfrac{8\sqrt{2}P}{13}$
DB	1	0	1	0	0	$\dfrac{5P}{13}$
	$\sum$		$p_{yy_D} = -1\frac{1}{2}$	$p_{xx_D} = -2\frac{1}{2}$	$p_{xy_B} = 1/2$	

The stiffness coefficients p_{xx}, p_{yy} and p_{xy} at joints B and D are obtained by summation of the appropriate quantities in columns 4, 5 and 6 of the table. To determine the remaining terms in equations (i) we note that the only member having both ends capable of displacement is BD; we therefore simply make use of the appropriate quantity in the table in the line BD (or DB).

At joint B, for example, $\cos^2 \theta_{BD}$ and $\sin \theta_{BD} . \cos \theta_{BD}$ are both zero, and there is therefore no term in either Δ_{x_D} or Δ_{y_D} in the equation. $\sin^2 \theta_{BD}$, however, equals 1, so that we have to include a term $\dfrac{\sin^2 \theta_{BD} . \Delta_{y_D}}{\rho_{BD}} = 1$. Δ_{y_D} in the equilibrium equation for the y-direction.

86

Equations (i) then become:

Joint B:

$$x\text{-direction: } 0 - 1\tfrac{1}{2}\Delta_{x_B} + \tfrac{1}{2}\Delta_{y_B} = 0$$
$$y\text{-direction } 0 + \tfrac{1}{2}\Delta_{x_B} - 1\tfrac{1}{2}\Delta_{y_B} + \Delta_{y_D} = 0$$

Joint D:

$$x\ 0 - 2\tfrac{1}{2}\Delta_{x_D} + \tfrac{1}{2}\Delta_{y_D} = 0$$
$$y - P + \tfrac{1}{2}\Delta_{x_D} - 1\tfrac{1}{2}\Delta_{y_D} + \Delta_{y_B} = 0$$

.... (ii)

The solution to equations (ii) is as follows:

$$\Delta_{x_B} = \frac{-5P}{13}, \quad \Delta_{y_B} = \frac{-15P}{13}, \quad \Delta_{x_D} = \frac{-4P}{13}, \quad \Delta_{y_D} = \frac{-20P}{13}$$

Substitution in equation [4.4] will now give the forces in the members. These are recorded in column 7 of the table. As an example of this calculation,

$$F_{DA} = \frac{1}{\rho_{DA}}\left[\left(\Delta_{x_A} - \Delta_{x_D}\right)\cos\theta_{DA} + \left(\Delta_{y_A} - \Delta_{y_D}\right)\sin\theta_{DA}\right]$$
$$= 1\left[\left(0 + \frac{4P}{13}\right)\left(-\frac{1}{\sqrt{2}}\right) + \left(0 + \frac{20P}{13}\right)\left(\frac{1}{\sqrt{2}}\right)\right]$$
$$= +\frac{8\sqrt{2}P}{13}$$

Problems for Solution

4.2. Solve *Problems 2.5, 2.20* and *4.8* by means of stiffness coefficients.

4.3. If all the members of the frame shown have the same cross-sectional area, find the forces in members *AB, EF* and *BF*.

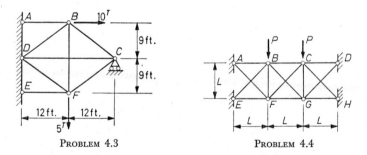

PROBLEM 4.3   PROBLEM 4.4

4.4. Find the forces in all chord and vertical members of the frame shown if ρ is the same for all members.

4.3. FRAMEWORK ANALYSIS BY RELAXATION

It is not intended here to add to the discussion of relaxation methods in Volume I [Chapter 4]. The student is recommended to attempt the solution of *Problems 4.1, 4.2, 4.3* and *4.4* by relaxation.

4.4. PIN-JOINTED FRAMEWORKS (Compatibility method)

4.4.1. THE MAXWELL-MOHR EQUATIONS FOR BRACED STRUCTURES

The method of stiffness coefficients dealt with in Volume I, Chapter 4, Section 4.2 and in Section 2 of the present chapter is an instance of an *equilibrium method*, in which the unknown quantities are displacements. In contradistinction, the method now to be considered—the Maxwell-Mohr method for braced structures—is an example of a *compatibility method*. In such methods the redundant forces in the structure are treated as the unknowns. The more fundamental distinction between the two general approaches is discussed fully in Volume I.

The Maxwell-Mohr equations in generalized form are as follows:

$$0 = \Sigma F_n(F_o + X_a F_a + X_b F_b + \ldots + X_n F_n)\rho \qquad \ldots . [4.8]$$

Where there is an initial lack of fit in a redundant the left hand side of the equation becomes λ, the lack of fit. The symbols are defined in Volume I [Chapter 4, Section 4.5.1].

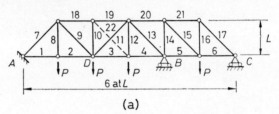

(a)

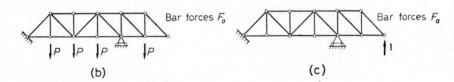

(b)   Bar forces F_o

(c)   Bar forces F_a

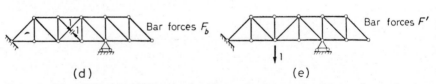

(d)   Bar forces F_b

(e)   Bar forces F'

PROBLEM 4.5. (a) Pin-jointed framework with a redundant support, here taken to be the vertical reaction at C. In part (b) of the problem the truss also has the redundant member 22. (b) Bar forces F_o in the primary structure obtained by removing the support at C. (c) Bar forces F_a caused by unit load at C. (d) Bar forces F_b caused by unit tensile load in member 22. (e) Bar forces F', caused by dummy unit load at D, for the deflexion of D.

Problem 4.5—We take as our first example the truss illustrated. It has members numbered 1 to 21, with cross-sectional areas as follows:

Members 1-6, 2 in.²

Members 7-17, 1 in.²

Members 18-21, 3 in.²

(a) Find the value of the reaction at C due to the loads P.

(b) If the truss has another member (No. 22, shown dotted) having a cross-sectional area of 1 in.², find the force in this member and the reaction at C when the loads P act as shown.

(c) What initial lack of fit (i) at the support C, or (ii) in the member 22, would give an upward reaction of $0.25P$ at C when the loads P are acting?

(d) If the temperature of the top chord and end diagonal members rises by $t°$ find the forces in the two redundants, assuming that there is no initial lack of fit in either.

(e) Find the vertical deflexion at D in part (b) above.

(a) The Maxwell-Mohr equation [4.8] for a framework with one redundant is

$$0 = \sum F_o F_a \rho + X_a \sum F_a^2 \rho \qquad \dots \text{ (i)}$$

In this case we choose the reaction at C as the redundant quantity X_a.

We remove this redundant force leaving a statically determinate primary structure (see diagram (b)); F_o is the force in any member of this structure when it is subjected to the applied loads P (diagram (b)) and F_a the force in any member when a unit load acts at C in place of the reaction there (diagram (c)).

The calculations are best arranged in tabular form (see TABLE 4.5). Then taking the summed values for $F_o F_a \rho$ and $F_a^2 \rho$ from columns 6 and 7, the Maxwell-Mohr equation becomes

$$0 = -\frac{4.16PL}{E} + X_a \frac{17.82L}{E}$$

giving
$$X_a = +0.233P.$$

The positive sign indicates that the reaction at C is in the same direction as the unit load which was applied at C to give the forces F_a; i.e. it acts upwards.

The forces in the members of the frame may now be obtained by means of the equation

$$F = F_o + X_a F_a.$$

(b) When two redundants X_a and X_b are present, the Maxwell-Mohr equations [4.8] are:

$$0 = \sum F_o F_a \rho + X_a \sum F_a^2 \rho + X_b \sum F_a F_b \rho \qquad \dots \text{ (ii)}$$

$$0 = \sum F_o F_b \rho + X_a \sum F_a F_b \rho + X_b \sum F_b^2 \rho \qquad \dots \text{ (iii)}$$

In this part of the problem, we take X_a as before, and X_b as the force in the additional member 22. We make a cut in the member 22, thus rendering it inactive as a part of the primary structure. It is now necessary to calculate the forces F_b produced in the members of the primary structure by unit loads acting on the two portions of member 22 (diagram (d)). These forces are tabulated in column 8 of TABLE 4.5. The products $F_o F_b \rho$, $F_b^2 \rho$ and $F_a F_b \rho$ are then calculated (columns 9, 10 and 11) and summed. On substituting in the two Maxwell-Mohr equations (ii) and (iii) we then have:

$$0 = -\frac{4.16PL}{E} + X_a \frac{17.82L}{E} - X_b \frac{1.295L}{E} \qquad \dots \text{ (iv)}$$

$$0 = \frac{0.88PL}{E} - X_a \frac{1.295L}{E} + X_b \frac{4.245L}{E} \qquad \dots \text{ (v)}$$

89

TABLE 4.5

1	2	3	4	5	6	7	8	9	10	11	12	13	14	15	16
Member	Length $\times L$	Area	$F_o \times P$	F_a	$F_o F_a \rho \times PL/E$	$F_a^2 \rho \times L/E$	F_b	$F_a F_b \rho \times PL/E$	$F_b^2 \rho \times L/E$	$F_a F_b \rho \times L/E$	$F_a \alpha l \times \alpha L$	$F_b \alpha l \times \alpha L$	F'	$F \times P$	$F'F\rho \times PL/E$
1	1	2	$5/4$	$1/2$	$5/16$	$1/8$	0	0	0	0	0	0	$1/2$	$1{\cdot}362$	$0{\cdot}341$
2	1	2	$5/4$	$1/2$	$5/16$	$1/8$	0	0	0	0	0	0	$1/2$	$1{\cdot}362$	$0{\cdot}341$
3	1	2	$3/4$	$3/2$	$9/16$	$9/8$	$-1/\sqrt{2}$	$-3/8\sqrt{2}$	$1/4$	$-3/4\sqrt{2}$	0	0	$1/2$	$1{\cdot}184$	$0{\cdot}296$
4	1	2	$3/4$	$3/2$	$9/16$	$9/8$	0	0	0	0	0	0	$1/2$	$1{\cdot}085$	$0{\cdot}271$
5	1	2	-1	2	-1	2	0	0	0	0	0	0			
6	1	1	0	1	0	$1/2$	0	0	0	0	-1	0			
7	$\sqrt{2}$	1	$-5\sqrt{2}/4$	$-1/\sqrt{2}$	$5\sqrt{2}/4$	$1/\sqrt{2}$	$-1/\sqrt{2}$	0	$1/2\sqrt{2}$	0	0	0	$-1/\sqrt{2}$	$-1{\cdot}926$	$1{\cdot}926$
8	1	1	1	0	0	0	1	$3/2$	$1/2$	0	0	0			
9	$\sqrt{2}$	1	$\sqrt{2}/4$	$1/\sqrt{2}$	$\sqrt{2}/4$	$1/\sqrt{2}$	$-1/\sqrt{2}$	$-1/\sqrt{2}$	0	0	0	0	$1/\sqrt{2}$	$0{\cdot}512$	$0{\cdot}512$
10	1	1	0	0	0	0	0	0	0	-1	0	0			
11	$\sqrt{2}$	1	$3\sqrt{2}/4$	$-1/\sqrt{2}$	$-3\sqrt{2}/4$	$1/\sqrt{2}$	0	0	0	-1	0	0	$1/\sqrt{2}$	$0{\cdot}762$	$0{\cdot}762$
12	1	1	1	0	0	0	0	0	0	0	0	0			
13	$\sqrt{2}$	1	$-7\sqrt{2}/4$	$1/\sqrt{2}$	$-7\sqrt{2}/4$	$1/\sqrt{2}$	$-1/\sqrt{2}$	0	$1/6$	0	0	0	$-1/\sqrt{2}$	$-2{\cdot}315$	$2{\cdot}315$
14	1	1	-1	1	-1	1	0	0	0	0	0	0			
15	$\sqrt{2}$	1	$\sqrt{2}$	$-\sqrt{2}$	$-2\sqrt{2}$	$2\sqrt{2}$	0	0	0	0	0	0			
16	1	1	0	1	$2\sqrt{2}$	1	0	0	0	0	0	$-1/\sqrt{2}$			
17	$\sqrt{2}$	1	0	-1	$1/2$	$2\sqrt{2}$	$-1/\sqrt{2}$	$1/2\sqrt{2}$	$\sqrt{2}$	$1/3\sqrt{2}$	-2	0	-1	$-1{\cdot}723$	$0{\cdot}574$
18	1	3	$-3/2$	-1	$1/2$	$1/3$	0	0	0	0	-1	0	-1	$-1{\cdot}624$	$0{\cdot}541$
19	1	3	$-3/2$	-2	$-2/3$	$1/3$	0	0	0	0	-1	0			
20	1	3	1	-1	0	$4/3$	0	0	0	0	-2	0			
21	1	3	0	-1	0	$1/3$	0	0	0	0	-1	0			
22	$\sqrt{2}$	1	0	0	0		1	0	0	0	0	0			
				Σ	$-4{\cdot}16$	$17{\cdot}82$	Σ	$0{\cdot}88$	$4{\cdot}245$	$-1{\cdot}295$	-8	$-1/\sqrt{2}$			$7{\cdot}879$

The solution to these equations is

$$X_a = 0 \cdot 223P$$

$$X_b = - 0 \cdot 139P$$

The forces in the members of the primary structure may now be calculated by the use of the formula

$$F = F_o + X_a F_a + X_b F_b$$

An interesting point is brought out if we calculate the force in bar 11. This is:

$$F_{11} = \frac{3\sqrt{2}P}{4} - \frac{0 \cdot 223P}{\sqrt{2}} - 0 \cdot 139P = 0 \cdot 764P$$

The force in the other diagonal in this panel (bar 22) is $X_b = - 0 \cdot 139P$. It is sometimes assumed in design that in a doubly braced panel the two diagonals share the shearing force equally; for the present problem, at least, this assumption is seen to be far from the truth.

(c) (i) The Maxwell-Mohr equations for this case are:

$$\lambda_a = \sum F_o F_a \rho + X_a \sum F_a^2 \rho + X_b \sum F_a F_b \rho \qquad \dots \cdot (vi)$$

$$0 = \sum F_o F_b \rho + X_a \sum F_a F_b \rho + X_b \sum F_b^2 \rho \qquad \dots \cdot (vii)$$

where λ_a is the amount by which the support at C is initially out of level. On the assumption that X_a is positive when it acts upwards, λ_a is positive when the support is *above* the correct level at C.

Substituting in the above for the summed terms and putting $X_a = 0 \cdot 25P$, we have:

$$\lambda_a = - \frac{4 \cdot 16PL}{E} + 0 \cdot 25P \frac{17 \cdot 82L}{E} - X_b \frac{1 \cdot 295L}{E} \qquad \dots \cdot (viii)$$

$$0 = \frac{0 \cdot 88PL}{E} - 0 \cdot 25P \frac{1 \cdot 295L}{E} + X_b \frac{4 \cdot 245L}{E} \qquad \dots \cdot (ix)$$

From which $\qquad \lambda_a = + \dfrac{0 \cdot 46PL}{E}$

The positive sign indicates that the support at C has to be jacked *upwards* by an amount $\dfrac{0 \cdot 46PL}{E}$ in order that the desired effects may be achieved.

(c) (ii) In this case the left hand side of equation (vi), above, becomes zero, and that of equation (vii) becomes λ_b, where λ_b is the amount by which member 22 must be inserted *too short* in the unloaded truss. The other terms remain as in (viii) and (ix). On solving, we find that $\lambda_b = \dfrac{1 \cdot 51PL}{E}$ i.e. X_b must be *too short* on erection by this amount.

(d) The first term in each Maxwell-Mohr equation may be written

$$\sum \frac{F_o L}{AE} F_a, \quad \sum \frac{F_o L}{AE} F_b, \text{ etc.}$$

$\dfrac{F_o L}{AE}$ is the change of length of each member of the primary structure under applied loads. If the distortion of the truss is due to temperature change the term $\dfrac{F_o L}{AE}$ is replaced by the term $\alpha_t t L$, which represents the free change of length of each

91

member of the primary structure. The Maxwell-Mohr equations are now as follows:

$$0 = \sum F_a \, \alpha_t t L + X_a \sum F_a^2 \rho + X_b \sum F_a F_b \rho$$
$$0 = \sum F_b \, \alpha_t t L + X_a \sum F_a F_b \rho + X_b \sum F_b^2 \rho$$

In the expressions $\sum F_a \alpha_t t L$ and $\sum F_b \alpha_t t L$, α_t is the coefficient of linear expansion of the material and L is the length of a member. These terms are calculated for the problem in hand in columns 12 and 13 of TABLE 4.5. Using the totals at the feet of these columns the Maxwell-Mohr equations become:

$$0 = -8\alpha_t t L + X_a \frac{17 \cdot 82 L}{E} - X_b \frac{1 \cdot 295 L}{E}$$

and

$$0 = -\frac{\alpha_t t L}{\sqrt{2}} - X_a \frac{1 \cdot 295 L}{E} + X_b \frac{4 \cdot 245 L}{E}$$

from which

$$\left. \begin{aligned} X_a &= 0 \cdot 471 \alpha_t t E \\ X_b &= 0 \cdot 311 \alpha_t t E \end{aligned} \right\}$$

(e) In determining the deflexions of hyperstatic structures it is unnecessary to apply the dummy unit load to the complete structure, but only to the primary structure (see Volume 1, Chapter 4, Section 4.8). Thus in finding the vertical deflexion of D in part (b) of this problem we apply a unit load at D to the primary structure which has already featured in the calculation (diagram (e)). If the force in any member of the primary structure due to this unit load is F', then

$$\varDelta_D = \sum F'F\rho \qquad \dots \text{[3.13]}$$

In TABLE 4.5, column 14, the values of F' are recorded, and in column 15 the values of F for those members which have a force F'. The products $F'F\rho$ are then summed (Column 16) giving

$$\varDelta_D = +\frac{7 \cdot 879 PL}{E}$$

We take for a second example a three-dimensional problem.

Problem 4.6—All the members of the frame shown in the diagram have the same value of ρ. If an additional member AC, also with the same value of ρ, is inserted find the forces in the members of the frame under the action of the load P.

The Maxwell-Mohr equation is

$$0 = \sum F_o F_a \rho + X_a \sum F_a^2 \rho$$

In this problem the additional member is obviously the one to consider as the redundant. We have already calculated the forces F_o due to the load P acting on the primary structure, i.e. with AC cut. This was done in *Problem 3.7*, in which the same frame was used, and the values obtained there are set out in column 2 of TABLE 4.6. It is next necessary to determine the forces F_a caused by unit loads acting on the two cut portions of AC (diagram (b)). These forces are confined to the members 2, 3, 5 and 7; for if we resolve at either B or C perpendicular to the zy-plane only one force, the bar force in either member 1 or 6, is involved so that both must be zero. By plane statics we then find the forces F_a tabulated in column 3.

The remainder of the solution follows the procedure already outlined. From the summations in TABLE 4.6 the Maxwell-Mohr equation becomes:

$$0 = -1 \cdot 37 P\rho + 3 \cdot 64 X_a \rho$$

so that

$$X_a = 0 \cdot 376 P$$

Then for any other member

$$F = F_o + X_a F_a$$

The terms $X_a F_a$ are calculated in column 6, and finally column 7 gives the values of the forces F.

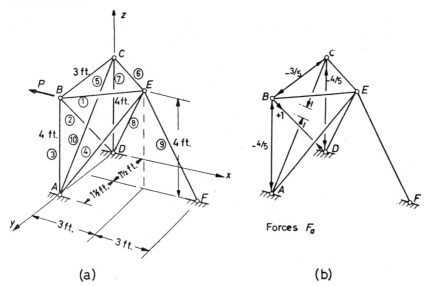

(a)　　　　　　　　　　　　　　(b)

PROBLEM 4.6. (a) Space frame with a redundant member 10. (b) Forces F_a caused by unit load in member 10.

TABLE 4.6

1	2	3	4	5	6	7
Member	$P \times F_o$	F_a	$\dfrac{F_o F_a \rho}{\times P\rho}$	$\dfrac{F_a^2 \rho}{\times \rho}$	$X_a F_a$	$\begin{array}{c}F \\ = F_o + X_a F_a\end{array}$
1	1·12	0	0	0	0	1·12P
2	− 0·83	1	− 0·83	1·0	0·38P	− 0·45P
3	0·67	− 4/5	− 0·54	0·64	− 0·30P	0·37P
4	− 1·31	0	0	0	0	− 1·31P
5	0	− 3/5	0	0·36	− 0·23P	− 0·23P
6	0	0	0	0	0	0
7	0	− 4/5	0	0·64	− 0·30P	− 0·30P
8	0·44	0	0	0	0	0·44P
9	0·83	0	0	0	0	0·83P
10	0	1	0	1·0	0·38P	0·38P
		Σ	− 1·37	3·64		

93

4.4.2. Design of Hyperstatic Braced Frameworks

Reference is made in Volume I [Appendix B] to the problem of the design of hyperstatic braced frameworks, as opposed to their analysis, and a simple example is given of a procedure in which it is possible, if desired, to employ prestressing in order to gain economy. The prestressing is achieved either by inserting a member of incorrect length or by producing a displacement at a reactive restraint.

We may systematize the approach as follows. The Maxwell-Mohr equation for a framework with one redundant with an initial lack of fit λ is:

$$\lambda = \Sigma F_a (F_o + X_a F_a) \rho$$

$$= \sum \frac{F_a F L}{AE}$$

where $F = F_o + X_a F_a$ is the force in any member of the complete structure. If the stress in any member is f the above equation becomes

$$\lambda = \sum \frac{F_a f L}{E} \qquad \dots \text{(i)}$$

The design problem is to proportion the members so that the stresses in the members will satisfy equation (i) when the structure carries the load it is designed to support. Without prestressing the left hand side of the equation becomes zero and there is then some restriction on the stresses that will satisfy it; if prestressing is permissible there is complete freedom of choice, and every member may be designed to carry any desired stress under the design load.

The following problem further illustrates the procedure.

Problem 4.7—The two-hinged arch shown is to be designed with prestressing so that under the loads on the top chord the stress in all members is $\pm f_w$. An alternative design is also to be made without prestressing.

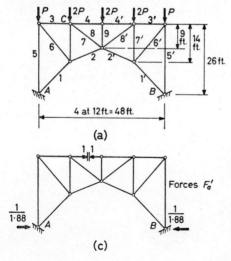

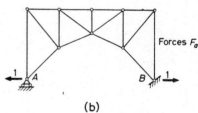

PROBLEM 4.7. (a) Spandrel-braced arch for design so that all the members have stress $\pm f_w$ under the loads shown. (b) Forces F_a caused by unit outward forces at A and B. (c) The effect of inserting member 4 with an incorrect length is found by finding the forces F'_a caused by unit force in this member.

Design with Prestressing

We will first take as the redundant the horizontal thrust at A or B. If we choose a value for this thrust the forces in all the members can be calculated by statics. In deciding on the value to choose we should bear in mind that in an economical arch design the line of resultant thrust should keep within the depth of the arch throughout the span. A horizontal thrust of $1.8P$ will meet this requirement. Then by calculation or graphically the forces F are determined (TABLE 4.7, column 3).

TABLE 4.7

1	2	3	4	5	6	7	8	9	10
				With Prestressing			Without Prestressing		
Member	Length L ft.	F $\times P$	F_a	Stress f $\times f_w$	F_aLf/E $\times f_w/E$	Area $\times P/f_w$	Stress f $\times f_w$	F_aLf/E $\times f_w/E$	Area $\times P/f_w$
1,1′	17·0	− 2·55	1·41	− 1	− 48·2	2·55	− 1	− 48·2	2·55
2,2′	13·0	− 0·83	2·01	− 1	− 52·2	0·83	− 1	− 52·2	0·83
3,3′	12·0	− 1·03	− 0·86	− 1	20·6	1·03	− 0·453	9·3	2·27
4,4′	12·0	− 1·92	− 1·88	− 1	45·2	1·92	− 0·453	20·5	4·23
5,5′	26·0	− 2·20	− 1·00	− 1	52·0	2·20	− 0·453	23·6	4·85
6,6′	18·5	1·58	1·32	1	48·8	1·58	0·453	22·2	3·49
7,7′	14·0	− 2·67	− 0·77	− 1	21·6	2·67	− 0·453	9·8	5·88
8,8′	15·0	1·12	1·28	1	38·4	1·12	0·453	15·2	2·47
9	9·0	− 2·00	0	− 1	0	2·00	− 1	0	2·00
				Σ	+ 126·2		Σ	0	

Next we find the forces F_a caused by unit horizontal loads acting outwards at A and B (diagram (b)). The terms $\dfrac{F_a fL}{E}$ are then calculated (column 6) on the basis of a stress equal to $\pm f_w$ in each member (column 5). The initial lack of fit λ is then given by

$$\lambda = \sum \frac{F_a fL}{E} = + \frac{126 \cdot 2 f_w}{E}$$

The positive sign here means that the support at A must be moved in the assumed direction of the horizontal thrust, i.e. outwards; in other words, the pinned supports at A and B must be forced apart a distance $\dfrac{126 \cdot 2 f_w}{E}$. This will induce stresses in the unloaded arch. These stresses together with those caused by the applied loads will amount in all members to $\pm f_w$.

The final step is to divide the force F in each member by the stress f_w, giving the cross-sectional area (column 7).

It may sometimes be more convenient to prestress the frame internally rather than externally. Thus if we wish to prestress member 4, for example, we regard this member as the redundant, cut it, and apply unit loads (see diagram (c)) to obtain forces F'_a. For each member $F'_a = -\dfrac{F_a}{1\cdot88}$, so that

$$\sum \frac{F'_a f L}{E} = -\sum \frac{F_a f L}{1\cdot88}$$

The lack of fit λ' in member 4 is therefore

$$\lambda' = -\frac{126\cdot2 f_w}{1\cdot88E} = -\frac{67\cdot2 f_w}{E},$$

and the member must be inserted *too long* by this amount.

Design without Prestressing

In this case equation (i) becomes

$$0 = \sum \frac{F_a f L}{E} \qquad \text{.... (ii)}$$

A study of TABLE 4.7, column 6, shows that in order to satisfy this equation we must reduce the stresses in members $3,3'$ to $8,8'$ inclusive. This can be done in any number of ways: perhaps the simplest is to reduce all the stresses in the same proportion (column 8). This brings the summation $\sum \dfrac{F_a f L}{E}$ to zero (column 7). Finally, as before, we obtain the cross-sectional area of each member by dividing F by f.

There is a very substantial saving in weight in this structure when prestressing is adopted: the prestressed design has approximately only one-half the weight of the unprestressed design.

Problems for Solution

4.8. Find the force in DE, the vertical movement of B and the horizontal movement of D. ρ is the same for all members.

(Birmingham, 1939)

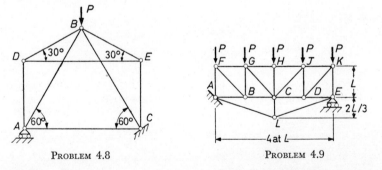

PROBLEM 4.8   PROBLEM 4.9

4.9. Find the force in LC if all members have the same value of ρ. What initial lack of fit of LC would be necessary for there to be no force in GH when the loads P are applied?

(Melbourne, 1953)

4.10.   The cross-sections of the members are as follows:

$$AD, BE : A$$

$$\text{All other members} : 2A$$

Find the ratio of the forces in these diagonals and the deflexions of C and D.

(Birmingham, 1931)

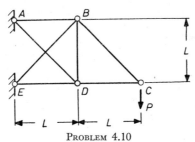

PROBLEM 4.10

4.11.   All members have the same value of ρ. Find the horizontal pull on the walls and the force in the diagonals BE and CF.

(Birmingham, 1934)

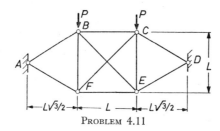

PROBLEM 4.11

4.12.   All members have the same value of ρ. Find the force in AF.

(Manchester, 1957)

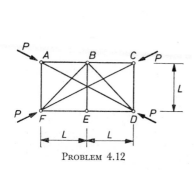

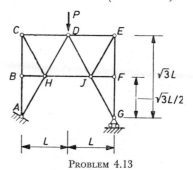

PROBLEM 4.12   PROBLEM 4.13

4.13.   The diagram illustrates a temporary gantry for bridge erection. It is suggested that the frame could carry more load for the same allowable stresses if a tie were inserted between A and G, and the question arises whether the tie should be just taut before the load comes on or whether some prestressing would be advantageous.

Investigate this matter on the assumption that all members, including the tie, have the same cross-sectional area.

(Manchester, 1955)

4.14. The cross-sectional area of each vertical rod is A, that of each inclined member is $20A$, and the effective cross-sectional area of the truss EF for changes in the length EF is $16A$. The inclined members are beams capable of carrying transverse loads. The vertical rods AE and FD are prestressed so that when the structure is under load they remain in tension. Find the changes in the force in FD caused by:

(a) a vertical load P midway along CF, together with a settlement Δ of the foundation at C in the direction FC;

(b) a rise in temperature t_1° in AE and a rise t_2° in the truss EF simultaneously, the coefficient of linear expansion of the material being α_t.

(Melbourne, 1953)

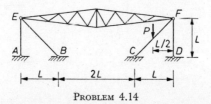

PROBLEM 4.14

4.15. In the steel framework shown a manufacturing tolerance of $\pm x$ in. is to be allowed on the lengths of all bars. Assuming that during assembly the bars are forced into position, find the maximum permissible value of x so that the stress in the diagonals shall not exceed 5000 lb./in.² with the most adverse combination of manufacturing errors. Cross-sectional areas:

$$AB, CD, BD \text{ and } AC: 0.25 \text{ in.}^2$$

$$BC, AD \text{ } 1.0 \text{ in.}^2$$

(London, 1956)

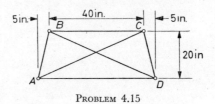

PROBLEM 4.15

4.16. Calculate the forces in the members of this steel framework if the member EF is 1/40 in. too short before insertion. All the members have a cross-sectional area of 1 in.²

(After Birmingham, 1955)

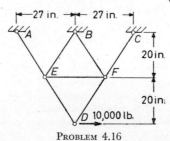

PROBLEM 4.16

4.17. The symmetrical arch shown consists of a number of equilateral triangles of side a. The cross-sectional areas are:

$$AB, BC, DE \text{ etc.}: \quad A_1$$
$$AE, EB, DB, DC \text{ etc.}: A_2$$

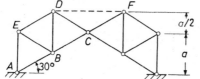

PROBLEM 4.17

The dotted member is inserted to exert a thrust R. Find the elongation of the length DF. If the cross-section of this member is A, by what length should it be made in excess of the original length DF so that it exerts a thrust R?

4.18. The framework shown is pinned to a wall at A, B, C and D. ρ is the same for all members. An additional member DF is inserted. Find the force in DF, due to the load P, (a) if it is of correct length and (b) if it is $\varDelta$ too long when inserted.

(Birmingham, 1942)

PROBLEM 4.18

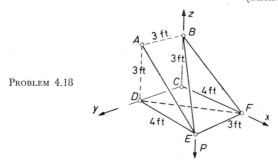

4.19. Prove that when it is known that the values of all the statically indeterminate quantities in a braced framework are equal, as in the following example, the Maxwell-Mohr equations reduce to:

$$X = - \frac{\sum F_o F_s \rho}{\sum F_s^2 \rho}$$

where $F_s = (F_a + F_b + \ldots)$ i.e. the force in a member under unit values of all the statically indeterminate quantities applied simultaneously.

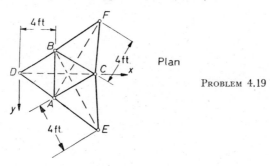

Plan

PROBLEM 4.19

The triangular frame ABC is horizontal and 4 ft. above the plane xy, in which the three supports D, E and F are symmetrically located. The framework is stiffened by

99

three further members *AF*, *BE* and *CD*, shown dotted.

$$AB, BD, CA : 4 \text{ ft.}$$

$$AD, BD, \text{ etc.}: 6 \text{ ft.}$$

$$AF, BE, CD: 8 \cdot 468 \text{ ft.}$$

All members have the same cross-sectional area *A*. Loads *P* are hung from *A*, *B* and *C*. Find the force in the members *AF*, *BE* and *CD* and the horizontal displacement of *C*.

(Birmingham, 1949)

4.20.   Show that equations additional to those of statics may be written for a redundant space frame as

$$\sum t\left(\frac{\partial t}{\partial t_1}\right)\frac{L^3}{AE} = 0$$

where *L* is the length of a member, *A* its cross-sectional area, *t* its tension coefficient and t_1 the tension coefficient for any one of the redundant members.

If *xy* defines the horizontal plane and *z* the vertical, find the forces in the bars of a pinned space structure consisting of 4 bars *AE*, *EB*, *EC* and *ED*, all of the same material and cross-section, when a load of 4 tons applied vertically downwards at *E*. The coordinates are $A(-9, 0, 0)$, $B(+9, 0, 0)$, $C(0, -5, 0)$, $D(0, +5, 0)$, $E(0, 0, +12)$.

(Leeds, 1957)

4.21.   Calculate the forces in the frame shown. The pins *A,B,C* and *D* are fixed to unyielding supports on a rigid floor, and *E,F* and *G* are all 10 ft. above floor level. All members have the same value of L^3/AE. The pins *E*, *F* and *G* each carry 10-ton vertical loads.

(Leeds, 1953)

PROBLEM 4.21

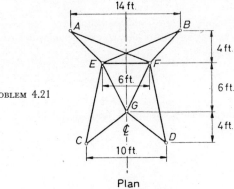

Plan

4.22.   The frame of *Problem 4.10* is to be designed on an elastic basis so that as many members as possible carry the maximum permissible stress $\pm f$ when the load *P* acts. (a) Show that by prestressing *EB* all members may be designed to carry a stress $\pm f$ and find the required lack of fit of *EB*.

(b) If *EB* is not to be prestressed, find what stress in *AD* is necessary for all other members to be fully stressed.

(c) Hence obtain in this case the cross-sectional areas of the members for the loads in the diagonals *AD* and *EB* to be equal in magnitude and opposite in sign.

(Melbourne, 1952)

4.23.   The frame shown is to be designed so that when the load P is acting all tension members carry a stress f and all compression members a stress $2f/3$. If the tension diagonal in each panel is to carry $2/3$ of the shearing force, find the areas of the members AE and BD and by how much they have to be inserted out of fit in the unloaded structure to achieve these stresses.

(After Melbourne, 1955)

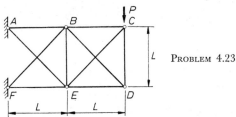

PROBLEM 4.23

4.24.   The frame illustrated has members all of length L and is to be so designed that under the loads P every member is stressed to the permissible value $\pm f$ and the force in any member is $\pm P/2$. What initial lack of fit is necessary in GD? Find also the initial stresses in the members.

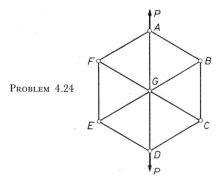

PROBLEM 4.24

4.5.   RIGIDLY JOINTED FRAMEWORKS (Compatibility Methods)

Two methods of analysis of frames in which bending stress predominates are discussed in Volume I, Chapter 4: the $\varDelta_{ik}$ method and Castigliano's Theorem of Compatibility.

4.5.1. THE $\varDelta_{ik}$ METHOD [Volume I, Chapter 4, Section 4.6]

This is based on the flexibility coefficient equations of Müller-Breslau (here written for a structure with two redundants).

$$0 \text{ (or } \lambda_a) = \varDelta_{ao} + X_a\varDelta_{aa} + X_b\varDelta_{ab} \left.\right\}$$
$$0 \text{ (or } \lambda_b) = \varDelta_{bo} + X_b\varDelta_{ba} + X_b\varDelta_{bb} \left.\right\} \quad \dots . [4.7]$$

In calculating the $\varDelta$'s in these equations it is necessary to evaluate integrals of the type $\int \dfrac{M_i M_k dx}{EI}$, where M_i is the bending moment due to unit load acting on the primary structure in place of one of the redundants, and M_k is the bending moment in the primary structure due to the applied loads.

H   101

It is shown in Volume I that, for any length of member within which the M_i diagram varies in a linear manner,

$$\frac{1}{EI}\int M_i M_k dx = \frac{\eta_i A_k}{EI}$$

where A_k is the area of the M_k diagram over the length under consideration and η_i is the value of the moment M_i at the centroid of this portion of the M_k diagram. In the above it is assumed that the members of the structure are prismatic.

The method is illustrated in Volume I, Chapter 4, Section 4.6.2. We shall further illustrate it by a problem involving distributed loads.

Problem 4.25—The steel pin-based frame shown in the diagram (a) consists of a 15 in. × 6 in. × 45 lb. R.S.J. throughout, for which $I = 492$ in.[4]. It is required to find the bending moments in the frame due to the uniformly distributed loads shown and the change in the distance between the eave joints B and D.

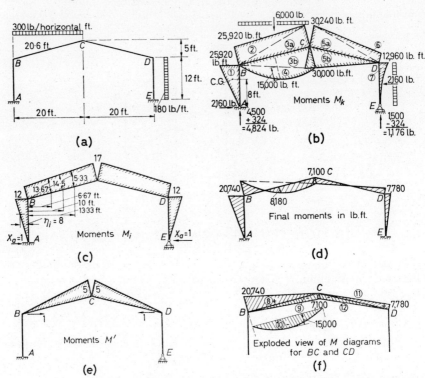

PROBLEM 4.25 (a) Rigidly jointed frame for solution by the Δ_{ik} method. (b) Moments M_k caused by the actual applied loads acting on the primary structure. (c) Moments M_i caused by unit horizontal thrust at the abutments. (d) Final bending moment diagram. (e) In order to find the relative movement of B and D dummy unit loads are applied there to give the bending moment diagram shown. (f) Exploded view of the M-diagram for BC and CD.

We take as the redundant the horizontal thrust at the base E. The primary structure is then pinned at A and supported on horizontal rollers at E (diagram (b)).

102

The compatibility equation is

$$0 = \Delta_{ao} + X_a \Delta_{aa}$$

in which Δ_{ao} is the inward movement of E in the primary structure due to the applied loads (diagram (b)) and Δ_{aa} is the inward movement of E due to a unit horizontal load applied at E (diagram (c)).

We first calculate the movement Δ_{ao}. This is given by the expression

$$\Delta_{ao} = \int_A^E \frac{M_i M_k \, ds}{EI} = \sum \frac{\eta_i A_k}{EI}$$

TABLE 4.25

Δ_{ik} CALCULATIONS

1	2	3	4	5	6	7
	Member	M_k diag.	Area of M_k diagram A_k	Position of centroid	η_i	$\eta_i A_k$
	AB	1	$25920 \times \dfrac{12}{2}$ $= 155 \cdot 5 \times 10^3$	8 ft. above A	8	$124 \cdot 4 \times 10^4$
Δ_{ao}	BC	2	$25920 \times \dfrac{20 \cdot 6}{2}$ $= 267 \cdot 0 \times 10^3$	6·67 ft. to right of B	13·67	$365 \cdot 0 \times 10^4$
		3	$240 \times \dfrac{20 \cdot 6}{2}$ $= 2 \cdot 5 \times 10^3$	13·33 ft. to right of B	15·33	$3 \cdot 8 \times 10^4$
		4	$- 15000 \times \dfrac{2}{3} \times 20 \cdot 6$ $= - 206 \times 10^3$	10 ft. to right of B	14·50	$- 298 \cdot 7 \times 10^4$
	CD	5	$240 \times \dfrac{20 \cdot 6}{2}$ $= 2 \cdot 5 \times 10^3$	13·33 ft. to left of D	15·33	$3 \cdot 8 \times 10^4$
		6	$12960 \times \dfrac{20 \cdot 6}{2}$ $= 133 \cdot 5 \times 10^3$	6·67 ft. to left of D	13·67	$182 \cdot 5 \times 10^4$
	DE	7	$12960 \times \dfrac{12}{3}$ $= 51 \cdot 8 \times 10^3$	9 ft. above E	9·00	$46 \cdot 6 \times 10^4$
					Σ	$427 \cdot 4 \times 10^4$

TABLE 4.25—*(cont.)*

Δ_{ik} CALCULATIONS

1	2	3	4	5	6	7
	Member	M_k diag.	Area of M_k diagram A_k	Position of centroid	η_i	$\eta_i A_k$
Δ_{aa}	AB		$12 \times \dfrac{12}{2} = 72$	8 ft. above A	8	576
	BC		$12 \times \dfrac{20 \cdot 6}{2} \times 123 \cdot 6$	6·67 ft. to right of A	13·67	1690
			$17 \times \dfrac{20 \cdot 6}{2} = 175 \cdot 1$	13·33 ft. to right of A	15·33	2684
	CD		As for BC			2684 1690
	DE		As for AB			576
					Σ	9900
Δ_{bd}	BC	8	$20740 \times \dfrac{20 \cdot 6}{2}$ $= 213 \cdot 6 \times 10^3$	6·67 ft. to right of B	1·67	$356 \cdot 7 \times 10^3$
		9	$- 7100 \times \dfrac{20 \cdot 6}{2}$ $= - 73 \cdot 1 \times 10^3$	13·33 ft. to right of B	3·33	$- 243 \cdot 4 \times 10^3$
		10	$- 15000 \times \dfrac{20 \cdot 6 \times 2}{3}$ $= - 206 \times 10^3$	10 ft. to right of B	2·50	$- 515 \cdot 0 \times 10^3$
	CD	11	$7780 \times \dfrac{20 \cdot 6}{2}$ $= 80 \cdot 1 \times 10^3$	6·67 ft. to left of D	1·67	$133 \cdot 8 \times 10^3$
		12	$7100 \times \dfrac{20 \cdot 6}{2}$ $= - 73 \cdot 1 \times 10^3$	13·33 ft. to left of D	3·33	$- 243 \cdot 4 \times 10^3$
					Σ	$- 511 \cdot 3 \times 10^3$

where M_i and M_k are the bending moments shown in diagrams (b) and (c) respectively, in which the moments are plotted on the tension sides of the members (moments are positive when they produce tension on the *outside* of a member).

In diagram (b) the moment diagrams due to the different loads are drawn separately, the negative diagrams being due to the load on BC and the positive diagrams being due to the load on DE.

Considering first the member AB, we note that the M_i diagram is linear over the complete length AB, and that therefore we may apply the above formula to AB as a whole. The area A_k of the diagram is $25920 \times \dfrac{12}{2} = 155.5 \times 10^3$, and its centroid is 8 ft. above A. At this point $M_i = \eta_i = 8$. Hence for AB the product

$$\eta_i A_k = 155.5 \times 10^3 \times 8 = 124.4 \times 10^4.$$

These calculations are arranged in TABLE 4.25 in the first line, columns 4 to 7.

In BC, M_i is again linear over the whole of the member. It is however convenient here to take the M_k diagram in three parts 2, 3 and 4. For diagram 2 $A_k = 25920 \times \dfrac{20.6}{2} = 267 \times 10^3$, and its centroid is one-third of the way from B towards C, at which point $M_i = 13.67$. Hence

$$\eta_i A_k = 267 \times 10^3 \times 13.67 = 365 \times 10^4.$$

The algebraic sum of diagrams 3a and 3b gives a small positive bending moment diagram, with a value of $+240$ at C. $A_k = 2.5 \times 10^3$ and the centroid is 13.33 ft. to the right of B. The moment η_i is therefore 15.33 and

$$\eta_i A_k = 2.5 \times 10^3 \times 15.33 = 3.8 \times 10^4.$$

Diagram 4 is parabolic and its area is $15000 \times 20.6 \times \dfrac{2}{3}$, the centroid being midway between B and C.

The only other point requiring comment in the derivation of $\varDelta_{ao}$ is that diagram 7, which is also parabolic, has an area $12960 \times \dfrac{12}{3}$ and its centroid is 9 ft. above E.

The calculations are arranged in TABLE 4.25 which should be followed through carefully.

The term $\varDelta_{aa}$ is given by the expression

$$\varDelta_{aa} = \int_A^E \frac{(M_i)^2 ds}{EI} = \sum \frac{\eta_i A_i}{EI}$$

in which A_i is now the area of a portion of the M_i diagram, and η_i is the moment M_i at the centroid of this same M_i diagram. These values are also set out in TABLE 4.25. From the summations for $\varDelta_{ao}$ and $\varDelta_{aa}$ the compatibility equation becomes

$$0 = 427.4 \times 10^4 + 9900 X_a$$

so that
$$X_a = -431.7 \text{ lb.}$$

It may be remarked that proper regard must always be paid to the signs of M_i and M_k. Thus had we chosen to take $X_a = 1$ acting to the right at E, the M_i diagram would have been negative throughout, and $\varDelta_{ao}$ (but not $\varDelta_{aa}$) would have been negative in sign.

It is also required to find the relative movement of B and D.

This is given by the expression

$$\varDelta_{bd} = \int \frac{M'M ds}{EI}$$

where M' is the moment at any point due to unit loads acting towards each other at B and D, in the *primary structure* [see Volume I, Chapter 4, Section 4.8]. These moments are shown in diagram (e).

The moments M have already been calculated, and are shown in diagram (d). In evaluating $\int \dfrac{M'M\,ds}{EI}$ we may conveniently make use of the Δ_{ik} method again. In this case A_k is the area of a part of the M diagram, and η_i is the value of M' at the centroid of the parts of the M diagram. We first explode the M diagram for BC and CD (diagram (f)) for convenience in handling the areas. The working is set out in TABLE 4.25, and further comment is scarcely necessary. From the summation we have

$$\Delta_{bd} = \frac{-511\cdot3 \times 10^3 \times 1728}{30 \times 10^6 \times 492} = -0\cdot06 \text{ in. (i.e. } B \text{ and } D \text{ move apart).}$$

4.5.2. Castigliano's Theorem of Compatibility

This has been discussed in Volume I and in Chapter 2 of the present volume, and it is only necessary to refer here to the general form of the theorem for a structure with one redundant X_a, when axial and shearing forces are taken into account as well as bending, is as follows:

$$0 = \sum \int M \frac{dM}{dX_a} \frac{ds}{EI} + \sum \int F \frac{dF}{dX_a} \frac{ds}{AE} + \sum \kappa \int Q \frac{dQ}{dX_a} \frac{ds}{AN}$$

It will be instructive to solve *Problem 4.25* by the use of Castigliano's Theorem, first taking account of bending deformations only, and the including the effect of axial and shearing deformations.

Problem 4.26—The first part of the problem already solved in *4.25* (the calculation of the bending moment diagram) is to be dealt with by the method of Castigliano.

(a) *Taking account of bending deformations only:*

Castigliano's equation for this case reduces to:

$$0 = \sum \int M \frac{dM}{dX_a} \frac{ds}{EI}$$

where M is the bending moment in the complete structure due to the applied loads.

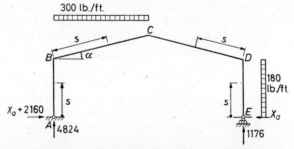

PROBLEM 4.26. The frame of *Problem 4.25* arranged for analysis by means of Castigliano's Theorem of Compatibility.

We will again take X_a as the horizontal thrust at E. Then from statics we obtain the reactions at A and E shown in the diagram.

We now proceed to write down M and $\dfrac{dM}{dX_a}$ for each member of the frame (the sign convention for M is the same as that adopted in *Problem 4.25*).

$AB:$ $M = (X_a + 2160)s$ $\dfrac{dM}{dX_a} = s$

$BC:$ $M = (X_a + 2160)(12 + s \sin \alpha) - 4824s \sin \alpha + \dfrac{300.(s \cos \alpha)^2}{2}$

$\dfrac{dM}{dX_a} = 12 + s \sin \alpha$

$CD:$ $M = X_a(12 + s \sin \alpha) + 2160 (6 + s \sin) - 1176s \cos \alpha$

$\dfrac{dM}{dX_a} = 12 + s \sin \alpha$

$DE:$ $M = X_a s + \dfrac{180s^2}{2}$ $\dfrac{dM}{dX_a} = s$

Then

$$0 = \sum \int M \frac{dM}{dX_a} \cdot \frac{ds}{EI} = \left(\frac{X_a + 2160}{EI}\right) \int_0^{12} s^2 ds \qquad (AB)$$

$$+ \left(\frac{X_a + 2160}{EI}\right) \int_0^{20\cdot6} (12 + s \sin \alpha)^2 ds - \frac{4824 \cos \alpha}{EI} \int_0^{20\cdot6} s(12 + s \sin \alpha) ds$$

$$+ \frac{150 \cos^2 \alpha}{EI} \int_0^{20\cdot6} s^2(12 + s \sin \alpha) ds \quad (BC)$$

$$+ \frac{X_a}{EI} \int_0^{20\cdot6} (12 + s \sin \alpha)^2 ds + \frac{2160}{EI} \int_0^{20\cdot6} (6 + s \sin \alpha)(12 + s \sin \alpha) ds$$

$$- \frac{1176}{EI} \cos \alpha \int_0^{20\cdot6} s(12 + s \sin \alpha) ds \quad (CD)$$

$$+ \frac{1}{EI} \int_0^{12} (X_a s + 90s^2) s ds \quad (DE)$$

which reduces to

$$0 = 427\cdot4 \times 10^4 + 9900 X_a$$

giving, as before

$$X_a = - 431\cdot7 \text{ lb.}$$

The main difficulty in solving this type of problem by either of the above methods is in the arithmetic. In the $\varDelta_{ik}$ method the integrations are performed much more simply than in Castigliano's method, and there is correspondingly less chance of error. The $\varDelta_{ik}$ method cannot, however, be used when it is desired to take account of axial and shearing deformations, as in the following:

(b) *Taking account of bending, axial and shearing deformations:*

We must now include the actual values of I and A for the 15 in. × 6 in. R.S.J. These are:

$$I = 492 \text{ in.}^4 \quad = 0\cdot0237 \text{ ft.}^4$$
$$A = 13\cdot24 \text{ in.}^2 = 0\cdot092 \text{ ft.}^2$$
$$A_{web} = 5 \text{ in.}^2 \quad = 0\cdot0347 \text{ ft}^2$$

In calculating the shear terms $\kappa \int Q \dfrac{dQ}{dX_a} \dfrac{ds}{AN}$ it is sufficiently accurate for joist sections (Volume I, Chapter 3, Section 3.2.2) to take κ as unity and A as the area of the web. N, the modulus of rigidity, may be taken for steel as $0.4E$.

We now proceed to evaluate the terms $\displaystyle\sum \int F \dfrac{dF}{dX_a} \dfrac{ds}{AE}$ and $\displaystyle\sum \int Q \dfrac{dQ}{dX} \dfrac{ds}{A_{\text{web}}N}$ for axial and shearing effects respectively. We adopt the following as our convention of signs:

F positive when compressive on a section;

Q positive at a section when the portion nearest A tends to move inwards relative to the other side of the section.

The following values of $F, \dfrac{dF}{dX_a}$ etc. emerge:

AB: $F = 4824$; $\dfrac{dF}{dX_a} = 0$

$\qquad Q = X_a + 2160$; $\dfrac{dQ}{dX_a} = 1$

BC: $F = (4824 - 300s \cos \alpha) \sin \alpha + (X_a + 2160) \cos \alpha$; $\dfrac{dF}{dX_a} = \cos \alpha$

$\qquad Q = (300s \cos \alpha - 4824) \cos \alpha + (X_a + 2160) \sin \alpha$; $\dfrac{dQ}{dX_a} = \sin \alpha$

CD: $F = 1176 \sin \alpha + (X_a + 2160) \cos \alpha$; $\dfrac{dF}{dX_a} = \cos \alpha$

$\qquad Q = 1176 \cos \alpha - (X_a + 2160) \sin \alpha$; $\dfrac{dQ}{dX_a} = - \sin \alpha$

DE: $F = 1176$; $\dfrac{dF}{dX_a} = 0$

$\qquad Q = - (X_a + 180s)$; $\dfrac{dQ}{dX_a} = - 1$

Then
$$\sum \int F \dfrac{dF}{dX_a} \dfrac{ds}{AE} = \frac{1}{AE} \int_0^{20 \cdot 6} (4824 - 300s \cos \alpha) \cos \alpha \sin \alpha\, ds$$
$$+ \frac{1}{AE} \int_0^{20 \cdot 6} (X_a + 2160) \cos^2 \alpha\, ds \qquad (BC)$$
$$+ \frac{1}{AE} \int_0^{20 \cdot 6} \{1176 \sin \alpha + (X_a + 2160) \cos \alpha\} \cos \alpha\, ds \quad (CD)$$
$$= \frac{1}{AE} (98 \cdot 3 \times 10^3 + 38 \cdot 8 X_a)$$

and
$$\sum \kappa \int Q \dfrac{dQ}{dX_a} \dfrac{ds}{AN} = \frac{1}{A_{\text{web}} N} \int_0^{12} (X_a + 2160) ds \qquad (AB)$$
$$+ \frac{1}{A_{\text{web}} N} \int_0^{20 \cdot 6} (- 4824 + 300s \cos \alpha) \cos \alpha \sin \alpha\, ds$$
$$+ \frac{1}{A_{\text{web}} N} \int_0^{20 \cdot 6} (X_a + 2160) \sin^2 \alpha\, ds \qquad (BC)$$

$$+ \frac{1}{A_{web}\, N} \int_0^{20 \cdot 6} \{- 1176 \cos \alpha + (X_a + 2160) \sin \alpha\} \sin \alpha \; ds \qquad (CD)$$

$$+ \frac{1}{A_{web}\, N} \int_0^{12} (X_a + 180s)ds \qquad\qquad (DE)$$

$$= \frac{1}{A_{web}\, N} (29 \cdot 6 \times 10^3 + 26 \cdot 4 X_a)$$

Substituting in the complete expression for $\dfrac{dU}{dX_a}$ we then have

$$0 = \frac{1}{0 \cdot 0237E} (427 \cdot 4 \times 10^4 + 9900 X_a) \qquad \text{(bending moment)}$$

$$+ \frac{1}{0 \cdot 092E} (98 \cdot 3 \times 10^3 + 38 \cdot 8 X_a) \qquad \text{(direct force)}$$

$$+ \frac{1}{0 \cdot 0347 \times 0 \cdot 4E} (29 \cdot 6 \times 10^{\cdot} + 26 \cdot 4 X_a) \quad \text{(shearing force)}$$

from which $\qquad\qquad\qquad X_a = - 437 \text{ lb.}$

This result bears out the statement made in Volume I [Chapter 4, Section 4.7.3] that direct and shearing effects may often be ignored; in the present example they alter the value of the redundant by only about one per cent. It may be remarked that the type of frame analysed in this problem is common in single storey factory construction, and that the joint section normally adopted for a 40 ft. span is likely to be a little lighter than a 15 in. × 6 in. R.S.J. Direct and shearing effects may, therefore, justifiably be ignored in calculation of the forces in this type of frame; they have a more important effect, however, on deflexions.

Problem 4.27—The curved steel beam *ABC* shown in plan in the diagram lies in the horizontal plane *ABC* and is fixed to a wall at *A* and supported at *C* in such a way that

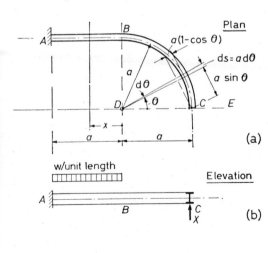

PROBLEM 4.27 (a) and (b) The curved cantilever shown in plan and elevation has a redundant reaction at the prop at *C*. (c) In order to find the rotation of *C* a unit torque is applied to the primary structure at that point.

the reaction there is vertical. The beam is of joist section. A uniformly distributed load of intensity w acts vertically downwards on the beam over the length AB.

Find the value of the reaction at C and also the angular rotation of the beam at C in the vertical plane DCE.

This is another class of problem—the three dimensional rigidly jointed frame—in which Castigliano's method is useful. In this particular case we may neglect shearing effects, and axial effects are absent in any case; but we must take account of torsional effects, since they involve large deformations and therefore large amounts of strain energy. There is only one redundant, which is most conveniently taken as the upward vertical reaction at C, and the appropriate equation in this case is

$$0 = \sum \int M \frac{dM}{dX_a} \cdot \frac{ds}{EI} + \sum \int T \frac{dT}{dX_a} \cdot \frac{ds}{NJ}$$

where NJ is the torsional rigidity of the beam at any point.

We first evaluate M, $\frac{dM}{dX_a}$, T and $\frac{dT}{dX_a}$ in the two sections CB and BA of the beam. Since there is only one redundant we will discard the suffix a. We assume that bending moments producing tension on the top fibres of the beam are positive, and that positive torsional moments are clockwise when viewed from the end C of the beam looking towards the end A.

$$CB: \quad M = -Xa \sin\theta; \qquad \frac{dM}{dX_a} = -a\sin\theta$$

$$T = Xa(1-\cos\theta); \qquad \frac{dT}{dX} = a(1-\cos\theta)$$

$$BA: \quad M = \frac{wx^2}{2} - X(a+x); \qquad \frac{dM}{dX} = -(a+x)$$

$$T = +Xa: \qquad \frac{dT}{dX} = +a$$

Then in the above equation we have:

$$0 = \int_0^{\pi/2} \frac{Xa^2\sin^2\theta \cdot ad\theta}{EI} + \int_0^{\pi/2} \frac{Xa^2(1-\cos\theta)^2 \, ad\theta}{NJ} \qquad (CB)$$

$$+ \int_0^a \left\{ X(a+x) - \frac{wx^2}{2} \right\} \frac{(a+x) \cdot dx}{EI} + \int_0^a \frac{Xa^2 \cdot dx}{NJ} \qquad (BA)$$

which reduces to

$$0 = \frac{Xa^3\pi}{4EI} + \frac{Xa^3}{NJ}\left(\frac{3\pi}{4} - 2\right) + \frac{7a^3}{24EI}(8X - wa) + \frac{Xa^3}{NJ}$$

from which

$$X = \frac{\dfrac{0\cdot292wa}{EI}}{\dfrac{3\cdot118}{EI} + \dfrac{1\cdot356}{NJ}} = \frac{0\cdot292wa}{3\cdot118 + 1\cdot356 \, EI/NJ}$$

According to Dobie[†] the values of EI/NJ for British Standard Beams range from 230 for No. 123 (12 in. + 6 in. H) to 770 for No. 140 (24 in. + 7½ in.) with an

---

† Dobie, W. B., 'Torsional strength of Structural Members', *Structural Engineer*, 1952, p. 34.

average of about 450. I-beams are specifically designed to resist bending and have an inherently low torsional resistance; it therefore appears that in rigidly jointed steel space structures torsional effects are likely to play an important part.

In calculating the rotation of the end C in the vertical plane DCE we apply a unit torque to the end C in the plane CDE (diagram (b)). As before, we apply this torque not to the hyperstatic structure but to the primary structure remaining when X is removed. At C the moment is purely torsional, but gradually becomes purely bending in its effect as B is approached.

We have

$$\theta_c = \sum \int \frac{M_t' M ds}{EI} + \sum \int \frac{T_t' T ds}{NJ}$$

where M_t' and T_t' are the bending and torsional moments due to unit torque applied at C, while M and T are the bending and torsional moments in the hyperstatic structure caused by the applied loads.

Then in CB: $M_t' = \sin \theta$; $T_t' = \cos \theta$

and in BA: $M_t' = 1$; $T_t' = 0$

We already have expressions for M and T and so

$$\theta_C = \int_0^{\pi/2} \frac{\sin \theta \, (- Xa \sin \theta) \, ad\theta}{EI} + \int_0^a 1 \left\{ \frac{wx^2}{2} - X(a + x) \right\} \frac{dx}{EI}$$
$$+ \int_0^{\pi/2} \cos \theta \, Xa(1 - \cos \theta) \frac{ad\theta}{NJ}$$

which reduces to

$$\theta_C = Xa^2 \left(\frac{0 \cdot 215}{NJ} - \frac{2 \cdot 285}{EI} \right) + \frac{wa^3}{6EI}$$

Substitution of the value of X previously derived will give θ_C in terms of the load w and the properties of the beam.

Problems for Solution

The following problems are to be solved both by the Δ_{ik} method and by Castigliano's Theorem of Compatibility.

4.28. The rigidly jointed bent shown is of uniform flexural rigidity EI throughout. Find the normal reaction at D and the movement at D.

(Birmingham, 1952)

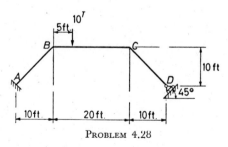

PROBLEM 4.28

4.29. In the frame $ABCDE$, the flexural rigidity of the columns is EI, and that of the beam BCD is $2EI$. Determine the horizontal and vertical forces at E, forming the

111

primary structure in the following ways:
    (a) providing a third pin at A;
    (b) providing horizontal rollers at E.

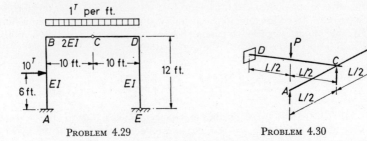

PROBLEM 4.29   PROBLEM 4.30

4.30.   The beam DC is rigidly fixed to a wall at D and simply supported at C by an identical beam ACB set at right angles to it. Find the reaction and the deflexion at C.
(Manchester)

4.31.   Find the reaction at G and the horizontal components of the reaction at E.

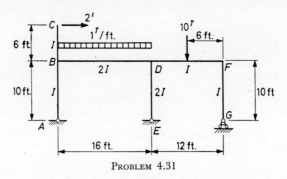

PROBLEM 4.31

Problems for Solution by Castigliano's Theorem of Compatibility

4.32.   The second moment of area of the steel beam AD illustrated is I and its cross-sectional area A. It is stiffened by steel members of cross-sectional area a. If the trussing members can carry only direct stress, find the force in EF.
(Birmingham, 1928)

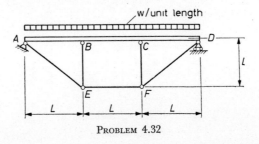

PROBLEM 4.32

4.33.   The beam AB has a second moment of area I and the tie an area a. Neglecting axial effects in AB, find:

112

(a) the force in the tie;

(b) the deflexion under the load;

(c) the equation for the influence line for the force in the tie if the unit load is distant x from B.

(Birmingham)

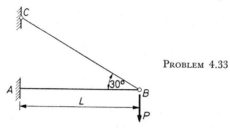

PROBLEM 4.33

4.34. The symmetrical frame shown consists of a single steel member $ABCD$, of flexural rigidity EI, braced by five bars each of cross-sectional area a and capable of carrying axial forces only. Neglecting the axial effects in $ABCD$, find the force in EF.

(Melbourne, 1951)

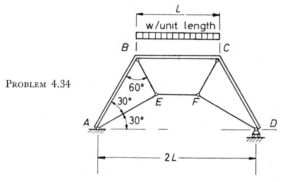

PROBLEM 4.34

4.35. The members of the steel cantilever frame $ABECD$ have the second moments of the area shown and it is stiffened by two steel ties EC and ED having cross-sectional area A, where $I/A = 10$ ft.² Neglecting the axial strain of BCD and ABE find the forces in the ties EC and ED. By how much should the tie ED be too short when inserted for the bending moment at C to be half the value without such prestressing?

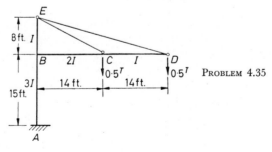

PROBLEM 4.35

4.36. The mast shown, whose flexural rigidity is EI, is supported by four guys of equal cross-sectional area a which are prestressed so that they are always in tension.

113

If a horizontal wind load F, uniformly distributed up the height of the mast, acts as shown in plan, find the changes in the forces in the four guys. Axial effects in the mast may be neglected.

(Melbourne, 1957)

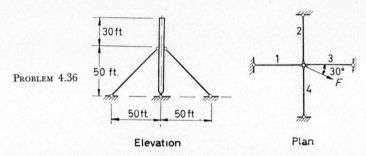

PROBLEM 4.36

Elevation   Plan

4.37. The diagram shows a portal frame with a beam in the form of a truss. The two columns ABC, $A'B'C'$ are of equal uniform cross-section. Axial effects may be ignored throughout the structure. Show that under the action of the load F a point of contraflexure occurs in the columns at a distance $\dfrac{3aH}{6a + 2}$ below B, where $a = H/h$.

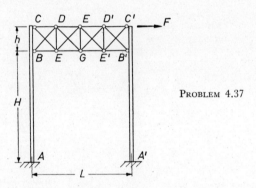

PROBLEM 4.37

When $a = 4$, find the ratio of the maximum bending moment in the columns with that calculated on the common assumption that the truss 'direction-fixes' the columns at B and B'.

(Melbourne, 1956)

4.38. The symmetrical frame shown consists of a continuous member $ADBEC$, 6 in. wide × 12 in. deep. The cross-sectional area of the ties DE and AC is $\frac{1}{2}$ in.², and their modulus of elasticity is 15 times that of the members AB and BC.

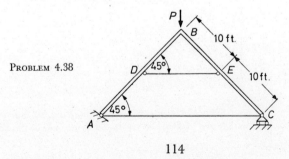

PROBLEM 4.38

Neglecting axial and shearing strains in $ADBEC$, find the forces in the ties and the vertical deflexion of B.

(Birmingham, 1932)

4.39. The frame shown, which is initially unstressed, consists of a beam ABC, whose second moment of area is 288 in.[4], and bars 0·8 in.[2] in cross-sectional area of the same material. Find the force in ED and the maximum bending moment in the beam.

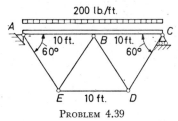

PROBLEM 4.39

By how much should the initial length of ED be changed in order to produce the optimum bending moment distribution in the beam? What is then the force in ED and the maximum bending moment in the beam under load?

4.40. The chain link shown has a uniform circular cross-section. Prove that if d is small compared with R, the mean radius of the ends, then the maximum bending moment occurs at the point of application of the load and is equal to $\dfrac{PR}{2}\left(\dfrac{L+2R}{L+\pi R}\right)$

(London, 1954)

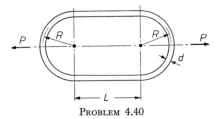

PROBLEM 4.40

4.41. The diagram shows a fuselage frame, rigidly jointed at A and C. $I_{ABC} = 5I$, $I_{ADC} = I$. Find the bending moments at B and D due to the couples M' acting at

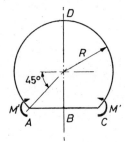

PROBLEM 4.41

A and C as shown. Neglect direct and shearing strain energy in comparison with bending strain energy.

(Glasgow, 1957)

115

4.42. The bow-girder shown in plan carries a uniformly distributed load of w per unit length. It is made of tube of circular cross-section for which the modulus of rigidity is three-eighths of Young's Modulus. Find the value of the bending and twisting moments at A and D and at the mid-point of BC.

(St. Andrews, 1956)

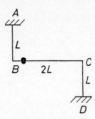

PROBLEM 4.42

4.43. A ring girder to support a water-tank is shown in plan in the figure. It is carried on six columns, spaced equally around the girder, and is connected to the

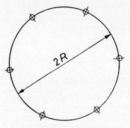

PROBLEM 4.43

columns in such a way that no change of slope or deflexion takes place there. Find the magnitude of the support bending and twisting moments if the ratio $\dfrac{EI}{NJ}$ is 5. It may be assumed that the girder is loaded uniformly at w tons per ft. run.

(After St. Andrews, 1955)

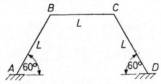

PROBLEM 4.44

4.44. The frame $ABCD$ shown in plan in the figure is of uniform solid circular cross-section. A load P is applied at C normal to the plane of the frame. Find the components of reaction at D, taking $N = 2E/5$.

(Birmingham, 1956)

116

CHAPTER 5

MOVING LOADS ON STRUCTURES

5.1. INTRODUCTION

In Volume 1, Chapter 5 was mainly devoted to a discussion of the determination of influence lines for hyperstatic structures and of structural models, although Section 5.2 dealt with influence lines generally. The same sequence is followed here; Section 5.2 contains a few typical problems on determinate beams and trusses while later sections are devoted to hyperstatic frames of various kinds. Some examples of rigid frames are also included but continuous beams and arches are treated in Chapters 6 and 7 respectively.

More extensive treatments of the problem of rolling loads on determinate structures will be found, for example, in works by Marshall† and by Ashby and Chilver.‡

5.2 INFLUENCE LINES FOR STATICALLY DETERMINATE STRUCTURES

5.2.1. STATICALLY DETERMINATE BEAMS [Volume 1, Section 5.2.1]

Problem 5.1—(a) Draw the influence lines for shearing force and bending moment at a point C 24 ft. from the left hand support of a simply supported beam AB of span 80 ft.

(b) Find the maximum positive and negative shearing force and the maximum bending moment at this point caused by a uniformly distributed load, longer than the span, of 1·5 tons per foot and by the train of concentrated loads shown; the 5-ton load leads and the train may go in either direction.

(Manchester College of Science and Technology)

The influence line for shearing force is shown at (b) in the diagram. When the unit load is in CB the shearing force at C is negative and is numerically equal to the vertical reaction at A, while when the load is in AC the shearing force at C is positive and is numerically equal to the vertical reaction at B. Under the uniformly distributed load the worst conditions are when the load extends from A or B to C: hence

$$\text{Max. Positive S.F. at } C = 1·5 \times \text{area } acd$$
$$= 1·5 \times \tfrac{1}{2} \times 24 \times 0·3 = 5·4 \text{ tons}$$
$$\text{Max. Negative S.F. at } C = 1·5 \times \text{area } bce$$
$$= 1·5 \times \tfrac{1}{2} \times 56 \times 0·7 = 29·4 \text{ tons}$$

The worst positions of the train of loads are found by inspection and are as shown.

---

† Marshall, W. T. *Solution of Problems in Structures.* Pitman.
‡ Ashby, R. J. and Chilver, A. H. *Problems in Engineering Structures.* Arnold.

$$\text{Max. Positive S.F. at } C = 10 \times \frac{4}{24} \times 0.3 + 8 \times \frac{14}{24} \times 0.3 + 8 \times 0.3$$

$$= 4.3 \text{ tons}$$

$$\text{Max. Negative S.F. at } C = 5 \times \frac{28}{56} \times 0.7 + 10 \times \frac{36}{56} \times 0.7$$

$$+ 8 \times \frac{46}{56} \times 0.7 + 8 \times 0.7$$

$$= 16.45 \text{ tons}$$

The influence line for bending moment at C, shown at (c), is obtained from the consideration that the maximum bending occurs when unit load is at C itself.

PROBLEM 5.1. (a) The influence lines for shearing force and bending moment at C are required. (b) The positions of the train of loads for maximum values of the positive and negative shear at C are given. (c) The train of loads produces the maximum bending moment at C when in the position shown.

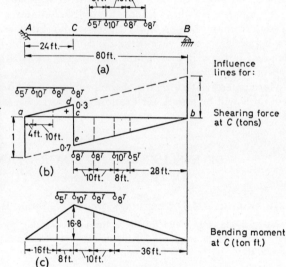

The maximum effect of the uniformly distributed load is when it covers the whole span; the bending moment at C is then $\frac{1}{2} \times 16.8 + 80 \times 1.5 = 1008$ ton ft. The maximum effect of the train of loads is found by inspection or trial and occurs when the loads are as shown.

$$\text{Max. B.M. at } C = \left(5 \times \frac{16}{24} + 10 + 8 \times \frac{46}{56} + 8 \times \frac{36}{56}\right) 16.8$$

$$= 420.8 \text{ ton ft.}$$

Problems for Solution

5.2. A beam of span L is crossed by two equal concentrated loads distant α apart. Prove that the maximum bending moment at any point of the beam due to these loads cannot exceed the maximum bending moment at the centre by more than $12\frac{1}{2}$ per cent whatever the values of α and L.

(Manchester College of Science and Technology)

5.3. A beam of span L carries a dead load of 1·5 tons per foot and is crossed by a uniformly distributed load, longer than the span, of 2 tons per foot. Find graphically and by calculation the length of the girder in which the shearing force can have both positive and negative values.

5.4. The beam *AB*, of span 60 ft., is simply supported at its ends and is indirectly loaded through a system of stringers and cross girders. Draw influence lines for

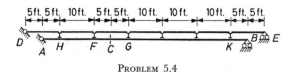

PROBLEM 5.4

the reaction at *A*, the shearing force at *C* and the bending moment at *C* and determine the maximum values produced by a live load of 2 tons per foot of length greater than 70 ft.

(Manchester)

5.5. A theorem of virtual work states that no work is done when a system of forces in equilibrium undergoes a small displacement. Show how this theorem is applied, as Müller-Breslau's principle, in the determination of influence lines.

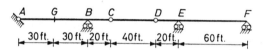

PROBLEM 5.5

Using this principle, or otherwise, obtain the influence lines for shearing force and bending moment at the point G and for reaction and bending moment at the point B in the cantilever-type bridge outlined in the diagram.

(Leeds, 1957)

5.6. In the structure shown in the diagram *D* and *E* are hinges. Sketch the influence lines, for vertical unit load, for the following: θ_C, θ_B, R_C, M_F. The cross-section is uniform throughout.

(Melbourne)

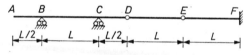

PROBLEM 5.6

5.2.2. STATICALLY DETERMINATE TRUSSES [Volume I, Section 5.2.3]

Problem 5.7—Draw the influence lines for the reactions at *A* and *B* and for the forces in the members 1, 2 and 3 as unit load crosses the top chord of the simply supported truss shown. Modify the diagram for member 2 to give the effect of a load crossing the lower chord.

(Manchester)

The influence lines for the reactions are obtained by taking moments about *A* and *B* respectively. To obtain the line for one of the members a suitable section is taken through the truss cutting the member; the section shown will serve for all three members.

The force in member 1 is obtained by taking moments about *P*, the point of intersection of members 2 and 3 (the centre of moments for member 1) and the

119

problem thus reduces to that of finding the influence line for bending at the point P of the simply supported beam AB with a linear extension to account for the overhang (diagram (d)).

The force in member 3 is similarly obtained, the centre of moments now being Q; since QP is vertical the lines for members 1 and 3 are mirror images (diagram (e)).

The force in member 2 is obtained by resolving vertically; when the load is to the right of R the force in member 2 is numerically equal to R_A, while when the load is to the left of Q the force in member 2 is numerically equal to R_B. The diagram (f) is completed by joining the points corresponding to Q and R since, when the top

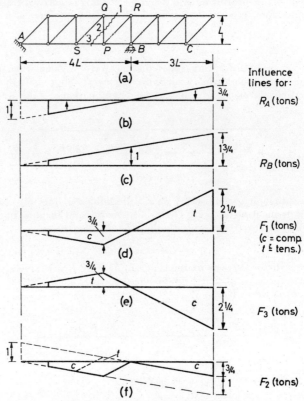

PROBLEM 5.7. (a) Influence lines for the reactions and for the forces in members 1, 2 and 3 are required. (f) The dotted lines in the centre of the diagram give the effect of loading the bottom chord instead of the top.

chord is loaded, member 2 belongs to the same panel as QR. When the lower chord is loaded the relevant panel is SP and the diagram is modified as shown by the dotted line. In this case the diagram will begin at A and terminate at C.

Problems for Solution

5.8. The height of the K-girder shown in the figure is 24 ft. and the span 120 ft. If the loads are carried by cross-girders at the lower joints draw the influence lines for the forces in the members GD, DE and FE. If the dead load is $\frac{1}{2}$ ton ft. and the live load is $1\frac{1}{2}$ tons ft. determine the maximum and minimum forces in the member FE. (Leeds, 1957)

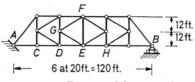

PROBLEM 5.8

5.9. The diagrammatic outline of a Pratt truss is shown in the figure. The truss consists of $2n$ equal panels of length L; the total span is thus $2nL$. If the dead load can

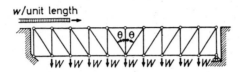

PROBLEM 5.9

be represented by equal loads W at each lower joint and the live load is a uniformly distributed load of w per unit length, show that

(a) the two middle panels will require counterbracing if

$$wL > \frac{2n-1}{(n-1)^2} W \quad \text{and}$$

(b) the four middle panels will require counterbracing if

$$wL > \frac{2n-1}{(n-2)^2} 3W$$

(Leeds, 1954)

5.10. The girder shown in the figure is one of two main girders of a deck-type

PROBLEM 5.10

bridge. Obtain influence lines for the forces in the members PQ, QS and RS.

(Manchester, 1946)

5.11. The outline of a cantilever bridge structure with a suspended girder span is

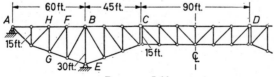

PROBLEM 5.11

shown in the diagram. All panel lengths are 15 ft. Draw the influence lines for the reactions at A and E and for the force in the member FG. Calculate the maximum

121

and minimum forces in the member *FG* if the loading consists of a uniformly distributed dead load of ¾ ton ft. over the whole span, a uniformly distributed live load of 1 ton ft. longer than the span and two wheel loads of 6 tons and 3 tons, spaced 10 ft. apart, with either wheel leading.

(Leeds, 1955)

5.12. Construct influence lines for the loads in the numbered members of the Baltimore truss shown in the diagram.

(St. Andrews, 1956)

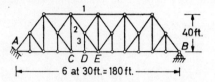

PROBLEM 5.12

5.3. INFLUENCE LINES FOR HYPERSTATIC STRUCTURES

5.3.1. BEAMS WITH A SINGLE REDUNDANT [Volume I, Section 5.3.1.1]

In Section 6.3.3 of the present volume the beam-line procedure for finding influence lines for continuous beams of many spans is described and illustrated. The following examples are more suitable for solution by the flexibility coefficient procedure of Volume I, Section 5.3.1.

Problem 5.13—Obtain an expression for the influence line for the redundant reaction of a beam continuous over three supports.

A continuous beam *ABC* of constant second moment of area is simply supported at *A*, *B* and *C*. $AB = 2d$; $BC = 3d$. Sketch the influence lines for the reactions at *B* and *C* and for the bending moment at *D*, the mid-point of the span *BC*. If the span *AB* carries a load of *W* tons at its mid-point, use the influence lines to obtain by calculation the bending moment at *D*.

The deflexion of the point *X* of the simply supported beam shown at (a) in the diagram is

$$\frac{Wbx}{EI(a+b)} \times \frac{a^2 + 2ab - x^2}{6} \qquad \text{when } x \leqslant a \qquad \dots \text{(i)}$$

(Manchester, 1952)

If R_B is chosen as the redundant reaction we have from the flexibility coefficient equation [4.7]

$$0 = -\Delta_{bm} + R_B \Delta_{bb}$$

i.e.
$$R_B = \frac{\Delta_{bm}}{\Delta_{bb}} = \frac{\Delta_{mb}}{\Delta_{bb}} \qquad \dots \text{(ii)}$$

The numerator and denominator of this equation are the deflexion of *m* and the deflexion of *B*, respectively, when unit upward load is applied in place of R_B; numerical values for a number of positions of *m* are obtained by substitution in the expression (i) and are plotted in diagram (c).

The influence line for R_C is obtained by taking moments about *A*;

$$R_C \times 5d + R_B \times 2d = 1 \times x \qquad \text{i.e.} \quad R_C = \frac{x}{5d} - \frac{2}{5}R_B \qquad \dots \text{(iii)}$$

122

This expression is plotted at (d).

For the bending moment at D we have

load to left of D: $M_D = R_C \times 3d/2$

load to right of D: $M_D = R_C \times 3d/2 - 1(x - 7d/2)$ $\Bigg\}$ .... (iv)

These expressions are plotted at (e). The bending moment at D when there is a load W at the mid-point of AB can be found by calculation as follows:

$$R_B = W\frac{\Delta_{eb}}{\Delta_{bb}} = \frac{\dfrac{3Wd}{5EI}\left(\dfrac{8d^2}{3} - \dfrac{d^2}{6}\right)}{12Wd^3/5EI} = \frac{5W}{8}$$

$$R_C = W\left(\frac{1}{5} - \frac{2}{5} \times \frac{5}{8}\right) = -\frac{W}{20}$$

$$M_D = \frac{W}{20} \times \frac{3d}{2} = \frac{3Wd}{40}$$

It can also be seen from (ii) that the influence line for R_B can be obtained by imposing unit displacement on the primary structure at B, for all other points on the beam will then be displaced by Δ_{mb}/Δ_{bb}. This is the basis of the indirect model

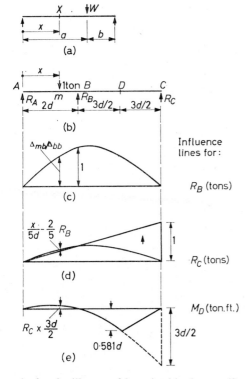

(a)

(b)

(c)

(d)

(e)

Influence
lines for:

R_B (tons)

R_C (tons)

M_D (ton.ft.)

PROBLEM 5.13. (a) Influence lines for the reactions of continuous beams can be obtained in terms of the deflexion of a simply supported beam. (b) The influence lines for R_B, R_C and M_D are required.

method to be illustrated later in this chapter (Section 5.4.2) but it can often be used to good advantage without recourse to experiment. Thus it is obvious that if unit displacement is imposed at B the beam must take up the general shape indicated

123

in diagram (c); the approximate influence line thus obtained may be adequate for the problem in hand or it may draw attention to salient points for which exact calculations can be made.

In the same way the influence line for R_C is obtained by imposing unit displacement at C. The influence line for bending moment at D is obtained by inserting an imaginary hinge at D and imposing unit rotation of DB relative to DC; the hinge at D will move upwards or downwards when this is done giving the diagram (e).

Problem 5.18 illustrates the above procedure.

Problems for Solution

5.14. Obtain the equation to the influence line for the force in the prop at B and use it to find the reaction at B caused by a uniformly distributed load of w per ft. over the beam. The beam is of uniform cross-section.

(Manchester, 1952)

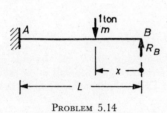

PROBLEM 5.14

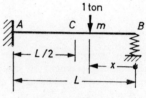

PROBLEM 5.15

5.15. A unit load moves from A towards B; the flexibility of the support at B is $L^3/12EI$. Sketch the influence lines for R_B, finding the ordinates at the quarter points and at mid-span. Hence sketch the influence line for the shearing force at mid-span. The beam is uniform in cross-section. (London, 1954)

5.16. A beam AB of relevant second moment of area I is fixed horizontally in a vertical wall at the end A. A tie of the same material, cross-sectional area a, is attached to the end B and to a point on the wall above A so that it is at an angle of 30° to the horizontal. Neglecting the axial compression of the beam find the influence line for the deflexion of B and for the tension in the tie as unit load moves over the beam.

(Manchester)

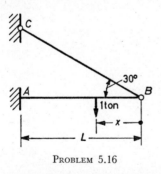

PROBLEM 5.16

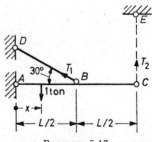

PROBLEM 5.17

5.17. ABC is a beam of flexural rigidity EI. It is pinned to a wall at A and supported by an inclined tie BD which can transmit axial forces only. The cross-section of the tie is such that its extension under unit load is one-sixteenth of the central deflexion of the beam ABC if the latter were supported at A and C and loaded with a unit load at B.

(a) Draw the influence line for T_1, the tensile force in DB, as unit vertical load traverses ABC.

(b) Draw the influence line for the vertical deflection of C.

(c) If C is supported by a second tie CE, identical with DB, draw the influence line for T_2, the tension in CE, if CE cannot resist compressive forces. Find the least value of x for which the tie CE is under load.

(The deflexion at a point distant x from one support of a simply supported beam of length L carrying a unit central load is $(3L^2x - 4x^3)/48EI$).

(Melbourne, 1954)

5.18. *ABC* is a prismatic beam with fixed ends and a pin at B. Sketch the influence lines for M_{AB}, V_A and θ_{BC} (the rotation of the end B of the part BC), the vertical displacement of B, and the shearing force at D for unit vertical load travelling across

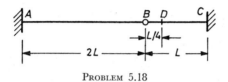

PROBLEM 5.18

the span AC. The sketches should show clearly the variations in curvature and the points of inflexion of the influence curves. Also calculate the values of the ordinates at point B of the influence lines for V_A and θ_{BC}.

Is there a discontinuity at B in the influence lines for M_{AB} and V_A? If so, why?

(Melbourne, 1954)

5.3.2. TRUSSES WITH A SINGLE REDUNDANT (Volume I, Sections 5.3.1.2 and 5.3.2]

The use of the flexibility coefficient equations to find influence lines for trusses is similar to their use in beam problems except that the necessary deflexions are now best found, in many cases, by means of Williot-Mohr diagrams [Volume I, Section 3.6.2]. Although the dummy unit load method [Volume I, Section 3.6.1] can be used to find these deflexions, as in *Problem 5.19* below, the procedure will be found to be tedious, when applied to a truss of many panels, in comparison with the alternative graphical construction.

Problem 5.19—A through Warren truss of four panels has lower panel points $L_0 - L_4$ and upper panel points $U_1 - U_4$. All the members have the same length d and cross-sectional area A.

If the truss is supported or anchored at L_0, L_2 and L_4 determine by calculation the influence lines for the reactions at L_0 and L_2 and deduce the influence line for the force in $L_1 L_2$.

(Manchester)

In order to find the deflexions of the joints L_1, L_2 and L_3 under unit load at L_2 it will be necessary to find the forces in the members under unit load at L_1 and at L_2; these are tabulated in TABLE 5.19, from which we see that $\Delta_{L_1} = 23d/6AE$ and $\Delta_{L_2} = 38d/6AE$. This allows the influence line for R_2 to be plotted at (b) the ordinates at L_1 and L_3 being $23/38 = 0.605$.

The influence line for R_0 is computed, as in *Problem 5.13*, by taking moments about L_4 and is plotted at (c).

The section shown at (a) allows the influence line for the force in L_1L_2 to be found, the centre of moments being U_2.

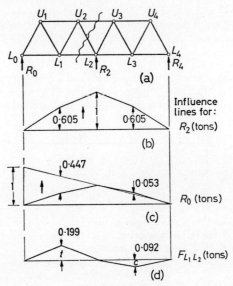

(a)

Influence lines for:
R_2 (tons)
(b)

R_0 (tons)
(c)

$F_{L_1L_2}$ (tons)
(d)

PROBLEM 5.19. (a) Influence lines are required for R, R_2 and for the force in L_1L_2.

TABLE 5.19

Member forces and joint deflexions

Member	F_{L_1}	F_{L_2}	$F_{L_1}F_{L_2}$	$F_{L_2}^2$
L_0U_1	$-\sqrt{3}/2$	$-1/\sqrt{3}$	$+1/2$	$1/3$
U_1U_2	$-\sqrt{3}/2$	$-1/\sqrt{3}$	$+1/2$	$1/3$
U_2U_3	$-1/\sqrt{3}$	$-2/\sqrt{3}$	$+2/3$	$4/3$
U_3U_4	$-1/2\sqrt{3}$	$-1/\sqrt{3}$	$+1/6$	$1/3$
U_4L_4	$-1/2\sqrt{3}$	$-1/\sqrt{3}$	$+1/6$	$1/3$
L_0L_1	$+\sqrt{3}/4$	$+1/2\sqrt{3}$	$+1/8$	$1/12$
L_1L_2	$+5/4\sqrt{3}$	$+\sqrt{3}/2$	$+5/8$	$3/4$
L_2L_3	$+3/4\sqrt{3}$	$+\sqrt{3}/2$	$+3/8$	$3/4$
L_3L_4	$+1/4\sqrt{3}$	$+1/2\sqrt{3}$	$+1/24$	$1/12$
U_1L_1	$+\sqrt{3}/2$	$+1/\sqrt{3}$	$+1/2$	$1/3$
L_1U_2	$+1/2\sqrt{3}$	$-1/\sqrt{3}$	$-1/6$	$1/3$
U_2L_2	$-1/2\sqrt{3}$	$+1/\sqrt{3}$	$-1/6$	$1/3$
L_2U_3	$+1/2\sqrt{3}$	$+1/\sqrt{3}$	$+1/6$	$1/3$
U_3L_3	$-1/2\sqrt{3}$	$-1/\sqrt{3}$	$+1/6$	$1/3$
L_3U_4	$+1/2\sqrt{3}$	$+1/\sqrt{3}$	$+1/6$	$1/3$
		Σ	$23/6$	$38/6$

126

Problems for Solution

5.20. Unit load at *B*, applied to the simply supported truss *AC*, produces the following deflexions at the lower joints: 0; 7·1; 12·4; 16·4; 12·4; 7·1; 0 (all × 10⁻² in.).

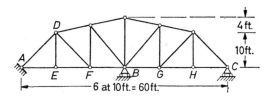

PROBLEM 5.20

Sketch the influence lines for R_A, R_B and the force in *DF*.

(London, 1957)

5.21. The diagram shows a mild-steel pin-jointed frame.

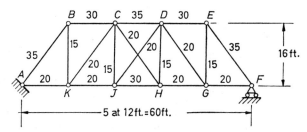

PROBLEM 5.21

Draw the influence line for the force in *CH* for a single concentrated load of 100 tons passing across the bottom chord. The cross-sectional areas in square inches are shown against the members.

(Birmingham, 1952)

5.22. The framework shown by the full lines in the figure is pinned at *A* and supported on frictionless rollers at *K*. The value of ρ (L/AE) of all members may be taken as the same.

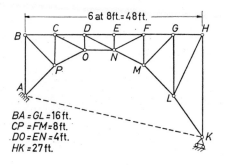

PROBLEM 5.22

Determine

(a) the reactions at *A* and *K* and the force in the member *CO* when a unit vertical load is applied at *D*;

127

(b) the movement of K when a unit load is applied at K in the direction of the dotted line.

If K is pinned as well as A, determine the influence lines (when the top chord is loaded) for

(c) the thrust in the direction of the dotted line;
(d) the reaction at K;
(e) the component of the reaction at A perpendicular to AK;
(f) the force in CO.

When a unit load is applied at D what is the change, due to the pin at K, in

(g) the reaction at A;
(h) the force in CO;
(i) the vertical deflexion at D?

(Birmingham, 1941)

5.23. The Warren girder shown in the figure is pinned to a rigid wall at R, and the joint B is supported by a tie. All the members of the truss and the tie have the same cross-sectional area A. The tie is first adjusted so that under the dead load the joint B is at the same level as R.

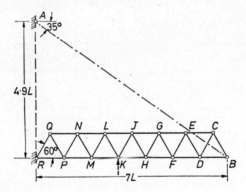

PROBLEM 5.23

(a) Find the reaction at R when there is a unit load at K.

(b) Find the influence line for the deflexion of the joint K as unit load crosses the chord RB (a rotation diagram must be constructed to correct the Williot diagram for the known movement of the joint B relative to R and A).

(c) On the assumption that the tie can resist compressive forces, construct an influence line for the reaction at K if a support is inserted there at such a level that it is just in contact with the truss under dead load only.

(d) Modify this influence line so that it applies when the tie resists tensile forces only.

(e) Draw the influence lines for the tension in the tie and for the forces in the members GF and PM if the truss is supported at K as in (c) above. The tie resists tensile forces only.

(f) If the support at K, inserted as in (c) above, is elastic and compresses an amount $10L/AE$ under unit load, draw the influence line for the reaction at K; the tie resists tensile forces only and L is the length of a member of the truss.

(Birmingham, 1943)

5.3.3. Structures with two Redundants [Volume I, Section 5.3.3]

It has already been indicated in Section 5.3.1 that influence lines for continuous beams on rigid supports are best found by the beam-line method; examples will be found in Chapter 6. If the supports are elastic, as in *Problem 5.24*, or if the structure is braced, equations [5.2], obtained from the flexibility coefficient equations, can be used with advantage. In the case of trusses the necessary deflexions are best found graphically.

Problem 5.24—The uniform propped cantilever ABC is supported at B by a spring of stiffness EI/L^3. Find the influence lines for R_B and R_C.

If R_B and R_C are selected as the redundants we have

$$\left. \begin{aligned} R_B &= \Delta_{mb} \frac{\Delta_{cc}}{\Delta_{bc}^2 - \Delta_{bb}\Delta_{cc}} - \Delta_{mc} \frac{\Delta_{bc}}{\Delta_{bc}^2 - \Delta_{bb}\Delta_{cc}} \\ R_C &= \Delta_{mc} \frac{\Delta_{bc}}{\Delta_{bc}^2 - \Delta_{bb}\Delta_{cc}} - \Delta_{mb} \frac{\Delta_{bb}}{\Delta_{bc}^2 - \Delta_{bb}\Delta_{cc}} \end{aligned} \right\} \quad \dots \text{[5.2]}$$

where the various deflexions Δ_{bb}, Δ_{bc}, etc. refer to the primary structure shown at (b). The various deflexions required can all be found from the formulae for a cantilever with a point load which were derived in Volume I (Section 3.7.2.1, *Case 1*). Thus referring to diagram (c)

$$\Delta_x = \frac{1}{EI}\left(\frac{x^3}{6} - \frac{L^2 x}{2} + \frac{L^3}{3}\right) \quad \dots \text{(i)}$$

$$\Delta_u = \frac{1}{EI}\left(\frac{L^3}{3} + \frac{L^2 u}{2}\right) \quad \dots \text{(ii)}$$

Applying these equations to the primary structure, we have

$$\Delta_{bb} = \frac{L^3}{3EI} + \frac{L^3}{EI} \text{ (spring)} = \frac{4L^3}{3EI}$$

$$\Delta_{bc} = \frac{L^3}{3EI} + \frac{L^3}{2EI} \qquad = \frac{5L^3}{6EI}$$

$$\Delta_{cc} = \frac{(2L)^3}{3EI} \qquad\qquad = \frac{8L^3}{3EI}$$

Thus equations [5.2] become

$$\left. \begin{aligned} \frac{R_B L^3}{EI} &= -\frac{96}{103}\Delta_{mb} + \frac{30}{103}\Delta_{mc} \\ \frac{R_C L^3}{EI} &= -\frac{48}{103}\Delta_{mc} + \frac{30}{103}\Delta_{mb} \end{aligned} \right\} \quad \dots \text{(iii)}$$

Δ_{mb} and Δ_{mc} are found by inserting a series of values of x and u in equations (i) and (ii), as indicated in Table 5.24.

The values of R_B and R_C can now be calculated easily, as in Table 5.24; the final influence lines are shown in the diagram at (d) and (e).

Problems for Solution

5.25. Repeat *Problem 5.24* with C also supported by a spring of stiffness EI/L^3. Also draw the influence line for M_A.

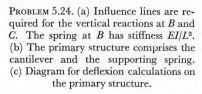

PROBLEM 5.24. (a) Influence lines are required for the vertical reactions at B and C. The spring at B has stiffness EI/L^3. (b) The primary structure comprises the cantilever and the supporting spring. (c) Diagram for deflexion calculations on the primary structure.

(a)

(b)

(c)

(d)

$R_B = 0.068$

Influence lines for:
R_B (tons)

(e)

R_C (tons)

$R_C = 1$

TABLE 5.24

Point m	x	u	Δ_{mb}†	Δ_{mb}† $\times \dfrac{96}{103}$	Δ_{mb}† $\times \dfrac{30}{103}$	x	Δ_{mc}†	Δ_{mc}† $\times \dfrac{48}{103}$	Δ_{mc}† $\times \dfrac{30}{103}$	R_B (tons)	R_C (tons)
1		L	0·833	0·776	0·243	0	2·667	1·242	0·776	0	1·0
2		0·8L	0·733	0·683	0·214	0·2L	2·269	1·057	0·661	0·022	0·843
3		0·6L	0·633	0·590	0·184	0·4L	1·878	0·875	0·547	0·043	0·691
4		0·4L	0·533	0·497	0·155	0·6L	1·503	0·701	0·438	0·059	0·546
5		0·2L	0·433	0·404	0·126	0·8L	1·152	0·537	0·336	0·068	0·411
6	0	0	0·333	0·311	0·097	1·0L	0·833	0·388	0·243	0·068	0·291
7	0·2L		0·235	0·219	0·068	1·2L	0·555	0·258	0·162	0·057	0·190
8	0·4L		0·146	0·136	0·043	1·4L	0·324	0·151	0·094	0·042	0·108
9	0·6L		0·066	0·062	0·019	1·6L	0·149	0·069	0·043	0·019	0·050
10	0·8L		0·019	0·018	0·005	1·8L	0·039	0·018	0·011	0·007	0·013

† L^3/EI omitted from these columns.

130

5.26. The flexural rigidity *(EI)* of the uniform beam shown in the figure is 1500 tons ft.² and the stiffness of the springs at *B* and *C* is 20 tons per ft. Draw the

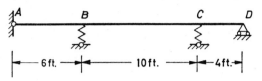

PROBLEM 5.26

influence lines for the reactions.

5.27. Draw the influence lines for the reactions at *A*, *B* and *C* of the beam shown in

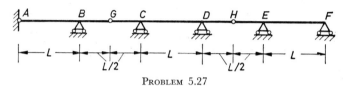

PROBLEM 5.27

the figure, which is of uniform flexural rigidity.

5.28. Draw the influence lines for the reactions at *B* and *C* of the through truss shown in the diagram. The members are identical.

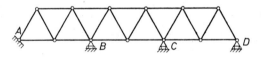

PROBLEM 5.28

5.29. The structure shown in the diagram is pinned to a rigid wall at *A*, *G* and *H*. The cross-sectional areas of the members are as follows:

All the chord members and *CB*,   4*a*
the web members,   2*a*
the tie *AE*.   *a*

The structure is loaded at the lower joints.

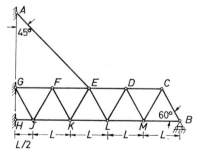

PROBLEM 5.29

131

(a) If the member AE is omitted and B is free to deflect draw the influence line for the deflexion at B. Find this deflexion if the loads are $3P$ at J, $4P$ at K, L and M, and $2P$ at B.

Also find what force acting at E in the direction EA would bring B to the same level as H under this loading.

(b) If the tie AE is inserted and B is supported so that it is at the same level as H, determine the influence lines for the reaction at B and the pull at A, if AE is just tight before the loads are applied.

Also find the influence lines for the forces in DC, FK and JK.

(c) State briefly what new elements would enter into the problem if the structure were erected by cantilevering it out as far as E, then inserting the tie AE and, after the remaining members were in position, propping B to the level of H.

(Birmingham, 1940)

5.3.4. RIGID FRAMES

The influence lines for highly redundant frames with rigid joints can be determined, in terms of the influence lines for the fixed-end moments at the ends of the beams, by means of the slope-deflexion equations [Volume I, Section 6.3].

Problem 5.30—Find the influence lines for M_{AB} and M_{BA} in the rigidly jointed bent shown in the diagram. The K-values are shown in circles.

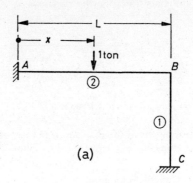

PROBLEM 5.30. (a) Influence lines are required for M_{AB} and M_{BA}. (b) The required influence lines.

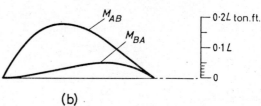

The relevant member equations are obtained by substitution in the slope-deflexion equations [6.5] and are:

$$M_{AB} = 4E(\theta_B) + M_{FAB} \qquad \cdots\cdots \text{(i)}$$

$$M_{BA} = 4E(2\theta_B) + M_{FBA} \qquad \cdots\cdots \text{(ii)}$$

$$M_{BC} = 2E(2\theta_B) \qquad \cdots\cdots \text{(iii)}$$

132

Adding (ii) and (iii) $\qquad \sum M_B = 0 = 12E\theta_B + M_{FBA}$

i.e. $\qquad\qquad\qquad E\theta_B = -\dfrac{1}{12} M_{FBA}$ $\qquad$ .... (iv)

Substituting in (ii) $\qquad M_{BA} = \dfrac{1}{3} M_{FBA} = \dfrac{x^2(L-x)}{3L^2}$ $\qquad$ .... (v)

Substituting in (i)

$$M_{AB} = -\frac{1}{3} M_{FBA} + M_{FAB}$$

$$= \frac{x^2(L-x)}{3L^2} - \frac{x(L-x)^2}{L^2} = -\frac{x(L-x)}{L^2}\left(L - \frac{2x}{3}\right) \qquad \text{.... (vi)}$$

Equations (v) and (vi), which are the required influence lines, have been plotted in diagram (b).

Problems for Solution

5.31. The diagram shows a two-hinged double cantilever framed girder for a bridge. The flexural rigidity of the girder is constant between the columns and

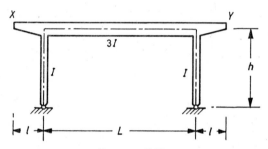

PROBLEM 5.31

three times that of the columns. Find the influence line for horizontal thrust as unit load passes from X to Y.

(Birmingham)

5.32. The members of the rigidly jointed frame shown are of uniform cross-section and material throughout. Find the influence line for bending moment in the beam

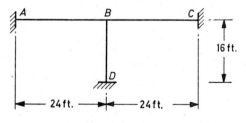

PROBLEM 5.32

at B. Use this influence line to find the approximate maximum value of the bending moment at B due to the passage from A to C of two axle loads of 2 tons, 6 ft. apart.

(London, 1957)

K $\qquad\qquad\qquad\qquad\qquad$ 133

5.4. STRUCTURAL MODELS

5.4.1. SCALE RELATIONSHIPS [Volume I, Section 5.4.2.1]

Problem 5.33—A portal frame is fabricated of 10 in. × 5 in. steel I-beam ($I = 146$ in.^{4}). A model is constructed of brass rod 0·2 in. dia. to a layout scale of 1/10. If the linear deflexion scale, considering bending only, is to be 1/30 find the scales for load, slope, strain and stress.

From equation [5.3(b)]

$$\frac{\Delta_p}{\Delta_m} = \frac{\left(\beta_1 \dfrac{FL^3}{EI}\right)_p}{\left(\beta_1 \dfrac{FL^3}{EI}\right)_m}$$

The suffix p refers to the prototype and the suffix m to the model.

i.e. $\quad 30 = \dfrac{F_p}{F_m}\left(\dfrac{Lp}{Lm}\right)^3 \dfrac{E_m}{E_p} \times \dfrac{I_m}{I_p}$

$$= s_F \, 10^3 \, \frac{16}{30} \times \frac{7\cdot85 \times 10^{-5}}{146} = 0\cdot00287 s_F$$

$$\therefore \quad s_F = \frac{30}{0\cdot00287} = 10{,}450$$

If deflexions are 1/30 of those on the prototype and the layout scale is 1/10, the slopes will be to the scale 10/30 = 1/3.

It is simplest next to consider the scale for stress.

Bending stress is proportional to $\dfrac{Md}{I} \propto \dfrac{FLd}{I}$

$$\therefore \text{ Stress scale} = \frac{s_F s_L s_d}{s_I} = \frac{10{,}450 \times 10\dfrac{10}{0\cdot2}}{\dfrac{146}{7\cdot85 \times 10^{-5}}} = 2\cdot81$$

$$\text{Strain scale} = \frac{s_f}{s_E} = \frac{2\cdot81}{30/16} = 1\cdot5$$

Problems for Solution

5.34. A test is to be made of a model of a large bridge in which the weight of the structure must be considered as well as the magnitude of the applied forces. The model is made of the same material as the prototype and all its linear dimensions are λ times those in the prototype. Show by dimensional reasoning that, if geometrical similarity of deflexion is to be preserved, two conditions are necessary:

  (a) the forces applied to the model should be λ^2 times those on the prototype;

  (b) the weights of the members of the model should (by means of additional loading) be increased to $1/\lambda$ times these weights determined on the basis of similarity. (Oxford, 1943)

5.35. Show that a model member of rectangular cross-section will correctly represent the behaviour of its prototype, both as regards bending and extensional deformations, if $d = 2\sqrt{3}\, s_L r$, where d is the depth of the model member and r is the radius of gyration of the prototype†.

---

† This result is due to M. N. Gogate.

5.36. The diagram represents a portal frame in which the columns are continuous and the bracing can be taken to be pin-jointed. A model is constructed to a layout scale of 1 in. equals 1 ft. in order to find the reactions at *B* by imposing suitable

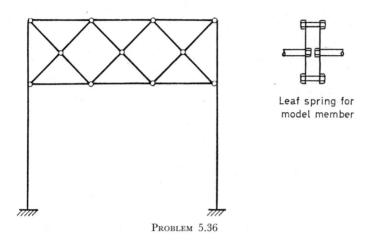

Leaf spring for
model member

PROBLEM 5.36

displacements there. The flexural rigidity of the model columns is $\dfrac{1}{1000}$ that of the prototype. The bracing is to be represented by rods having spring inserts to give the required axial stiffness. Find the required spring stiffness in terms of L/AE for the prototype bracing members.

5.4.2. DETERMINATION OF REDUNDANTS FROM MODELS [Volume I, Section 5.4.2.3]

Problem 5.37.—In order to determine the reactions at one of the abutments of an arch with fixed ends due to a single load acting vertically at a certain point (*C*) a model was constructed to a scale of 1 : 100. The following readings were taken during two tests on the model, in each of which displacements were applied to the same end, *B*, while the other end, *A*, was held fixed.

Test 1.	Upward displacement of end	0·05 in.
	Horizontal displacement of end	0·00 in.
	Clockwise rotation of end	0·02 rad.
	Corresponding displacement of *C*	− 0·03 in.
Test 2.	Clockwise rotation of end	− 0·06 rad.
	Vertical and horizontal displacements of end	0·00 in.
	Corresponding displacement of *C*	0·02 in.

Calculate for the full-scale arch the values of the fixing moment and of the vertical component of the reaction at the end under consideration, due to a load of 15 cwt. applied as above.

(Oxford, 1942)

The simplest way to evaluate the redundants from model experiments of this kind is by the use of Betti's Reciprocal Theorem [Volume I, Section 3.5.2] which states that if two groups of loads act on a structure the sum of the products of the forces of the first group and the corresponding displacements of the second is equal to the sum of the products of the forces of the second group and the corresponding displacements of the first.

Considering first the model without regard to scale, two groups of loads are shown in the diagram at (a) and (b) (Test 1). The first group comprises the applied

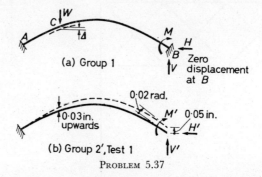

(a) Group 1

Zero displacement at B

(b) Group 2′, Test 1

PROBLEM 5.37

load at C and the reactions at B (M, H and V) which are produced when the displacements at B are zero. The second group consists of those forces, M', H' and V', which are required to produce the specified displacements at B, the figures from Tests 1 and 2 being used in turn. Thus we have:

		V	H	M	W
Group 1:	Forces	V	H	M	W
	Displacements	0	0	0	Δ
Group 2′:	Forces	V'	H'	M'	$W = 0$
(Test 1)	Displacements	0·05	0	0·02	$- 0·03$
Group 2″:	Forces	V''	H''	M''	$W = 0$
(Test 2)	Displacements	0	0	$- 0·06$	$+ 0·02$

Hence from Groups 1 and 2′,

$$V \times 0·05 + H \times 0 + M \times 0·02 - W \times 0·03$$
$$= V' \times 0 + H' \times 0 + M' \times 0 + 0 \times \Delta$$

Hence
$$0·05\,V + 0·02\,M = 0·03\,W \qquad \dots \text{(i)}$$

and from Groups 1 and 2″

$$V \times 0 + H \times 0 - M \times 0·06 + W \times 0·02$$
$$= V'' \times 0 + H'' \times 0 + M'' \times 0 + 0 \times \Delta$$

Hence
$$0·06M = 0·02\,W \qquad \dots \text{(ii)}$$

Solving (i) and (ii)
$$\left.\begin{array}{c} M = W/3 \\ V = 7W/15 \end{array}\right\} \qquad \dots \text{(iii)}$$

These are the reactions M and V that would be produced by the load W in the model arch fixed at A and B. We must now find out what would be the reaction in the prototype which is s_L times as large and elastically similar. So far as forces are concerned, we are making use of the fact that the ratio $V : W$ is equal to a ratio of linear displacements; this ratio is unaffected if both displacements are multiplied by the linear scale factor s_L. The ratio $M : W$ is also equal to a ratio of displacements, but this time one is linear and one angular.

i.e. $\quad M\theta = W\Delta$

$$M = \frac{W\Delta}{\theta}$$

136

If the experiment were carried out on the prototype the linear displacements would be s_L times as large while the angular displacements would be unchanged;

i.e. at full size
$$M = \frac{W \Delta s_L}{\theta}$$

In other words the moments obtained from a model test must be multiplied by the linear scale factor to obtain the corresponding prototype moments.
In this case, from (iii)

$$V = \frac{7W}{15} = \frac{7 \times 15}{15} = 7 \text{ cwt.} \qquad M = \frac{W}{3} \times 100 = \frac{15}{3} \times 100 = 500 \text{ cwt. in.}$$

Problems for Solution.

5.38. A model of an arch with fixed ends is constructed to a scale of 1 : 90 in order to obtain influence lines for the reactions at the ends. In each of three tests the left-hand end A of the model was fixed while displacements were imposed on the other end B. The resulting displacement of a certain load point C was measured with the following results.

Test	Displacement of end B			Resulting displacement of load point C downwards (in.)
	Upwards (in.)	Inwards (in.)	Clockwise rotation (rad.)	
1	+ 0·05	+ 0·6	+ 0·01	− 0·304
2	+ 0·04	+ 0·02	+ 0·1	+ 0·042
3	+ 0·4	− 0·01	− 0·05	− 0·105

Find the reactions of the prototype arch when there is a load of 1 ton at C. How should the tests have been conducted so as to give influence lines directly?

(after Manchester)

5.39. A test on a xylonite model arch of 10 in. span with fixed ends gave the following results:

Anti-clockwise rotation of left hand support: 0·5°.

Movement of point X on arch: 0·025 in. to the left and 0·011 in. upwards.

If a similar arch were constructed of 100 ft. span what would be the bending moment at the left hand support due to a load of 60 tons, acting at 30° to the vertical (downwards and towards the right), applied at a point corresponding to X?

(Oxford, 1945)

5.40. The diagram shows a model of a non-uniform beam constructed to a scale of 1 in. = 1 ft. Experiments with couples M_1 and M_2 give the slopes and deflexions

PROBLEM 5.40

shown. Find the moments produced at A and B in the prototype beam if it is fixed at the ends and carries a 5-ton load at C.

(London, 1956)

5.41. The diagram shows a spline pinned to a drawing board at *A*, *B*, *C* and *D*. The right-hand pin is removed and *D* is pushed 1·5 in. upwards. The resulting movements (in inches) of other points on the spline are:

Fractions of span	Vertical deflexion (in.)		
	AB	*BC*	*CD*
1/6	—	—	+ 0·13
1/3	+ 0·05	− 0·115	+ 0·32
1/2	—	—	+ 0·54
2/3	+ 0·09	− 0·15	+ 0·80
5/6	—	—	+ 1·10

PROBLEM 5.41

Find the right-hand reaction of a continuous beam of spans 12 ft., 18 ft., and 15 ft. carrying 5-ton loads at each of the third points and a uniformly distributed load of 10 tons on the right-hand span.

(London, 1954)

5.42. A model of the girder shown is constructed to a linear scale of 1 : 30. When point *B* is displaced 2·16 in. the model takes up the shape indicated, displacements being measured at equal intervals. Find the reactions at *A*, *B* and *C* when the prototype girder carries the loads shown at *D*, *E* and *F* and sketch the bending moment diagram.

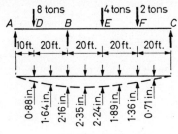

PROBLEM 5.42

An alternative way of carrying out the model test would have been to insert a hinge in the model girder at *B* and to impose an angular displacement there of *BA* relative to *BC*, keeping *B* at the same level. If an angular displacement of 5° had been imposed what shape would the model have taken up?

(after Leeds, 1951)

138

CHAPTER 6

FRAMES WITH RIGID JOINTS

6.1. INTRODUCTION

The analysis of reinforced concrete or steel building frames with rigid joints has been very much developed over recent years and a great many different procedures have been developed. The most important of these were discussed in Volume I (Chapter 6) and a number of examples were worked.

In this chapter the arrangement is by type of structure—continuous beam, portal frame with sway and so on—so that the reader can decide for himself which is the best method of analysis or, having tried several, may be given some basis for making future decisions.

In this book the solutions to the problems will be found at the end, but in the design office all calculations must be checked. A good way of doing this, which ensures that the calculations are really independent, is to insert the solutions obtained by moment distribution into, say, the slope deflexion equations, a process which immediately reveals the existence of errors. It is thus advantageous for the designer to have more than one method of analysis at his command.

The special procedures of Naylor and Bolton are not further discussed but some of the examples given will be found suitable for these and other quick methods.

The chapter closes with a few examples on the beam-line method and on the determination of collapse loads by the plastic method.

6.2. BEAMS WITH FIXED ENDS [Volume I, Section 6.2.2]

The importance of this problem arises from the fact that both the slope-deflexion and the moment distribution methods of rigid frame analysis use it as a starting point. It is therefore convenient to have a list of the 'fixing' or 'fixed end' moments which are developed under commonly occurring load systems. It is often possible to use equations [6.1(a)],

$$
\left.
\begin{aligned}
M_{F_{AB}} &= + \sum \frac{Pab^2}{L^2} \\
M_{F_{BA}} &= + \sum \frac{Pa^2b}{L^2}
\end{aligned}
\right\} \qquad \dots \dots [6.1(a)]
$$

which applies to case (a) of FIGURE 6.1, to obtain these moments for distributed loads of various kinds; the solution to case (b) of FIGURE 6.1, for example, was obtained in Volume I by integrating these expressions (after writing wdx for P) between the limits of $\pm d/2$. In other cases, as in *Problem 6.1* below, it is necessary to use the moment-area method, or some other, to express in algebraic terms the fact that the slope and deflexion are zero at both ends of the beam.

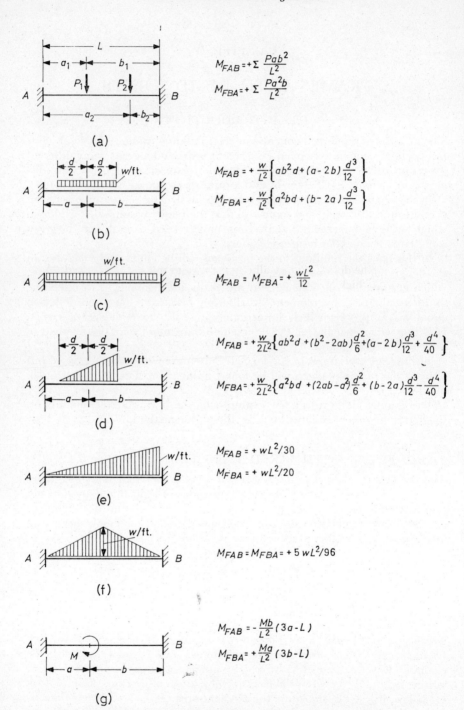

FIGURE 6.1. Fixed end moments for various loadings. Hogging bending moments are positive.

Problem 6.1—Find the fixed end moments for the beam shown at (a) and sketch the bending moment diagram when $a = 3L/8$ and $b = 5L/8$, and also when $a = b = L/2$.

The primary structure, at (b), is the simply supported beam AB which deflects as shown at (c) and has the bending moment diagram shown at (d). Using the moment area method we have from equation [3.22(a)]

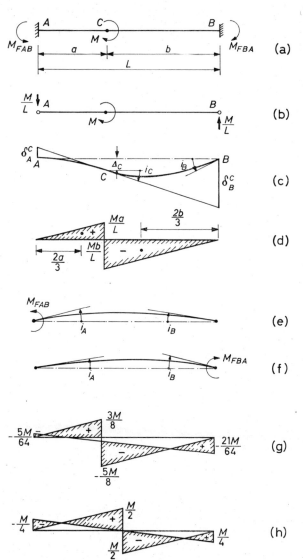

PROBLEM 6. 1. (a) Beam with fixed ends loaded by a couple M. (b) The primary structure is the simply supported beam AB. (c) The deflected shape of the primary structure. (d) The corresponding bending moment diagram. (e) and (f) The primary structure loaded by couples acting at A and B respectively. (g) The final bending moment diagram when $a = \dfrac{3L}{8}$.

(h) The bending moment diagram when $a = b = L/2$.

$$\delta_A^C = \left[\frac{A_m \bar{x}}{EI}\right]_A^C \qquad \dots \text{[3.22(a)]}$$

$$= \frac{Ma^3}{3EIL}$$

and

$$\delta_B^C = \frac{Mb^3}{3EIL}$$

hence

$$i_C = \frac{M}{3EIL^2}(a^3 + b^3) \qquad \dots \text{(i)}$$

we also have

$$i_C - i_A = \left[\frac{A_m}{EI}\right]_A^C \qquad \dots \text{[3.21(a)]}$$

i.e.

$$i_A = i_C - \frac{Ma^2}{2EIL} \qquad \dots \text{(ii)}$$

similarly

$$i_B = i_C - \frac{Mb^2}{2EIL} \qquad \dots \text{(iii)}$$

If positive couples M_{FAB} and M_{FBA} are applied at the ends A and B respectively it can readily be shown (for example by means of equations [6.9] and [6.10]) that

$$i_A = -\frac{L}{EI}\left(\frac{M_{FAB}}{3} + \frac{M_{FBA}}{6}\right)$$

and

$$i_B = +\frac{L}{EI}\left(\frac{M_{FAB}}{6} + \frac{M_{FBA}}{3}\right) \qquad \dots \text{(iv)}$$

If now M_{FAB} and M_{FBA} are of such a value that when applied in conjunction with M at C they bring the slopes at A and B to zero we have, from equations (ii), (iii) and (iv)

$$\frac{M}{3L^2}(a^3 + b^3) - \frac{Ma^2}{2L} - \frac{L}{3}M_{FAB} - \frac{L}{6}M_{FBA} = 0$$

$$\frac{M}{3L^2}(a^3 + b^3) - \frac{Mb^2}{2L} + \frac{L}{6}M_{FAB} + \frac{L}{3}M_{FBA} = 0 \qquad \dots \text{(v)}$$

Solving (v) simultaneously gives

$$M_{FAB} = \frac{2M}{L^3}(a^3 + b^3) - \frac{M}{L^2}(2a^2 + b^2) = -\frac{Mb}{L^2}(3a - L)$$

$$M_{FBA} = -\frac{2M}{L^3}(a^3 + b^3) + \frac{M}{L^2}(a^2 + 2b^2) = +\frac{Ma}{L^2}(3b - L)$$

These are the required fixed end moments. When $a = 3L/8$ and $b = 5L/8$ we have

$$M_{FAB} = -\frac{5M}{8}\left(\frac{3 \times 3}{8} - 1\right) = -\frac{5M}{64}$$

$$M_{FBA} = +\frac{3M}{8}\left(\frac{3 \times 5}{8} - 1\right) = +\frac{21M}{64}$$

142

The final bending moment diagram, shown at (g), is obtained by combining these results with the simply supported diagram (d). The corresponding values when the couple is applied centrally can be found in the same way or, more easily, by a simple moment distribution. The resulting bending moment diagram is shown at (h). Throughout these calculations the bending moment convention of signs ('hogging' moments positive) has been used.

Problems for Solution

6.2. Verify the values of the fixed end moments given in FIGURE 6.1(d), (e) and (f).

6.3. Find the fixed end moments produced in the beam *AB* when the load *P* is carried on a bracket.

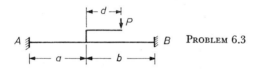

PROBLEM 6.3

6.4. The ends of a beam *AB* are attached to rigid walls by fittings which exert a resisting moment $\alpha\theta$ when the slope at the end of the beam is θ. Obtain an expression for θ when the beam carries a uniformly distributed load, over its whole length, of w per foot and find the value of α which gives the least value of the maximum numerical bending moment.

(Birmingham)

6.5. Repeat *Problem 6.4* when the beam carries a central point load *P*.

6.6. Find the end moments and the central deflexion of a beam with fixed ends carrying a uniformly distributed load w over the left half-span. What central point load would reduce the central deflexion to zero?

6.7. Find the central deflexion of the beam carrying a uniformly distributed load shown in FIGURE 6.1(c).
  Hence find the thrust in a rigid central prop so placed that the central deflexion is
  (a) zero, and
  (b) one-half of the value without the prop.
  Also find the thrust in an elastic prop, having a stiffness k lb. per in. in compression, which is placed a distance $wL^4/768EI$ below the beam before the load w is applied.

6.3. CONTINUOUS BEAMS

6.3.1. CONTINUOUS BEAMS WITH UNYIELDING SUPPORTS OR WITH SUPPORTS THAT SUBSIDE A KNOWN AMOUNT

In Volume I, Section 6.2.3, Clapeyron's Equation [6.3] was introduced and illustrated by means of a worked example; the same example was also worked by the slope-deflexion method (Section 6.3.2) and by moment distribution (Section 6.4.2).

  Clapeyron's Equation [6.3] for the support moments M_P, M_Q and M_R, applies to two adjacent spans *PQ* and *QR* of a continuous beam, as in FIGURE 6.2.

$$M_P \frac{L_1}{E_1 I_1} + 2M_Q \left\{ \frac{L_1}{E_1 I_1} + \frac{L_2}{E_2 I_2} \right\} + M_R \frac{L_2}{E_2 I_2}$$

$$+ 6 \sum \frac{A_m \bar{x}}{EIL} = 6 \left\{ \frac{\Delta_P - \Delta_Q}{L_1} + \frac{\Delta_R - \Delta_Q}{L_2} \right\} \quad \dots \quad [6.3]$$

If the beam is uniform and there are no reaction displacements this becomes

$$M_P L_1 + 2M_Q (L_1 + L_2) + M_R L_2 = -6 \sum \frac{A_m \bar{x}}{L} \quad \dots \quad [6.3(a)]$$

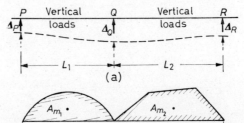

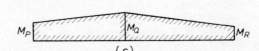

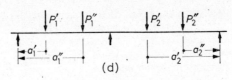

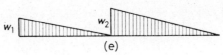

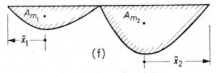

FIGURE 6.2. (a) Two adjacent spans, PQ and QR, of a continuous beam with an indefinite number of spans. Vertical loads act on the beam and the supports subside by amounts Δ_P, Δ_Q and Δ_R respectively. (b) The primary bending moment diagrams, here assumed positive, have areas A_{m_1} and A_{m_2} respectively. (c) The moments over the supports M_P, M_Q and M_R are given by Clapeyron's Equation. (d) Nomenclature for point loads. (e) Hydrostatic loading. (f) The corresponding primary bending moment diagrams (negative if the loads are downwards).

144

If there are point loads on each span, as in FIGURE 6.2(d), the right hand side of equation [6.3(a)] becomes

$$- 6 \sum \frac{A_m \bar{x}}{L} = + \sum \frac{Pa(L^2 - a^2)}{L} \quad \quad \dots \text{[6.4(a)]}$$

while if there are uniformly distributed loads completely covering each span it becomes

$$- 6 \sum \frac{A_m \bar{x}}{L} = + \sum \frac{wL^3}{4} \quad \quad \dots \text{[6.4(b)]}$$

With hydrostatic loads on each span, as in FIGURE 6.2(e), it can readily be shown by integration that the right hand side of equation [6.3(a)] becomes

$$- 6 \left\{ \frac{A_{m1} \bar{x}_1}{L_1} + \frac{A_{m2} \bar{x}_2}{L_2} \right\} = + \frac{7}{60} w_1 L_1^3 + \frac{2}{15} w_2 L_2^3$$

In using this last result, which is illustrated by the simple problem below, it is necessary to ensure that $\bar{x}$ is correctly measured outwards in each span.

Problem 6.8—The uniform continuous beam shown at (a) is fixed at the end A and pinned to supports at B and C; its second moment of area is 2,880 in.^{4} Sketch the bending moment diagram and find the reactions (1) for the hydrostatic loading shown and (2) if the support C sinks 0·0018 ft.

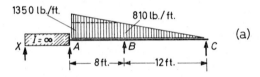

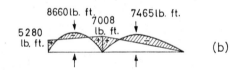

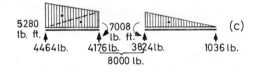

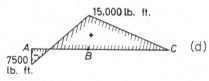

PROBLEM 6.8. (a) In order to apply Clapeyron's Equation to this beam, which is fixed at A, an imaginary span XA of infinite stiffness is considered. (b) The complete bending moment diagram. (c) Calculation of the reactions. (d) Bending moments caused by the subsidence of C.

145

(1) *Solution using Clapeyron's Equation*

The fixed end A is dealt with by imagining a span XA of infinite second moment of area; the trapezoidal load in span AB is regarded as being made up of a uniform and of a triangular load.

Applying equation [6.3(a)] to the spans XA and AB:

$$2M_A \times 8 + M_B \times 8 = \left(810\,\frac{8^3}{4} + 540\,\frac{2}{15}\,8^3\right)_{AB} \qquad \cdots \text{(i)}$$

and for spans AB and BC:

$$M_A \times 8 + 2M_B \times 20 = \left(810\,\frac{8^3}{4} + 540\,\frac{7}{60}\,8^3\right)_{AB} + \left(810\,\frac{2}{15}\,12^3\right)_{BC} \qquad \cdots \text{(ii)}$$

Solving (i) and (ii) simultaneously

$$M_A = 5{,}280 \text{ lb. ft.} \qquad M_B = 7{,}008 \text{ lb. ft.}$$

These values have been combined with the primary moments to give the bending moment diagram (b). The reactions are found by isolating the spans, as at (c), and taking moments in the usual way. Thus in the span AB

$$R_A = \frac{1}{8}\left(\frac{1}{2} \times 1350 \times 8 \times \frac{2 \times 8}{3} + \frac{1}{2} \times 810 \times 8 \times \frac{8}{3} - 7008 + 5280\right) = 4{,}464 \text{ lb.}$$

and

$$R_B = \frac{1}{8}\left(\frac{1}{2} \times 1350 \times 8 \times \frac{8}{3} + \frac{1}{2} \times 810 \times 8 \times \frac{2 \times 8}{3} + 7008 - 5280\right) = 4{,}176 \text{ lb.}$$

while in span BC

$$R_B = 3{,}824 \text{ lb. and } R_C = 1{,}036 \text{ lb.}$$

The total reaction at B is thus 8,000 lb.

Slope-deflexion Solution

The slope-deflexion equations, which give the relationships between the couples

FIGURE 6.3. Nomenclature for the slope-deflexion equations [6.5]. The moments, slopes and deflexions are here shown in the positive sense (clockwise).

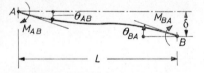

acting on the ends of a beam and the slopes and relative displacements of the ends (see FIGURE 6.3) are:

$$M_{AB} = \frac{2EI}{L}\left(2\theta_{AB} + \theta_{BA} - 3\frac{\delta}{L}\right) + M_{FAB} \left.\vphantom{\frac{2EI}{L}}\right\}$$
$$M_{BA} = \frac{2EI}{L}\left(2\theta_{BA} + \theta_{AB} - 3\frac{\delta}{L}\right) + M_{FBA} \qquad \cdots \text{[6.5]}$$

The first step in applying these equations to *Problem 6.8* is to obtain the fixed end moments from the formulae given in FIGURE 6.1.

Thus:

$$M_{FAB} = \frac{540 \times 8^2}{20} + \frac{810 \times 8^2}{12} = 6{,}048 \text{ lb. ft.}$$

similarly,

$$M_{FBA} = 5{,}472 \text{ lb. ft.}; \ M_{FBC} = 5{,}832 \text{ lb. ft.}; \ M_{FCB} = 3{,}888 \text{ lb. ft.}$$

These moments must be given a positive sign if they act on the beam in a clockwise sense and a negative sign if they act in an anti-clockwise sense. Successive applications of equation [6.5], omitting the constant $2E$ and arbitrarily taking $I = 24$, give the member equations:

$$M_{AB} = 3(\theta_B) - 6{,}048 \qquad \dots \text{(iii)}$$

$$M_{BA} = 3(2\theta_B) + 5{,}472 \qquad \dots \text{(iv)}$$

$$M_{BC} = 2(2\theta_B + \theta_C) - 5{,}832 \qquad \dots \text{(v)}$$

$$M_{CB} = 2(\theta_B + 2\theta_C) + 3{,}888 \qquad \dots \text{(vi)}$$

The joint equations express the equilibrium of B and C.
From (iv) and (v)

$$M_{BA} + M_{BC} = 0 = 10\theta_B + 2\theta_C - 360 \qquad \dots \text{(vii)}$$

From (vi)

$$M_{CB} = 0 = 2\theta_B + 4\theta_C + 3{,}888 \qquad \dots \text{(viii)}$$

Solution of equations (vii) and (viii) gives

$$\theta_B = +256 \text{ and } \theta_C = -1{,}100$$

Substitution in the member equations (iii) to (vi) gives

$$M_{AB} = 3 \times 256 - 6{,}048 = -5{,}280 \text{ lb. ft.}$$

$$M_{BA} = 6 \times 256 + 5{,}472 = +7{,}008 \text{ lb. ft.}$$

$$M_{BC} = 2(2 \times 256 - 1{,}100) - 5{,}832 = -7{,}008 \text{ lb. ft.}$$

$$M_{CB} = 2(256 - 2 \times 1{,}100) + 3{,}888 = 0.$$

These end moments are numerically the same as were obtained above but their signs correspond to the slope deflexion convention.

Moment Distribution Solution

As the beam BC is pinned at its end C the distribution factors at joint B, given by equation [6.12], are in the ratio $\dfrac{1}{8} : \dfrac{3}{4} \times \dfrac{1}{12} = 2 : 1$. The actual distribution process is as follows:

AB	BA	BC	CB	
	2/3	1/3	1	Distribution factors
− 6,048	+ 5,472	− 5,832	+ 3,888	Fixed end moments
			− 3,888	Balance C
		− 1,944		Carry over
	+ 1,536	+ 768		Balance B
+ 768				Carry over
− 5,280	+ 7,008	− 7,008	0	TOTAL

(2) *Solution Using Clapeyron's Equation*

Applying equation [6.3(a)] to the spans XA and AB, we have

$$2M_A + M_B = 0$$

and for spans AB and BC, with $\delta_c = 0 \cdot 0018$ ft.

147

$$M_A \times 8 + 2M_B \times 20 = \frac{30 \times 10^3 \times 2,880}{12 \times 12} \left(\frac{6 \times 0 \cdot 0018}{12} \right) = 54 \times 10^4$$

The solution of these equations is

$$M_A = - 7,500 \text{ lb. ft.}; \ M_B = + 15,000 \text{ lb. ft.}$$

giving the bending moment diagram (d).

Slope-deflexion Solution

The member equations are:

$$M_{AB} = \frac{2 \times 30 \times 10^3 \times 2,880}{96} (\theta_B) = 18\theta_B \times 10^3 \qquad \ldots \ldots \text{(ix)}$$

$$M_{BA} = \frac{2 \times 30 \times 10^3 \times 2,880}{96} (2\theta_B) = 36\theta_B \times 10^3 \qquad \ldots \ldots \text{(x)}$$

$$M_{BC} = \frac{2 \times 30 \times 10^3 \times 2,880}{144} \left(2\theta_B + \theta_C - \frac{3 \times 0 \cdot 0018}{12} \right)$$

$$= 24\theta_B \times 10^8 + 12\theta_C \times 10^3 - 54 \times 10^4 \qquad \ldots \ldots \text{(xi)}$$

$$M_{CB} = \frac{2 \times 30 \times 10^3 \times 2,880}{144} \left(\theta_B + 2\theta_C - \frac{3 \times 0 \cdot 0018}{12} \right)$$

$$= 12\theta_B \times 10^8 + 24\theta_C \times 10^8 - 54 \times 10^4 \qquad \ldots \ldots \text{(xii)}$$

As before, the joint equations are

$$M_{BA} = M_{BC} = 0$$

and $\qquad M_{CB} = 0$

giving

$$\left. \begin{array}{l} 60\theta_B \times 10^4 + 12\theta_C \times 10^4 = 54 \\ 12\theta_B \times 10^4 + 24\theta_C \times 10^4 = 54 \end{array} \right\} \qquad \ldots \ldots \text{(xiii)}$$

from which we obtain

$$\theta_B \times 10^4 = 0 \cdot 5 \text{ and } \theta_C \times 10^4 = 2 \cdot 0$$

substitution in equations (ix) to (xii) gives

$$M_{AB} = + 90,000 \text{ lb. in.} = + 7,500 \text{ lb. ft.}$$

$$M_{BA} = + 15,000 \text{ lb. ft.}$$

$$M_{BC} = - 15,000 \text{ lb. ft.}$$

$$M_{CB} = 0.$$

When these results are converted to the beam convention of signs they yield the same bending moment diagram (d) as before.

Moment Distribution Solution

The procedure is now to imagine that the joint C is forced into the displaced position while joints B and C are prevented from rotating by imaginary clamps.

Moments

$$M_{BC} = M_{CB} = -\frac{6EI\Delta}{L^2} \qquad \dots \text{[6.13]}$$

$$= -\frac{6 \times 30 \times 10^6 \times 2{,}880 \times 0\cdot0018}{144 \times 144}$$

$$= -45{,}000 \text{ lb. ft.}$$

are thus produced in BC; these are distributed as follows:

AB	BA	BC	CB	
	2/3	1/3	1	Distribution factors
		− 45,000	− 45,000	Fixed end moments
			+ 45,000	Balance C
		+ 22,500		Carry over
	+ 15,000	+ 7,500		Balance B
+ 7,500				Carry over
+ 7,500	+ 15,000	− 15,000	0	TOTAL

The reactions are found by subdividing the beam and taking moments, as above, and are

$$R_A = 2812\cdot5 \text{ lb.}; \quad R_B = + 4062\cdot5 \text{ lb.}; \quad R_C = -1{,}250 \text{ lb.}$$

where the negative sign signifies a downward reaction.

Problems for Solution

6.9. A beam ABC of length L is simply supported at its ends A and C and is continuous over a support B, which is L_1 from A and L_2 from C. The second moment of area of the beam varies linearly from zero at A and C to I at B. Find the reaction at the support B, when the beam carries a uniformly distributed load of intensity w over its whole length.

(St. Andrews, 1953)

6.10. A continuous beam has three equal spans, is simply supported at each end and supports a uniformly distributed load of w per unit length throughout its length. Find the values of the interior support moments.

(after Sheffield, 1950)

6.11. A horizontal continuous beam of uniform section is 60 ft. long and is supported with vertical restraint only by four level and equidistant supports. A dead load of 1 ton ft. covers the entire beam and, in addition, a superload of 2 tons ft. may or may not be carried by each of the three spans. Calculate the value of the maximum reaction at an intermediate support.

(Leeds, 1954)

6.12. A continuous beam $ABCDE$ rests on supports at A, B, C and D, all of which are at the same level. $AB = CD = 10$ ft., $BC = 16$ ft. and $DE = 6$ ft. The flexural rigidity EI for the span BC and the overhanging end DE is twice that for spans AB and CD.

If the beam weighs $\frac{1}{2}$ ton ft. run and carries loads of 10 tons at E and at the mid point of BC, draw the bending moment and shearing force diagrams for the beam.

(Oxford, 1944)

L   149

6.13. Find the support moments, calculate the reaction at A and sketch the bending moment diagram for the uniform continuous beam $ABCD$.

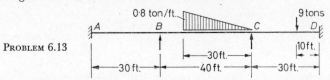

PROBLEM 6.13

(a) with D fixed, as shown
(b) with D simply supported
(c) with D free (i.e. CD is a cantilever).

(after Manchester College of Science and Technology)

6.14. A continuous beam $ABCD$ is of constant flexural rigidity throughout. $AB = BC = L$; $CD = L/4$. It is fixed at A and simply supported at B and C, the three supports being co-linear. It carries a uniformly distributed load of w per unit length on BC and a point load of $wL/2$ at D. Determine the slope of the beam at C in terms of w, L and EI.

(St. Andrews, 1952)

6.15. The beam $ABCD$ shown in the diagram is of constant section and has flexural

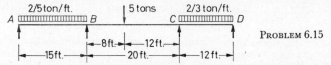

PROBLEM 6.15

rigidity $EI = 15 \times 10^7$ tons in.^{2} Find the deflexion of the mid-point of BC.

(St. Andrews, 1955)

6.16. *Subject of Problem:* To determine the bending moment and shearing force

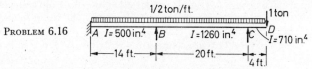

PROBLEM 6.16

diagrams for the continuous steel beam shown in the diagram.

Answers required: The support moments and reactions for the beam
(a) due to the loading shown and
(b) after support B has settled $\frac{1}{4}$ in.

(after Durham, 1955)

6.17. A continuous beam $ABCD$ extends over three spans of 24 ft., 32 ft. and 24 ft. respectively. It has a uniform flexural rigidity of 48,000 ton ft.^{2} and rests on rigid supports. The support at C has settled $\frac{1}{2}$ in. below the horizontal line across the other three supports. Find the reactions and the support moments induced in the beam when it carries a uniformly distributed load of 1 ton ft. over the entire length.

(Leeds, 1955)

6.18. *Subject of Problem:* Continuous beam $ABCD$ of three spans resting on supports originally all at the same level. The supports settle differentially.

Dimensions and Data:

	Span AB	Span BC	Span CD
Length:	20 ft.	60 ft.	40 ft.
Load:	1 ton ft. U.D.L.	2 tons ft. U.D.L.	4 tons ft. U.D.L.

Settlement from original level:

   Support A: Nil   Support B: 3/8 in.
   Support C: 3/16 in.   Support D: 1/4 in.

$EI = 37 \cdot 5 \times 10^{5}$ ton in.^{2}

Answers required:

  (a) The shearing force diagrams before and after settlement.
  (b) The bending moment diagram before and after settlement.

(Durham, 1951)

6.19.   A uniform beam of length 20 ft. rests freely at each end on fixed supports at the same level and has a central support whose height can be adjusted. It carries loads of 3 tons and 2 tons at 16 ft. and 15 ft. respectively from the left hand end. Show that when the bending moment at the centre is made zero by suitably adjusting the height of the central support the deflexion at that point will be about one-quarter of what it would be if the central support were removed.

(Oxford, 1942)

6.20.   Find the pressure which is exerted on each of a long line of circular pegs by a long steel strip laced through them as shown. The pegs (which may be treated as rigid)

   PROBLEM 6.20

are $\frac{1}{2}$ in. diameter and spaced at equal intervals of 1 ft., with their centres lying on the same straight line; the strip is of steel, 1 in. wide and 1/16 in. thick.

(Oxford, 1933)

6.21.   A continuous beam *ABCD*, of uniform flexural rigidity *EI*, extends over four level rigid supports spaced 12 ft., 8 ft. and 16 ft. apart respectively, and is subjected to a uniformly distributed loading of 1 ton ft. over its entire length. With the supports at *B* and *C* removed, the loading produces deflexions at *B* and *C* as shown in the table below, which also gives the deflexions due to unit loads applied separately at *B* and *C* respectively. From this information, or otherwise, calculate the reactions at *B* and *C*, and sketch the bending moment diagram for the beam.

Deflexions at	B	C
due to U.D.L. on *BC*	1,782	2,020 $\times (AD)^4/24EI$
due to unit load at *B*	108	112 $\times (AD)^3/EI$
due to unit load at *C*	112	$133\frac{1}{3} \times (AD)^3/EI$

(Leeds, 1956)

6.3.2. CONTINUOUS BEAM ON ELASTIC SUPPORTS

The methods of the previous section, in which redundant bending moments are found by one method or another, are not convenient for the present type of problem. Here the forces in the supports must be regarded as the redundants since the deflexions of the supports, and hence the displaced position of the beam, depend on them. In simple cases the direct comparison of displacements introduced in Volume I, Section 1.3 will suffice, but in more complex problems the flexibility coefficient equations, applied to the primary structure consisting of the beam together with its supports, will be more convenient. An example of this was given in Volume I, Section 6.2.3.2.

These two methods are now illustrated by the following example.

151

Problem 6.22—Four identical beams are arranged as shown in diagram (a), the connexions at A, B and C, which are the mid-points of supporting beams being capable of transmitting upward or downward loads but not torsion. Find the central bending moment.

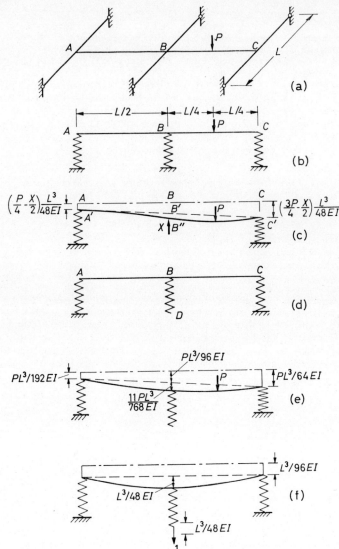

PROBLEM 6.22. (a) The beam ABC is simply supported by three identical beams. (b) The supporting beams can be represented as springs of flexibility $L^3/48EI$. (c) If the central spring is replaced by a variable force X the central deflexion BB'' can be calculated in terms of X. BB'' is also equal to the compression of the central spring under the force X. (d) In order to use the flexibility coefficient equation the primary structure is conveniently chosen as shown. (e) The primary structure under the actual load P. (f) The primary structure under unit load replacing the redundant reaction at D.

The arrangement can evidently be represented as shown at (b) where the springs have flexibility $L^3/48EI$ in./lb.

By direct comparison of displacements.

(1) *Solution by direct comparison of displacements.*
Here we seek to find the reaction between the central spring and the beam at B by equating the deflexion of the beam at that point with the compression of the spring. From diagram (c) it appears that the central deflexion of the beam is $BB'' = BB' + B'B''$

Now
$$BB' = \frac{1}{2} \times \frac{L^3}{48EI}\left\{\left(\frac{P}{4} - \frac{X}{2}\right) + \left(\frac{3P}{4} - \frac{X}{2}\right)\right\} = \frac{(P-X)L^3}{96EI}$$

and
$$B'B'' = \frac{11PL^3}{768EI} - \frac{XL^3}{48EI}$$

$$\therefore BB'' = \frac{19PL^3}{768EI} - \frac{XL^3}{32EI} \qquad \cdots \cdots \text{(i)}$$

The compression of the central spring is $BB'' = \dfrac{XL^3}{48EI}$ $\qquad \cdots \cdots$ (ii)

Hence equating (i) and (ii) we obtain $\qquad X = \dfrac{19P}{40}$

from which we find $(M_B = + PL/160)$.

(2) *Solution by the flexibility coefficient equation.*
Equations [4.7] now reduce to
$$\varDelta_d = 0 = \varDelta_{do} + X\varDelta_{dd} \qquad \cdots \cdots \text{(iii)}.$$
where the deflexions $\varDelta_{do}$ and $\varDelta_{dd}$ now refer to the point D of the primary structure shown in diagram (d). Under the actual load P we have, from diagram (c)
$$\varDelta_{do} = \frac{PL^3}{EI}\left(\frac{1}{96} + \frac{11}{768}\right) = \frac{19PL^3}{768EI}$$
while under unit load at D, as at (f), we have
$$\varDelta_{dd} = \frac{L^3}{EI}\left(\frac{1}{96} + \frac{1}{48} + \frac{1}{48}\right) = \frac{5L^3}{96EI}$$

Hence in (iii)
$$X = -\frac{\varDelta_{do}}{\varDelta_{dd}} = -\frac{19P}{768} \times \frac{96}{5} = -\frac{19P}{40} \quad \text{as before.}$$

Problems for Solution

6.23. The three span continuous beam $ABCD$ shown in the diagram has a constant second moment of area I and rests on elastic supports at B and C which each yield

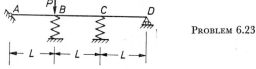

PROBLEM 6.23

an amount $L^3/6EI$ per unit load. Find the reactions when a load P acts at B.

(Melbourne, 1957)

6.24. A uniform beam ABC of length $2L$ rests on unyielding supports at its ends A and C while its mid-point B rests on a spring of flexibility kL^3/EI. A uniformly distributed load of w per unit length extends from A to C. Find the value of k which makes the greatest bending moment as small as possible.

6.25. A straight steel beam $ABCD$ has a constant second moment of area $I = 100$ in.[4] $AB = 10$ ft., $BC = CD = 3$ ft. The beam is fixed at A and supported at B and D by elastic props which sink $0 \cdot 10$ in. per ton. When the beam is unloaded the props just touch the beam but sustain no load. Find the bending moments at A, B, and C when there is a load of 1 ton at C.

6.26. $ABCDE$ is a pontoon bridge of uniform second moment of area I, supported at B, C and D on pontoons which sink Δ per unit load. A uniform load w per unit

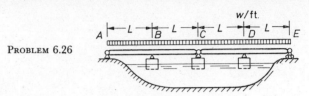

PROBLEM 6.26

length is applied to the full length of the bridge.

Calculate:
(a) the reaction at B
(b) the bending moment at B, if $\Delta = L^3/6EI$
(c) the value of Δ that makes $M_B = 0$.

(Melbourne, 1955)

6.3.3. INFLUENCE LINES FOR CONTINUOUS BEAMS

Two methods for finding influence lines were given in Volume I; in Section 5.3.3 the flexibility coefficient procedure for dealing with the two redundant reactions in a three-span continuous beam was described while in Section 6.2.3.3 Clapeyron's Equation was used to find the support moment influence

FIGURE 6.4. Convention of signs for the Beam-Line method.

lines for a similar beam. For beams with more than three spans these methods, which call for the solution of simultaneous equations, are very laborious and the following method, based on the Beam-Line method given in Volume I, Section 6.5.3, will be found to be more convenient.

Problem 6.27—A uniform continuous beam $ABCDE$ is simply supported at A, B, C, D and E. $AB = BC = CD = DE = L$. Find the influence lines for M_B, M_C, R_A, R_B and R_C.

We begin by recalling the general beam-line [6.23] for the beam LR shown in FIGURE 6.4.

$$M_L = M_{FL} + \frac{2}{n+4} M_{FR} - 4\left(\frac{n+3}{n+4}\right) EK\theta_L \qquad \dots \text{[6.23]}$$

where the restraint offered by the spans to the right of R is given by

$$M_R = nEK\theta_R \qquad \dots \text{(i)}$$

If the beam LR is not loaded,

$$M_{FL} = M_{FR} = 0$$

154

and
$$M_L = -4\left(\frac{n+3}{n+4}\right)EK\theta_L \qquad \ldots\text{(ii)}$$

This is written in the beam-line convention of signs, in which M_L and θ_L are positive when they are anti-clockwise and clockwise respectively; the restraint-line at L is

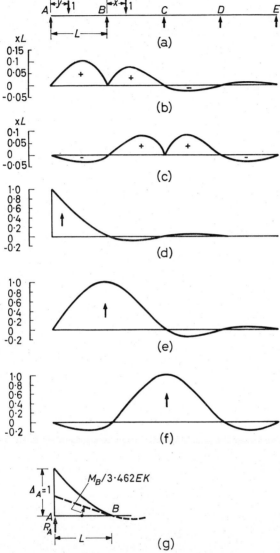

PROBLEM 6.27 (a) Uniform continuous beam with four equal spans. (b) Influence line for M_B. (c) Influence line for M_C. (d) Influence line for R_A. (e) Influence line for R_B. (f) Influence line for R_C. (g) Unit vertical displacement imposed at A.

thus given by

$$M_L = +4\left(\frac{n+3}{n+4}\right)EK\theta_L \qquad \ldots\text{(iii)}$$

155

By substituting equation (iii) in the slope-deflexion equations (written in the beam-line sign convention) we obtain for the unloaded beam

$$\theta_R = \frac{2}{n+4}\theta_L \qquad\qquad \dots\text{(iv)}$$

$$M_R = -\frac{n}{2(n+3)}M_L \qquad\qquad \dots\text{(v)}$$

The procedure is now to calculate the restraints at the supports beginning from the right hand end.

Thus at D, from [6.10]

$$M_D = 3EK\theta_D \qquad\qquad \text{i.e. } n_D = 3.$$

In span CD, at C, from (iii)

$$M_C = 4\left(\frac{n_D+3}{n_D+4}\right)EK\theta_C$$

$$= 4\frac{3+3}{3+4}EK\theta_C \qquad \text{i.e. } n_C = \frac{24}{7} = 3\cdot429.$$

Similarly, in span BC at B

$$n_B = 4\left\{\frac{\dfrac{24}{7}+3}{\dfrac{24}{7}+4}\right\} = \frac{45}{13} = 3\cdot462$$

We can now find all the support moments for various positions of the unit load, as follows.

When the unit load is in BC:

Applying [6.23] to the span BC

$$M_B = M_{FBC} + \frac{2}{\dfrac{24}{7}+4}M_{FCB} - 4\left\{\frac{\dfrac{24}{7}+3}{\dfrac{24}{7}+4}\right\}EK\theta_B$$

From the restraint offered by the span BA

$$M_B = 3EK\theta_B$$

Hence

$$M_B = \frac{x(L-x)^2}{L^2} + \frac{7}{26}\frac{x^2(L-x)}{L^2} - \frac{15}{13}M_B$$

$$= \frac{x(L-x)}{56L^2}(26L - 19x) \qquad\qquad \dots\text{(vi)}$$

Similarly,

$$M_C = M_{FCB} + \frac{2}{3+4}M_{FBC} - 4\left(\frac{3+3}{3+4}\right)\frac{M_C}{24/7}$$

$$= \frac{x(L-x)}{14L^2}(5x + 2L) \qquad\qquad \dots\text{(vii)}$$

156

From (v)

$$M_D = -\frac{3}{2(3+3)} M_C = -\frac{x(L-x)}{56L^2}(5x+2L) \qquad \dots \text{(viii)}$$

The point of this last calculation is that the value of M_D when the unit load is in span BC is equal to that of M_B when the unit load is in span CD.

When the unit load is in AB:

The calculations follow the same lines as above and lead to the results given below.

$$M_B = \frac{15}{56}\left\{\frac{y(L^2-y^2)}{L^2}\right\}$$

$$M_C = -\frac{1}{14}\left\{\frac{y(L^2-y^2)}{L^2}\right\}$$

$$M_D = \frac{1}{56}\left\{\frac{y(L^2-y^2)}{L^2}\right\}$$

When successive numerical values are given to x and y the influence lines given at (b) and (c) are obtained.

If the end A had been fixed we should have had

$$M_B = M_{FBC} + \frac{7}{26}M_{FCB} - \frac{45}{13}EK\theta_B$$

as before, when the load was in BC.

The restraint offered by BA would have given

$$M_B = 4EK\theta_B$$

Hence

$$M_B = M_{FBC} + \frac{7}{26}M_{FCB} - \frac{45}{52}M_B$$

$$= \frac{52}{97}\left(M_{FBC} + \frac{7}{26}M_{FCB}\right) \qquad \dots \text{(ix)}$$

At A, from (v)

$$M_A = -\frac{\infty}{2(\infty+3)}M_B = -\frac{1}{2}M_B \qquad \dots \text{(x)}$$

Similarly

$$M_C = M_{FCB} + \frac{2}{4+4}M_{FBC} - 4\left(\frac{4+3}{4+4}\right)\frac{M_C}{24/7}$$

$$= M_{FCB} + \frac{1}{4}M_{FBC} - \frac{49}{48}M_C$$

$$= \frac{48}{97}\left(M_{FCB} + \frac{1}{4}M_{FBC}\right) \qquad \dots \text{(xi)}$$

Similar calculations would have been used when the load was in CD, the restraint line at C then being

$$M_C = 4\frac{4+3}{4+4}EK\theta_C = \frac{7}{2}EK\theta_C \qquad \dots \text{(xii)}$$

Finally it is to be noted that if the spans have different K-values the calculations for any span must be made in terms of the K-value of that span.

157

Influence Lines for Reactions

The influence lines for the reactions can easily be obtained from those for the support moments; thus when the load is in AB

$$R_A = \frac{(L-y) - M_B}{L}$$

while when the load is elsewhere

$$R_B = - M_B/L$$

Values for the other reactions can be similarly obtained and yield the diagrams (d), (e) and (f).

Alternatively the whole problem can be approached by finding the reaction influence lines first by means of Müller-Breslau's Principle (Volume I, Section 5.2.4) from which it appears that the influence line for R_A, for example, is the shape of the beam when unit displacement is imposed at A. To calculate this we observe from diagram (g) that

$$\varDelta_A = 1 = R_A \frac{L^3}{3EI} + \frac{M_B L}{3 \cdot 462 EK}$$

$$= 0 \cdot 622 \frac{M_B L}{EK}, \quad \text{since } R_A = M_B/L$$

i.e.
$$M_B = 1 \cdot 608 \frac{EK}{L} = n_B EK \theta_B$$

$\therefore$
$$\theta_B = \frac{1 \cdot 608}{3 \cdot 462 L} = \frac{0 \cdot 465}{L}$$

From (v) above

$$M_C = - \frac{n_C}{2(n_C + 3)} M_B = - \frac{3 \cdot 429}{2(6 \cdot 429)} \times \frac{1 \cdot 608 EK}{L} = - 0 \cdot 430 \frac{EK}{L}$$

Hence
$$\theta_C = \frac{0 \cdot 430}{3 \cdot 429 L} = \frac{0 \cdot 125}{L}$$

Proceeding in this way one can obtain the bending moment and slope at D which are

$$M_D = 0 \cdot 107 \frac{EK}{L}$$

$$\theta_D = \frac{0 \cdot 036}{L} \quad \text{and also } \theta_E = \frac{0 \cdot 018}{L}$$

Since the bending moment and slope at all the supports are known the deflexion at intermediate points can be found by the moment area method.

The influence lines for the beam $ABCDE$ should now be recalculated in this manner.

Problems for Solution

6.28. Find the influence lines for the support moments and reactions for the following beams.

    (a) A uniform beam ABC continuous over two equal spans with simple supports at A,B and C.

    (b) A uniform beam ABC continuous over two equal spans but with A fixed and simple supports at B and C.

(c) A uniform beam ABC continuous over two equal spans but with A and C fixed and a simple support at B.

(d) A uniform beam $ABCD$ continuous over three equal spans with simple supports at A,B,C and D.

(e) A uniform beam $ABCD$ continuous over three equal spans but with A fixed and simple supports at B,C and D.

(f) A uniform beam $ABCD$ continuous over three equal spans but with A and D fixed and simple supports at B and C.

(g) The beam $ABCD$ of *Problem 6.16*.

6.29.   The beam $ABCD$ is of uniform cross-section and $M_A = 3EK_{AB}\theta_A$. A unit load travels from A to D. Obtain expressions for the influence line for the moment at B

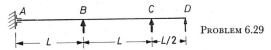

PROBLEM 6.29

in terms of the relevant fixing moments M_{FAB}, M_{FBA} etc.

(Birmingham, 1948)

6.30.   The uniform continuous beam shown is fixed at A and simply supported at B,C,D,E and F. Using the method of effective restraints, or any other method, find

PROBLEM 6.30

the slope of the influence lines for M_A and M_C at each of the points A, B, D, E and F.

(Melbourne, 1957)

6.4. RIGIDLY JOINTED FRAMES IN WHICH SWAY CANNOT OCCUR [Volume I, Sections 6.3.2 and 6.4.2]

The use of the slope deflexion equations and the moment distribution method for frames in which it is known that joint translation will not occur (either because the joints are not free to move or because of symmetry) has already been illustrated in *Problem 6.8* above. It is now only necessary to draw attention to the economy of effort that can be obtained when there is symmetry or anti-symmetry. Thus in FIGURE 6.5(b) it is obvious that $\theta_{BC} = -\theta_{CB}$ while at (d) $\theta_{BC} = +\theta_{CB}$. The number of unknown angles to be found by slope deflexion is in each case reduced by one.

The treatment of symmetrical loading by moment distribution was described in Volume I, Section 6.4.2 Example (b) where it was seen that the effective K-value of a symmetrically disposed member, such as BC in FIGURE 6.5(a), was reduced to $I/2L$. In the anti-symmetrical case (c) the structure can be replaced by that shown at (e) so that the effective K-value of BC' is $\frac{3}{4} \times \frac{I}{L/2} = 1 \cdot 5I/L$.

These shorts cut should be used wherever possible in the problems that follow.

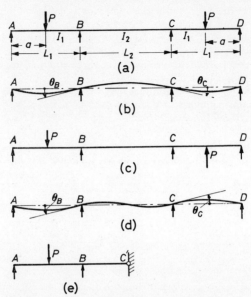

FIGURE 6.5. (a) Symmetrical continuous beam symmetrically loaded. (b) Shape of the deflected beam. (c) Symmetrical continuous beam anti-symmetrically loaded. (d) Shape of the deflected beam. (e) Curtailed beam statically equivalent to (c).

Problems for Solution

6.31. A duct for a heating system has frames as shown at frequent intervals along its length. Assuming that neighbouring sides are rigidly joined together, determine the bending moments at the corners and sketch the distribution of bending moments round the frame.

(London, 1954)

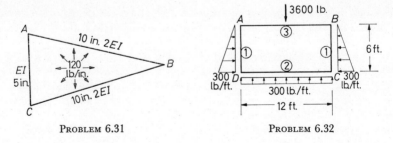

PROBLEM 6.31   PROBLEM 6.32

6.32. The figure represents a culvert supporting earth on either side and a point load on the roof. A length of 1 ft. perpendicular to the paper has been considered and the K-values of the members are given by the figures in circles.

   Find the bending moments at the corners of the culvert.

(Manchester, 1952)

6.33. The figure represents a framework with rigid joints, the K-values of the members being shown in circles. Investigate the bending moments produced in the

160

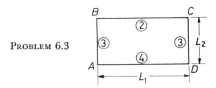

PROBLEM 6.3

frame if, because of unequal heating, member BC increases in length by the amount $2d$.

(Manchester, 1955)

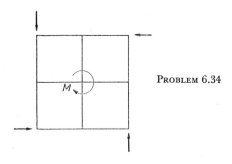

PROBLEM 6.34

6.34. Use the slope deflexion equations to find the angle of rotation of the centre joint of the framework shown in the figure if all the members are equal and of stiffness K.

(Manchester, 1955)

6.35. Obtain the slope deflexion equations for moments applied at each end of a member ABC whose flexural rigidity is EI over one-half its length AC and $EI/2$ over the other half CB.

(Manchester, 1956)

6.36. A long water tank is built against a rock face by erecting a reinforced concrete wall and slab, as shown, monolithic and built into the rock at A and C.

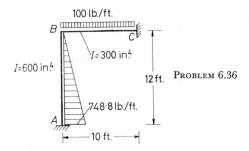

PROBLEM 6.36

Considering 1 ft. run of the tank the equivalent second moments of area are as shown. Calculate the bending moments in the frame and the support reactions at A and C.

(London, 1951)

6.37. The figure shows a rigidly jointed frame; joint A is pinned to its support and joint C is fixed to its foundation. The members have equal K-values. The unit load can occupy any position on the beam AB.

161

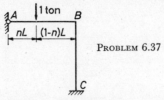

PROBLEM 6.37

Use the slope deflexion method to find the values of the bending moments at B and C in terms of n and L and plot the influence line for bending moment at B.

(Manchester, 1954)

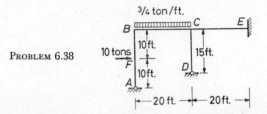

PROBLEM 6.38

6.38.   In the frame shown joints A and D are pinned, E is fixed and B and C are rigid. All the members have the same cross-section. Find the bending moments at B, C, E and F.   (London, 1951)

6.39.   The continuous structure shown in the figure is of uniform relevant second moment of area throughout and carries the loads shown. Obtain the diagram of

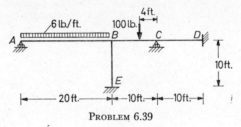

PROBLEM 6.39

bending moment for $ABCD$, giving all important values.   (after Melbourne, 1953)

6.40.   The diagram shows a reinforced concrete wharf framework, the figures in circles being the relative second moments of area of the members. The piles are driven into firm clay to a depth of about 20 ft.

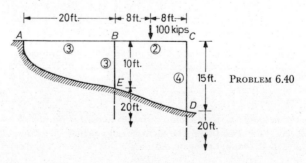

PROBLEM 6.40

162

Making the assumption that the piles are fixed at the points E and D, analyse the frame and compute the forces acting on the abutment at A under the live loading shown.

Discuss the validity of the assumption that the piles are fixed at E and D and suggest alternative assumptions that might be more appropriate showing how they would affect the previous results. (Melbourne, 1948)

6.41. The figure (a) shows a continuous beam of many equal spans rigidly attached, at B and C, to columns hinged at the feet E and F. All the spans of the beam and the columns have the same flexural rigidity and length.

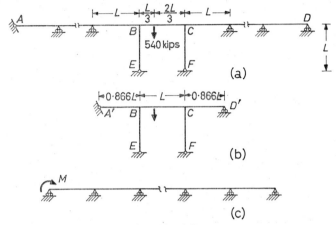

PROBLEM 6.41

(i) Show that when a couple M is applied to one end A of a uniform continuous beam of many equal spans, as at (c), the angle of rotation produced at A is

$$\theta_A = M/3 \cdot 464EK.$$

(ii) Hence show that the spans BA and CD in (a) can be replaced by single spans BA' and CD', of length $0 \cdot 866L$, hinged at A' and D' as shown at (b).

(iii) Hence analyse the structure (a) under the loads shown and find the axial force in the beam AB. (Manchester, 1958)

6.42. In the framework shown the beam and the columns are of equal cross-section. Joints B and C are welded, while at E and F the framework is hinged to its foundations.

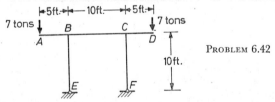

PROBLEM 6.42

Find the bending moments at the joints, sketch the bending moment diagram, and compute the reactions at E and F. (Manchester, 1954)

6.43. The roof shown in the figure is supported by a column fully restrained at the base and with rigid connections to the rafters at the column cap. The column shaft also supports a pair of open web crane brackets near mid-height. The left-hand rafter is subjected to a vertical suction upwards and the right-hand rafter to a vertical pressure downwards. The second moments of area are given alongside the respective

163

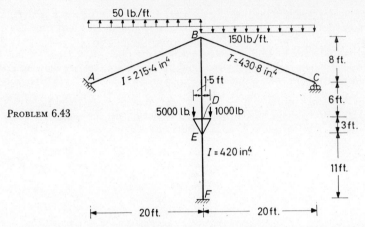

PROBLEM 6.43

members. Sketch the curve of bending moment for the 28 ft. long column and attach arithmetical values (in lb. ft.) at all the change points. (Edinburgh, 1957)

6.44. Find the bending moment diagram for the framework shown. The 4-ton load is centrally placed on the beam *CD*. (Manchester)

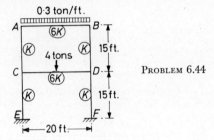

PROBLEM 6.44

6.45. The figure shows a two-storey portal frame, the columns of which are pinned at their bases. Assuming that the columns and beams all have an identical *EI* value, draw the bending moment diagram for the frame due to the loads shown. (Sheffield, 1956)

6.46. Find the bending moment diagram for the portal frame shown.
The supports *A*, *B*, *C* and *D* are pinned, all the other joints being rigid. The value of *EI* is the same for all the members. (after Sheffield, 1957)

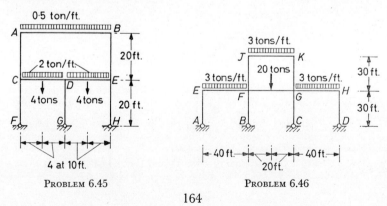

PROBLEM 6.45   PROBLEM 6.46

164

6.5. RIGIDLY JOINTED FRAMES IN WHICH SWAY CAN OCCUR

When translation of one or more of the joints of a frame can be accommodated by bending of the members the analysis, whether by slope-deflexion or moment distribution, must be modified to take account of this 'sway' unless it is obvious, from symmetry, that no such movement will occur in a particular case. Several possible methods of attack were described and illustrated in Volume I, Chapter 6, where it was indicated that after the recognition of the number of possible modes of sway the corresponding equations of equilibrium —the sway equations—must be developed. The process is illustrated below in *Problem 6.47*. Reference should be made to Volume I for an account of special methods, due to Naylor and Bolton, which are advantageous in certain circumstances.

Problem 6.47—The frame illustrated is a 'complex' one in which the relative

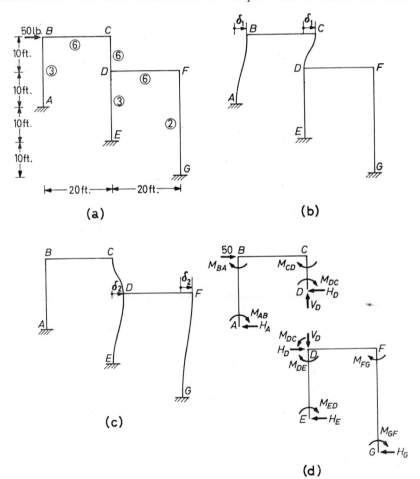

PROBLEM 6.47. (a) Complex frame. (b) Sway I. (c) Sway II. (d) Determination of sway equations.

movements of the joints depend on the relative stiffness of the members and cannot be found from geometry alone. This particular example was used by Grinter† to illustrate the shear distribution process; his solution can be usefully compared with those now given.

There are two modes of sway, shown at (b) and (c); the sway equations are found by isolating those parts of the frame involved in each type of sway, as at (d). Considering the equilibrium of the element $ABCD$ we have:

Post AB, moments about B: $M_{AB} + M_{BA} = -H_A \times 20$ .... (i)

Post CD, moments about C: $M_{CD} + M_{DC} = -H_D \times 10$ .... (ii)

Resolving horizontally $H_A + H_D = 50$ .... (iii)

Hence $M_{AB} + M_{BA} + 2(M_{CD} + M_{DC}) = -1,000$ I

This is the first sway equation. The second is obtained by considering the element $EDFG$ for which we have:

$$\frac{1}{20}(M_{DE} + M_{ED}) + \frac{1}{30}(M_{FG} + M_{GF}) = -H_D$$

$$= \frac{1}{10}(M_{CD} + M_{DC}) \qquad \text{from (ii)}$$

Hence

$$3(M_{ED} + M_{DE}) + 2(M_{FG} + M_{GF}) - 6(M_{CD} + M_{DC}) = 0 \qquad .... \text{II}$$

Slope deflexion Solution

The member equations, taking $2E = 1$, are:

$$\left.\begin{aligned}
M_{AB} &= 3\left(\theta_B - \frac{3\delta_1}{20}\right) \\[4pt]
M_{BA} &= 3\left(2\theta_B - \frac{3\delta_1}{20}\right) \\[4pt]
M_{BC} &= 6(2\theta_B + \theta_C) \\[4pt]
M_{CB} &= 6(\theta_B + 2\theta_C) \\[4pt]
M_{CD} &= 6\left\{2\theta_C + \theta_D - \frac{3(\delta_1 - \delta_2)}{10}\right\} \\[4pt]
M_{DC} &= 6\left\{\theta_C + 2\theta_D - \frac{3(\delta_1 - \delta_2)}{10}\right\} \\[4pt]
M_{DE} &= 3\left(2\theta_D - \frac{3\delta_2}{20}\right) \\[4pt]
M_{ED} &= 3\left(\theta_D - \frac{3\delta_2}{20}\right) \\[4pt]
M_{DF} &= 6(2\theta_D + \theta_F) \\[4pt]
M_{FD} &= 6(\theta_D + 2\theta_F) \\[4pt]
M_{FG} &= 2\left(2\theta_F - \frac{3\delta_2}{30}\right) \\[4pt]
M_{GF} &= 2\left(\theta_F - \frac{3\delta_2}{30}\right)
\end{aligned}\right\} \qquad .... \text{(iv)}$$

---

† *Theory of Modern Steel Structures*, Vol. II. Macmillan.

The joint equations are:

$$\sum M_B = \sum M_C = \sum M_D = \sum M_F = 0 \qquad \dots \text{(v)}$$

from which we obtain by substitution

$$18\theta_B + 6\theta_C - 0\cdot45\delta_1 = 0$$
$$6\theta_B + 24\theta_C + 6\theta_D - 1\cdot8\delta_1 + 1\cdot8\delta_2 = 0$$
$$6\theta_C + 30\theta_D + 6\theta_F - 1\cdot8\delta_1 + 1\cdot35\delta_2 = 0$$
$$6\theta_D + 16\theta_F - 0\cdot2\delta_2 = 0.$$

and from the sway equations we obtain

$$9\theta_B + 36\theta_C + 36\theta_D - 8\cdot1\delta_1 + 7\cdot2\delta_2 = -1{,}000$$
$$-108\theta_C - 81\theta_D + 12\theta_F + 21\cdot6\delta_1 - 25\cdot1\delta_2 = 0$$

$$\left. \rule{0pt}{110pt} \right\} \quad \dots \text{(vi)}$$

The solution of these equations is:

$$\theta_B = 16\cdot874; \quad \theta_C = 5\cdot004; \quad \theta_D = 18\cdot406; \quad \theta_F = 0\cdot065$$
$$\delta_1 = 741\cdot688; \quad \delta_2 = 557\cdot367$$

Substitution in equations (iv) gives:

$$M_{AB} = -283\cdot1 \quad M_{BA} = -232\cdot5 \quad M_{BC} = +232\cdot5$$
$$M_{CB} = +161\cdot3 \quad M_{CD} = -161\cdot3 \quad M_{DC} = -80\cdot9$$
$$M_{DE} = -140\cdot4 \quad M_{ED} = -195\cdot6 \quad M_{DF} = +221\cdot3$$
$$M_{FD} = +111\cdot2 \quad M_{FG} = -111\cdot2 \quad M_{GF} = -111\cdot3$$
$$\text{(all in lb. ft.)}$$

Moment Distribution Solutions

(a) Correction for sway effects by proportion [Volume I, Section 6.4.3.1].

Since there are no fixed end moments in this problem we begin by introducing sway moments corresponding to the two modes of sway. Thus for sway I,

$$M_{SAB} = M_{SBA} = -\frac{6EK_{AB}\delta_1}{L_{AB}} \qquad \alpha - 150$$

$$M_{SCD} = M_{SDC} = -\frac{6EK_{CD}\delta_1}{L_{CD}} \qquad \alpha - 600$$

while for sway II, similarly,

$$M_{SCD} = M_{SDC} = +\frac{6EK_{CD}\delta_2}{L_{CD}} \qquad \alpha \; 1{,}800$$

$$M_{SDE} = M_{SED} = -\frac{6EK_{DE}\delta_2}{L_{DE}} \qquad \alpha - 450$$

$$M_{SFG} = M_{SGF} = -\frac{6EK_{FG}\delta_2}{L_{FG}} \qquad \alpha - 200.$$

The distribution process, which follows the usual routine, is not given in full but the results are shown in TABLE 6.47(a).

When these moments are substituted in the two sway equations we obtain:

Sway I:

In I: $-145 - 140 + 2(-253 - 272) = -1{,}335$

in II: $3(+104 + 52) + 2(-26 - 13) - 6(-253 - 272) = +3{,}540$

$$\left. \rule{0pt}{30pt} \right\} \times x$$

TABLE 6.47(a).

Sway I Distribution

	AB	BA	BC	CB	CD	DC	DE	DF	FD	FG	GF	ED	
		1/3	2/3	1/2	1/2	2/5	1/5	2/5	3/4	1/4			Initial moments
	− 150	− 150			− 600	− 600							
				distribution as usual leads to									
	− 145	− 140	+ 140	+ 253	− 253	− 272	+ 104	+ 168	+ 26	− 26	+ 13	+ 52	

Sway II—Distribution

	AB	BA	BC	CB	CD	DC	DE	DF	FD	FG	GF	ED	
					+ 1800	+ 1800	− 450			− 200	− 200	− 450	Initial moments
				distribution as usual leads to									
	+ 72	+ 144	− 144	− 720	+ 720	+ 938	− 664	− 274	+ 98	− 98	− 149	− 557	

Final Summation

	AB	BA	BC	CB	CD	DC	DE	DF	FD	FG	GF	ED	
	− 323·3	− 312·1	+ 312·1	+ 564·0	− 564·0	− 606·4	+ 231·8	+ 374·6	+ 58·0	− 58·0	− 29·0	+ 115·9	Sway I × 2·23
	+ 40·3	− 80·6	− 80·6	− 402·9	+ 402·9	+ 524·9	− 371·6	− 153·3	+ 54·8	− 54·8	− 83·4	− 311·6	Sway II × 0·56
	− 282·0	− 231·5	+ 231·5	+ 161·1	− 161·1	− 81·5	− 139·8	+ 221·3	+ 112·8	− 112·8	− 112·4	− 195·7	Total

168

Sway II:

    in I: $+ 72 + 144 + 2(720 + 938) = + 3,532$

    in II: $3(- 557 - 664) + 2(- 98 - 149) - 6(720 + 938) = - 14,105$ $\left.\right\} \times y$

The simultaneous equations for x and y are:

$$\left. \begin{array}{c} - 1,335x + 3,532y = - 1,000 \\ 3,540x - 14,105y = 0 \end{array} \right\} \text{ i.e. } \begin{array}{c} x = 2{\cdot}23 \\ y = 0{\cdot}56 \end{array}$$

When the sway I and sway II distributions are multiplied by these factors and added the results given at the foot of TABLE 6.47(a) are obtained. As a final check substitution in the sway equations gives:

    in I: $- 282{\cdot}0 - 231{\cdot}5 + 2(- 161{\cdot}1 - 81{\cdot}5) = - 998{\cdot}7$

    in II: $3(- 195{\cdot}7 - 139{\cdot}8) + 2(- 112{\cdot}8 - 112{\cdot}4) - 6(- 161{\cdot}1 - 81{\cdot}5)$
$$= - 1{\cdot}3.$$

(b) Correction for sway effects by successive approximations.

Since the moments in member CD appear in both sway equations the method given under this heading in Volume I, Section 6.4.3.2 must be modified, as follows. Suppose that sways δ_1 and δ_2 are imposed simultaneously on the members AB and DF respectively; then the moments set up at the ends of the vertical members, taking $6E = 1$, are:

$$\left. \begin{array}{l} M_{SAB} = M_{SBA} = - \dfrac{K_{AB}}{L_{AB}} \delta_1 = - 0{\cdot}15\delta_1 \\[2mm] M_{SCD} = M_{SDC} = - \dfrac{K_{CD}}{L_{CD}} (\delta_1 - \delta_2) = - 0{\cdot}6(\delta_1 - \delta_2) \\[2mm] M_{SDE} = M_{SED} = - \dfrac{K_{DE}}{L_{DE}} \delta_2 = - 0{\cdot}15\delta_2 \\[2mm] M_{SFG} = M_{SGF} = - \dfrac{K_{FG}}{L_{FG}} \delta_2 = - 0{\cdot}0667\delta_2 \end{array} \right\} \quad \dots\text{ (ix)}$$

If the corrections required corresponding to the two sway equations are respectively S_{I} and S_{II} then from I we have

$$- 0{\cdot}15\delta_1 + 2\{- 0{\cdot}6(\delta_1 - \delta_2)\} = S_{\text{I}}/2$$

i.e. $- 2{\cdot}7\delta_1 + 2{\cdot}4\delta_2 = S_{\text{I}}$ $\dots\text{ (x)}$

and from II

$$3(- 0{\cdot}15\delta_2) + 2(- 0{\cdot}0667\delta_2) - 6\{- 0{\cdot}6(\delta_1 - \delta_2)\} = S_{\text{II}}/2$$

i.e. $7{\cdot}2\delta_1 - 8{\cdot}367\delta_2 = S_{\text{II}}$ $\dots\text{ (xi)}$

The solution of (x) and (xi) is $\delta_1 = - 1{\cdot}575\,S_{\text{I}} - 0{\cdot}452\,S_{\text{II}}$
$$\delta_2 = - 1{\cdot}356\,S_{\text{I}} - 0{\cdot}508\,S_{\text{II}}$$

from which the sway correction moments (ix) can be found.

At the outset, when $S_{\text{I}} = - 1,000$ and $S_{\text{II}} = 0$ we have $\delta_1 = 1,575$ and $\delta_2 = 1,356$ from which

$$M_{SAB} = - 236; \; M_{SCD} = - 131; \; M_{SDE} = - 203; \; M_{SFG} = - 90$$

These moments are entered in the first line of TABLE 6.47(b) and are followed by one cycle of distribution. The resulting moments are substituted in the two sway equations in TABLE 6.47(c) and S_{I} and S_{II} are then found to be $- 493$ and $+ 816$ respectively. Correction moments obtained as above are computed and entered in

TABLE 6.47(b)

SWAY CORRECTION BY SUCCESSIVE APPROXIMATIONS

	AB	BA	BC	CB	CD	DC	DE	DF	FD	FG	GF	ED
	1/3	1/3	2/3	1/2	1/2	2/5	1/5	2/5	3/4	1/4		
Initial sway moments	− 236	− 236			− 131	− 131	− 203			− 90	− 90	− 203
Balance B and D and C.O.	+ 34	+ 79	+ 157	+ 79	+ 67	+ 133	+ 67	+ 134	+ 67			+ 33
Balance C and F and C.O.			− 4	− 7	− 8	− 4		+ 8	+ 17	+ 6	+ 3	
Total after 1st cycle	(− 202)	(− 157)	(+ 153)	(+ 72)	(− 72)	(− 2)	(− 136)	(+ 142)	(+ 84)	(− 84)	(− 87)	(− 170)
1st sway correction	− 61	− 61			− 92	− 92	− 38			− 17	− 17	− 38
Balance B and D and C.O.	+ 11	+ 22	+ 43	+ 22	+ 25	+ 51	+ 25	+ 50	+ 25			+ 12
Balance C and F and C.O.			+ 11	+ 22	+ 23	+ 11		− 3	− 6	− 2	− 1	
Total after 2nd cycle	(− 252)	(− 196)	(+ 207)	(+ 116)	(− 116)	(− 32)	(− 149)	(+ 189)	(+ 103)	(− 103)	(− 105)	(− 196)
2nd sway correction	− 22	− 22			− 53	− 53	− 9			− 4	− 4	− 9
Balance B and D and C.O.	+ 2	+ 4	+ 7	+ 4	+ 11	+ 21	+ 11	+ 22	+ 11			+ 5
Balance C and F and C.O.			+ 9	+ 19	+ 19	+ 9		− 3	− 5	− 2	− 1	
Total after 3rd cycle	(− 272)	(− 214)	(+ 223)	(+ 139)	(− 139)	(− 55)	(− 147)	(+ 208)	(+ 109)	(− 109)	(− 110)	(− 200)

TABLE 6.47(b) and the whole process is repeated as often as found necessary. Three cycles are given here and it is evident that convergence is rather slow.

TABLE 6.47(c)

CALCULATION OF SWAY CORRECTION

Cycle	Substitution in I $M_{AB} + M_{BA} + 2(M_{CD} + M_{DC}) = -1{,}000$	R.H.S.	S_I
after 1st	$-202 - 157 + 2(-72 - 2)$	-507	-493
after 2nd	$-252 - 196 + 2(-116 - 32)$	-744	-256
after 3rd	$-272 - 214 + 2(-139 - 55)$	-874	-126

Cycle	Substitution in II $3(M_{DE} + M_{ED}) + 2(M_{FG} + M_{GF}) - 6(M_{CD} + M_{DC}) = 0$	R.H.S.	S_{II}
after 1st	$3(-136 - 170) + 2(-84 - 87) - 6(-72 - 2)$	-816	$+816$
after 2nd	$3(-149 - 196) + 2(-103 - 105) - 6(-116 - 32)$	-563	$+563$
after 3rd	$3(-147 - 200) + 2(-109 - 110) - 6(-139 - 55)$	-315	$+315$

Problems for Solution

6.48. Obtain the sway equations for the frames shown below and on the next page.

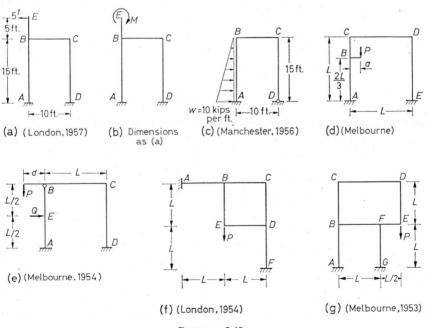

(a) (London, 1957)   (b) Dimensions as (a)   (c) (Manchester, 1956)   (d) (Melbourne)

(e) (Melbourne, 1954)   (f) (London, 1954)   (g) (Melbourne, 1953)

PROBLEM 6.48

171

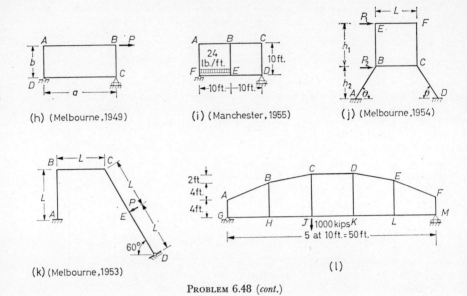

(h) (Melbourne,1949)

(i) (Manchester, 1955)

(j) (Melbourne,1954)

(k) (Melbourne,1953)

(l)

PROBLEM 6.48 (*cont.*)

6.49. The column shown in the figure is part of a building frame and is of uniform section. The lower end A is rigidly attached to the foundation and the upper end C is attached to the beams and columns above by heavy connections and is assumed to be is fixed. B is a rigid joint. Find the bending moments at A, B and C and sketch the bending moment and shearing force diagrams for the column.

Comment on the assumption that C is fixed from the point of view of the design of the column.

(Melbourne, 1947)

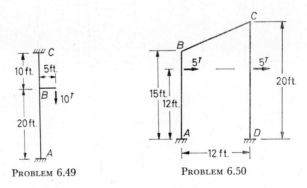

PROBLEM 6.49

PROBLEM 6.50

6.50. The figure shows a rigidly jointed frame constructed of members having the same constant second moment of area. Analyse the frame by moment distribution, or otherwise, and sketch the bending moment diagram.

(Manchester, 1953)

6.51. Use the method of moment distribution to analyse the portal frame shown in the figure if the hinged support D sinks an amount Δ. The members have the same uniform cross-section,

(Manchester, 1958)

172

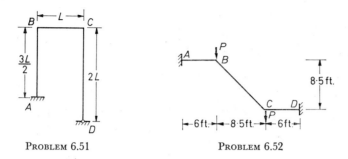

PROBLEM 6.51   PROBLEM 6.52

6.52.   The diagram represents a beam of uniform cross-section supporting a staircase. Use the slope-deflexion method to find the bending moments at the ends of the members.

(Manchester, 1954)

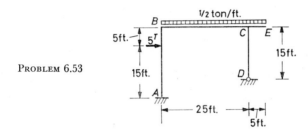

PROBLEM 6.53

6.53.   The members of the rigidly jointed frame shown in the figure have the same constant second moment of area. Sketch the deflected form of the frame, find the bending moments at the joints and sketch the bending moment diagram for *AB*.

(London, 1957)

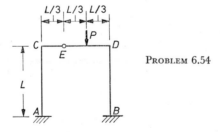

PROBLEM 6.54

6.54.   The second moment of area is uniform throughout the frame shown in the figure. Find the bending moments at the joints.

(London)

6.55.   In many frames there are members which are subjected to torsion: for instance the beam *BC* in the figure will be twisted as *AB* deflects in bending.
   (a) How will a couple be divided between two connected members when one is in torsion and the other is in bending?
   (b) What will be the carry over factor for a member in torsion?
   (c) Find the distribution of moments in the frame shown in the figure if the joint

173

B is prevented from moving laterally. AB and BC are identical and circular in cross-section; the modulus of rigidity is 2/5 of Young's modulus.

(d) If B is allowed to move laterally, derive the sway equation which will now be required.

(Manchester, 1955)†

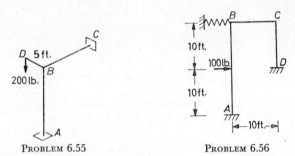

PROBLEM 6.55   PROBLEM 6.56

6.56. The rigidly jointed frame $ABCD$, all the members of which have a second moment of area I, is flexibly restrained by a spring at B attached to a rigid wall. This spring compresses or extends one inch under a force $EI/1,200$, where E is the modulus of elasticity of the frame material.

It is required to find the moments in the frame due to a horizontal load of 100 lb. acting as shown.

(Melbourne, 1952)

6.57. A rigidly jointed portal frame $ABCD$ has two columns AB and DC, of height L, and a horizontal beam BC, also of length L. All the members have the same second moment of area I. Foundation A is rigid but D yields elastically, rotating unit angle under a moment $20EI/L$ and settling vertically unit distance under a force $10EI/L^3$; it is not capable of horizontal displacement.

A vertical load P acts at the mid-point of BC, which is prevented from swaying sideways by a prop at C. Obtain the bending moments in the frame if $P = 40$ kips and $L = 20$ ft.

(Melbourne, 1953)

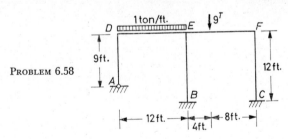

PROBLEM 6.58

6.58. In the frame shown the second moments of area are as follows:
Members DE and EF, I; BE, $2I$; AD and CF, $3I$.
Find the bending moments at the joints.

(Leeds, 1952)

---

† See J. A. L. Matheson, ' Moment distribution applied to rectangular rigid space frames', *J. Inst. Civ. Engrs*, Vol. 29, 1948, p. 221.

6.59. The frame shown is constructed of members having the same uniform cross-section. Find the bending moments at the joints.

(London, 1957)

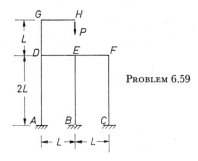

PROBLEM 6.59

6.60. Obtain the sway equations for the frame shown in the figure and find the bending moments at the joints if $P = W$, $a = b = c$ and the cross-section of the members is constant.

(Manchester, 1956)

PROBLEM 6.60

6.61. *ABC* (diagram (a)) is a composite member consisting of two equal members *AB* and *BC*, each of stiffness K, jointed rigidly at *B*. If *A* is fixed and *C* is pinned (so that the distance *AC* cannot change) determine the effective stiffness of the composite member, in terms of K, when a moment is applied at *C*. Find also the carry-over factor to *C*.

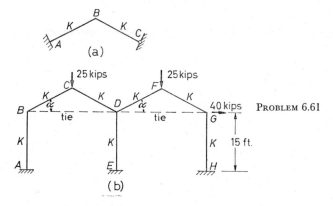

PROBLEM 6.61

In the two-bay gabled frame shown at (b), flexible ties incapable of transmitting bending moment are provided between *B* and *D* and between *D* and *G* so that

175

spread between these points is prevented. Each member has a stiffness K. The frame is loaded as shown. Assuming that axial deformations are to be neglected, calculate the bending moments in the frame, using the moment-distribution method and taking advantage of any simplification in procedure that appears to be admissible.

(Melbourne, 1952)

6.62. The members of the frame shown have equal K-values. Find the bending moments at the joints.

(Melbourne)

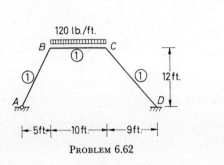

PROBLEM 6.62

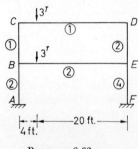

PROBLEM 6.63

6.63. The K-values of the members of the frame are shown in circles. Find the bending moments at the joints.

(Birmingham, 1940)

6.64. The figures in circles are the K-values of the members of the frame illustrated. Obtain the bending moment diagram for the frame under the wind loading shown.

(London, 1956)

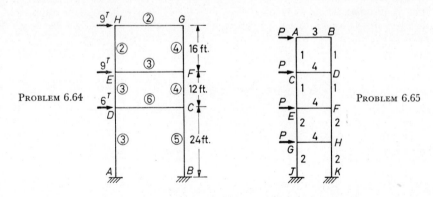

PROBLEM 6.64

PROBLEM 6.65

6.65. Plot the bending moments in the symmetrical single bay rigid frame. All members are of length L and the figures given are the relative second moments of area.

(Manchester College of Science and Technology, 1956)

176

6.66. The mine headgear shown diagrammatically in the figure is constructed of welded steelwork uniform in cross-section. Neglect axial changes of length and find the bending moments at the joints.

(Melbourne, 1950)

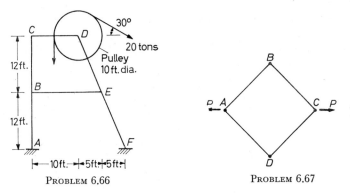

PROBLEM 6.66   PROBLEM 6.67

6.67. Find the bending moments at the corners of the square frame of side *L* shown in the figure and calculate the reduction of the diagonal *BD*. The members are identical.

(Manchester, 1956)

6.68. A rectangular closed rigid frame, of sides *L* and *B*, is under uniform external pressure. Find the ratio of *L* to *B* so that there is zero bending moment at the centre of the breadth *B*.   (London, 1956)

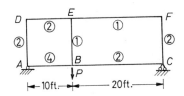

PROBLEM 6.69

6.69. Find the bending moments at the joints of the Vierendeel frame shown. The *K*-values of the members are given in circles.   (Melbourne)

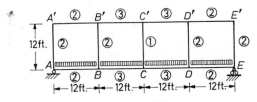

PROBLEM 6.70

6.70. The Vierendeel girder shown carries a uniformly distributed load of 1 ton ft. along the bottom chord. Calculate the bending moments and plot the bending moment diagram.   (Leeds, 1957)

177

6.6. FRAMES WITH SEMI-RIGID JOINTS

Some of the main features of the beam-line method, which is particularly suitable for analysing frames with cleated joints, have already been recalled in Section 6.3.3. It is now intended only to remind the reader of the remaining important points given in Volume I, Section 6.5.3 before giving some problems for solution.

In computing the total restraint at the end of a beam connected to other members by cleats the stiffness of a number of members 'in parallel' is obtained by adding the stiffnesses of the individual members, while the reciprocal of the stiffness (the flexibility) of a number of members 'in series' is equal to the sum of the reciprocals of their individual stiffnesses. Thus in *Problem 6.73*(a) at A, the total stiffness of the members AE and AG is the sum of their individual stiffnesses; for AE we have

$$M_{AE} = 3EK_{AE}\theta_A = 3 \times E \times \tfrac{1}{2} \times \theta_A \qquad \text{from [6.10]}$$

Hence stiffness of $AE + AG = 2(3 \times \tfrac{1}{2}) = 3$.

$$\therefore \quad \text{flexibility of } AE + AG = \frac{1}{3}$$
$$\text{and flexibility of cleat} = \frac{1}{3}$$

$$\therefore \quad \text{flexibility of joint} = \frac{1}{3} + \frac{1}{3} = \frac{2}{3}.$$

$$\therefore \qquad \text{stiffness of joint} = \frac{3}{2} \qquad \text{i.e.} \qquad M_A = \frac{3}{2}E\theta_A.$$

Problems for Solution

6.71. The relative K-values of the members are shown in circles. Find the moments at the ends of the beams AB and BC in terms of the fixing moments in the loaded beam AB,
  (a) if all the joints are rigid
  (b) if BC is attached to the wall and to BD by connexions with a moment-angle relation $M = 2EK_{BC}\theta$.

(Birmingham)

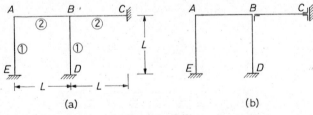

(a)   (b)

PROBLEM 6.71

6.72. Find the moments at B, C and D,
  (a) if $ABCD$ is continuous, pinned to the columns, and fixed at D.
  (b) if $ABCD$ is continuous, fixed at D and attached to BF and CG by yielding connexions;

(c) if *ABCD* consists of three separate beams attached to the columns at *B* and *C*
by yielding connexions; *A* is pinned and *B* fixed as before.

The *K*-values of the members are given in circles and for all connexions $M = 2EK_{BC}\theta$.

(Birmingham)

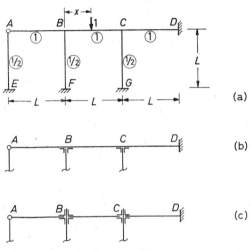

(a)
(b)
(c)

PROBLEM 6.72

6.73.   (a) Find the moments at the ends of the beam *AC* under the load *P*.
(b) A vertical prop is inserted at *B*, bringing it to the same level as *A* and *C*.
Find the bending moment at *B*.

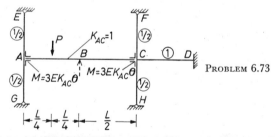

PROBLEM 6.73

(c) Find the change in the bending moment at *B* produced by adding a load
P at the mid point of *BC*.

(Birmingham)

6.7.   THE ANALYSIS OF COLLAPSE LOADS

The main features of elementary plastic theory were described in Volume I,
Section 6.6 and some of them are illustrated by the following problem.

Problem 6.74.   The members of the frame have the same value of the plastic moment
of resistance M_p. Find the collapse load.

Number of possible hinge positions   = 15 (see diagram (b))

Number of redundants   = 9

∴ Number of independent mechanisms = 6

179

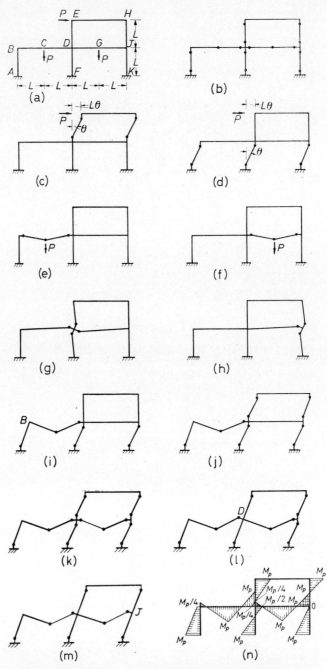

PROBLEM 6.74. (a) Frame, constructed of uniform members, whose collapse load is required. (b) Possible positions of plastic hinges. (c) to (h) Independent basic collapse mechanisms. (i) to (l) Combination of basic mechanisms. (m) Final collapse mechanism. (n) Corresponding bending moment diagram.

180

The basic mechanisms, and the corresponding equilibrium equations are:

Sway of top storey (c)	$PL\theta = 4M_p\theta$	.... (i)
Sway of bottom storey (d)	$PL\theta = 6M_p\theta$	.... (ii)
Collapse of beam BCD (e)	$PL\theta = 4M_p\theta$	.... (iii)
Collapse of beam DGJ (f)	$PL\theta = 4M_p\theta$	.... (iv)
Rotation of joint D (g)	$0 = 4M_p\theta$	.... (v)
Rotation of joint J (h)	$0 = 3M_p\theta$	.... (vi)

We now proceed to combine these elementary mechanisms so as to eliminate as many plastic hinges as possible. For example, we could proceed in the following order:

Combine (ii) and (iii), eliminating hinge at B (diagram (i)) and reducing the virtual work on the right hand side of each of equations (ii) and (iii) by $M_p\theta$. Hence adding (ii) and (iii) and deducting $2M_p\theta$ from right hand side,

$$2PL\theta = 10M_p\theta - 2M_p\theta = 8M_p\theta \qquad \text{.... (vii)}$$

Combine (i) and (vii) (diagram (j)); adding (i) and (vii)

$$3PL\theta = 12M_p\theta \qquad \text{.... (viii)}$$

Combine (iv) and (viii) (diagram (k)); adding (iv) and (viii)

$$4PL\theta = 16M_p\theta \qquad \text{.... (ix)}$$

Combine (v) and (ix) and eliminate three hinges at D (diagram (l)); adding (v) and (ix) and deducting $6M_p\theta$ to allow for the virtual work thus excluded

$$4PL\theta = 20M_p\theta - 6M_p\theta = 14M_p\theta \qquad \text{.... (x)}$$

Combine (vi) and (x) and eliminate two hinges at J (diagram (m)); adding (vi) and (x) and deducting $4M_p\theta$

$$4PL\theta = 17M_p\theta - 4M_p\theta = 13M_p\theta$$

$$\text{i.e.} \quad P = \frac{13}{4}\frac{M_p}{L.}$$

Since we have used all the basic mechanisms and as there seems to be no possibility of eliminating any more hinges this should be the collapse load. To check this we attempt to find the bending moment diagram from statical considerations; it is soon found that this cannot be done for the reason that the equations involving the nine plastic hinges are not independent. If one additional joint moment, say M_{DF}, is arbitrarily fixed then the moment everywhere can be found.

If M_{DF} is given the value $-M_p/2$ then

$$M_{DE} = -M_p/4; \quad M_{JH} = -M_p; \quad M_{JK} = 0$$

It has thus proved possible to find a bending moment diagram that satisfies statics and in which M_p is not exceeded at any point. It follows from the uniqueness theorem [Volume I, Section 6.6.3.1] that this is the required collapse mechanism.

Problems for Solution

6.75. Calculate the yield moment M_y and the full plastic moment M_p for the sections shown at (a) and (b). The yield stress is 15·25 ton sq. in.

(Melbourne, 1957)

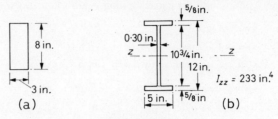

PROBLEM 6.75

6.76. Obtain the equilibrium equations for the assumed collapse mechanisms shown and hence estimate the collapse load. Draw the bending moment diagram for each case and determine whether the yield condition is satisfied at all points. If it is not, revise the collapse mechanism and obtain a better estimate for the collapse load. (Melbourne, 1957)

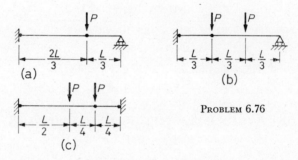

PROBLEM 6.76

6.77. Explain what is meant by the term 'shape factor' as used in the plastic theory of structures. What is the shape factor for a beam of circular cross-section?

The portal frame shown in the diagram is loaded to failure by the force P. Find the relationship between P, M_p and L at collapse if the plastic moment of AB is $1.5\ M_p$ while that of BC and CD is M_p. (Manchester, 1958)

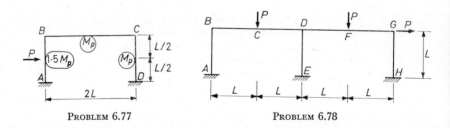

PROBLEM 6.77   PROBLEM 6.78

6.78. The two-bay portal frame shown in the diagram is loaded to failure by the load system P.

Assuming that M_p is the same for all members, find an expression for the collapse load in terms of M_p and L. (Manchester, 1956)

182

6.79. Find the value of *P* which brings about collapse of the rigid portal frame shown in the diagram.

(Melbourne, 1956)

PROBLEM 6.79

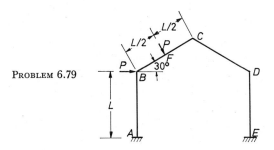

6.80. The design loads shown on the diagram are in tons and the figures in circles denote the plastic moments of the members in tons ft. Find the load factor at collapse.

(Melbourne, 1957)

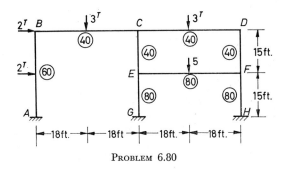

PROBLEM 6.80

CHAPTER 7

ARCHES

7.1. INTRODUCTION

The arch is a structural form of great importance and consequently its behaviour under fixed or moving loads has been extensively studied. While the usual theorems of structural theory are applicable to arches it is found that special methods of considerable utility and interest can be developed for dealing with arches of various types and some of these are illustrated in the problems that follow.

Although the three-hinged arch is statically determinate, and so really falls outside the scope of this book, some of the points that arise in its analysis also occur in connexion with two-hinged and fixed arches, the common hyperstatic types; the chapter therefore begins with some problems on three-hinged arches under fixed and moving loads.

7.2. THREE-HINGED ARCHES UNDER FIXED LOADS

[Volume I, Section 7.2]

Problem 7.1—BCD is a semi-circular three-hinged arch supported on two columns *AB* and *ED*. Find the horizontal reactions and the bending moments at *A* and *E* under the loads *P* and also the bending moment at *F*, the mid-point of *BC*.

(Melbourne, 1953)

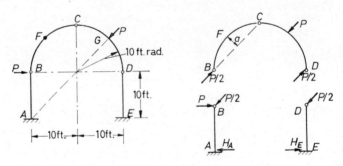

PROBLEM 7.1

The mode of action of the structure can best be appreciated by separating the arch from the columns as shown. We then have, from horizontal resolution,

$$H_A = P - \frac{P \cos 45°}{2} = 0\cdot646P \text{ tons}$$

$$H_E = \frac{P \cos 45°}{2} = 0\cdot354P \text{ tons}$$

Taking moments about A and E respectively, we have

$$M_A = 10\left(P - \frac{P\cos 45°}{2}\right) = 6\!\cdot\!46P \text{ ton ft.}$$

$$M_E = \frac{10P\cos 45°}{2} = 3\!\cdot\!54P \text{ ton ft.}$$

Taking moments about F, we have

$$M_F = Pa/2 = 10P\left(1 - \frac{1}{\sqrt{2}}\right)\bigg/2 = 1\!\cdot\!465P \text{ ton ft.}$$

Problems for Solution

7.2. A symmetrical three-hinged parabolic arch of 120 ft. span and 40 ft. rise has vertical loads of 9, 12 and 15 tons at 15 ft., 30 ft. and 90 ft. respectively measured horizontally from the left-hand support. Draw the linear arch and the bending moment diagram for the arch and find the bending moments at the load points.

(Manchester)

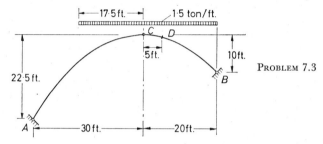

PROBLEM 7.3

7.3. The unsymmetrical three-hinged arch ACB shown in the figure is of parabolic form. Find the bending moment at D. (Manchester)

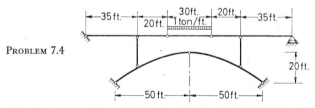

PROBLEM 7.4

7.4. Determine the bending moment at a quarter-chord point of the composite structure shown in the figure if the three-pinned arch component is (a) parabolic, (b) circular. (Manchester)

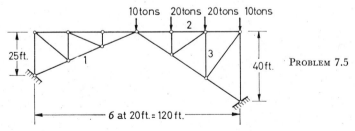

PROBLEM 7.5

7.5. Use graphical means to determine the forces in members 1, 2 and 3 of the three-hinged arch shown in the figure under the loads indicated. (Manchester)

185

7.3. INFLUENCE LINES FOR THREE-HINGED ARCHES
[Volume I, Section 7.2.4]

The first influence line to be obtained is usually that for the horizontal component of thrust and, in the case of the three-hinged arch, this is obtained from statical considerations. Influence lines for axial thrust, shearing force and bending moment at points on the rib, or for the force in members of a braced arch, can then be readily obtained.

Problem 7.6—Construct the influence lines for shear, axial thrust and bending moment for the left-hand quarter span section of a three-hinged parabolic arched rib of span 80 ft. and central rise 16 ft. Determine the maximum values of these load functions when a concentrated load of 10 tons rolls over the span.

(Manchester)

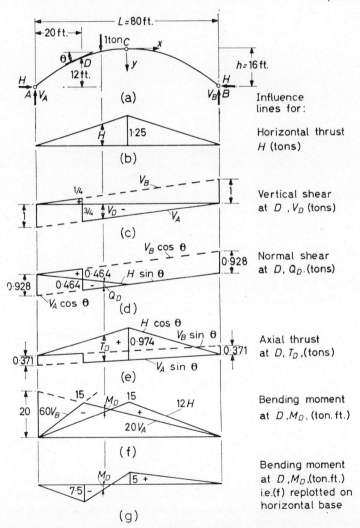

PROBLEM 7.6. Three-hinged parabolic arch, for which influence lines are required.

186

The centre line of the rib is shown at (a); its equation, with C as origin, is $x^2 = 100y$. The slope at D is given by differentiating:

$$2x = 100\frac{dy}{dx} \quad \text{i.e.} \quad \left(\frac{dy}{dx}\right)_D = \frac{2 \times 20}{100} = 0\cdot4$$

Hence $$\sin\theta = 0\cdot371; \quad \cos\theta = 0\cdot928.$$

Influence line for H. The general shape of this diagram will be as shown at (b); the centre ordinate corresponding to unit load at C, when $V_A = V_B = \frac{1}{2}$, is $L/4h = 1\cdot25$.

Influence line for V_D the vertical shear at D. This is the same as for a simply supported beam and is shown at (c).

Influence line for Q_D the normal shear at D. This is obtained by combining the influence line for V with that for H, for at D

$$Q_D = V_D\cos\theta + H\sin\theta \qquad \text{.... (i)}$$

this expression is plotted at (d) and it is seen that Q_D is zero when the moving unit load is in CB, for at C

$$V_D\cos\theta = -\tfrac{1}{2} \times 0\cdot928 = -0\cdot464$$

and $$H\sin\theta = +1\cdot25 \times 0\cdot371 = +0\cdot464$$

This is confirmed by the fact that when the load is to the right of C the reaction at A must act along the line AC; as the slope at D happens to equal the slope of AC there can be no normal shearing force at D.

Influence line for T_D the axial thrust at D. Here we have

$$T_D = H\cos\theta - V_D\sin\theta \qquad \text{.... (ii)}$$

which is plotted at (e).

Influence line for M_D the bending moment at D. When the moving unit load lies in AD

$$M_D = 12H - 60V_B \qquad \text{.... (iii)}$$

and when it is in DB

$$M_D = 12H - 20V_A \qquad \text{.... (iv)}$$

The two lines $60V_B$ and $20V_A$ intersect at D where both have the value 15; the final diagram is therefore as shown at (f).

For actual use these diagrams should be replotted on a horizontal base which has been done at (g) in the case of the bending moment influence line.

Problems for Solution

7.7.   Find the influence line for bending moment at X due to unit vertical load.

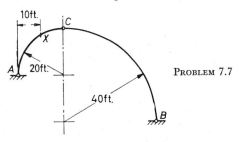

PROBLEM 7.7

Hence find the maximum bending moment at this point due to a uniformly distributed load, longer than the span, of 2 tons per foot.

(Sheffield, 1949)

7.8. A three-hinged symmetrical arched rib has a span of 60 ft. and a rise of 15 ft.; its centre-line is circular. A wheel load of 10 tons rolls over the arch. Using an influence line find the maximum positive and negative bending moments occurring anywhere in the rib.

(Sheffield, 1951)

7.9. A three-hinged parabolic arch has a rise of 12 ft. and a span of 100 ft. Determine the maximum bending moment at the quarter-span point due to the given reversible

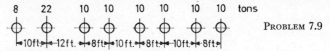

PROBLEM 7.9

live load. Obtain from an influence line the corresponding horizontal thrust in the arch.

(Manchester)

7.10. Show that a parabolic three-pinned arch rib carrying a uniform (per unit horizontal length) load will be subject to direct thrust only.

PROBLEM 7.10

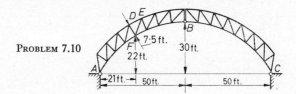

A symmetrical arch girder is pinned at *A*, *B* and *C*, as shown in the diagram. Derive an influence line for the force in member *DE* due to unit load moving along the lower chord of the girder.

(Sheffield, 1954)

7.4. ELASTIC PROPERTIES OF THE ARCHED RIB

Arches having two, one or no hinges are hyperstatic and their behaviour depends on the deflexions of the various parts of the rib caused by loads, changes of temperature or other agencies. The problems of this section are intended to demonstrate the calculation of the deflexions of arched ribs and the subsequent solution of arch problems by the direct comparison of deflexions.

Problem 7.11—A symmetrical parabolic arched rib *ACB* is fixed at the end *A* and free at the end *B*. It is so proportioned that the second moment of area of any cross-section is $I_0 \sec \alpha$, where I_0 is the second moment of area at the crown and α is the angle of inclination of the rib to the horizontal at the section.

(a) Find expressions for the horizontal, vertical and angular movements of the end *B* if a vertical load *P* is applied at the crown *C*.

(b) If the free end *B* had been pinned in its initial position before the application of *P* find the reactions at the pin and the angular movement there.

(after Melbourne, 1950)

188

The equation to the parabolic rib, with origin at A, is

$$y = \frac{4hx}{L^2}(L-x)$$

$$= \frac{x}{L}(L-x) \text{ when } h = L/4.$$

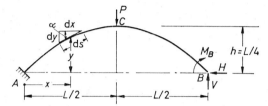

PROBLEM 7.11. In order to find the various components of deflexion of the free end B, imaginary horizontal, vertical and angular forces, H, V and M_B, are applied there.

(a) From Castigliano's Theorem, Part II.

$$\text{Horizontal movement of } B = \frac{\partial U}{\partial H} = \int_A^B M\frac{\partial M}{\partial H}\frac{ds}{EI} \qquad \dots \text{ (i)}$$

$$\text{Vertical movement of } B = \frac{\partial U}{\partial V} = \int_A^B M\frac{\partial M}{\partial V}\frac{ds}{EI} \qquad \dots \text{ (ii)}$$

$$\text{Angular movement of } B = \frac{\partial U}{\partial M_B} = \int_A^B M\frac{\partial M}{\partial M_B}\frac{ds}{EI} \qquad \dots \text{ (iii)}$$

where H, V and M_B are imaginary forces (i.e. numerically equal to zero) added for the purpose of obtaining the movement of B.

The bending moment M at any point is

$$M = P\left(\frac{L}{2}-x\right) + Hy - V(L-x) + M_B \qquad \dots \text{ (iv)}$$

where the first term applies only when $0 < x < L/2$, and the remaining terms are included for the sole purpose of obtaining the derivatives

$$\frac{\partial M}{\partial H} = y; \quad \frac{\partial M}{\partial V} = -(L-x); \quad \frac{\partial M}{\partial M_B} = 1$$

Hence (i) becomes

$$\int_0^{L/2} P\left(\frac{L}{2}-x\right)y\frac{ds}{EI} \qquad \dots \text{ (i')}$$

since

$$H = V = M_B = 0\dagger$$

This expression is awkward to handle if EI is constant but with 'secant' variation of I we have

$$I = I_0 \sec\alpha = I_0\frac{ds}{dx}$$

$$\therefore \quad \frac{ds}{I_0} = \frac{dx}{I}$$

Hence (i') becomes

$$\frac{P}{EI_0 L}\int_0^{L/2}\left(\frac{L}{2}-x\right)x(L-x)dx = \frac{PL^3}{64EI_0} \qquad \dots \text{ (v)}$$

† It is to be noted that $\partial M/\partial H$, $\partial M/\partial V$ and $\partial M/\partial M_B$ have real values even though H V and M_B, being imaginary, are zero.

Similarly (ii) becomes
$$-\int_0^{L/2} P\left(\frac{L}{2}-x\right)(L-x)\frac{ds}{EI}$$
$$= -\frac{P}{EI_0}\int_0^{L/2}\left(\frac{L}{2}-x\right)(L-x)dx = -\frac{5PL^3}{48EI_0} \dots \text{(vi)}$$

and (iii) becomes
$$\int_0^{L/2} P\left(\frac{L}{2}-x\right)\frac{ds}{EI} = \frac{P}{EI_0}\int_0^{L/2}\left(\frac{L}{2}-x\right)dx = \frac{PL^2}{8EI_0} \quad \dots \text{(vii)}$$

(b) If B is pinned before the load is applied forces H and V will develop at B. In order to find these forces we calculate the horizontal and vertical movements of the free end B of the cantilever arch under forces $H = V = 1$ acting in the directions shown in the diagram.

Horizontal movement of B under $H = 1$, $\Delta_{HH} = \int_A^B y^2\frac{ds}{EI} = \frac{1}{EI_0}\int_0^L y^2 dx = \frac{L^3}{30EI_0}$

Vertical movement of B under $H = 1$, $\Delta_{VH} = -\frac{1}{EI_0}\int_0^L y(L-x)dx = -\frac{L^3}{12EI_0}$

Horizontal movement of B under $V = 1$, $\Delta_{HV} = \Delta_{VH} = -\frac{L^3}{12EI_0}$

Vertical movement of B under $V = 1$, $\Delta_{VV} = \frac{1}{EI_0}\int_0^L (L-x)^2 dx = \frac{L^3}{3EI_0}$

The flexibility coefficient equations [4.7] now give
$$\left.\begin{array}{l} 0 = \dfrac{PL^3}{64EI_0} + \dfrac{HL^3}{30EI_0} - \dfrac{VL^3}{12EI_0} \\[3mm] 0 = -\dfrac{5PL^3}{48EI_0} - \dfrac{HL^3}{12EI_0} + \dfrac{VL^3}{3EI_0} \end{array}\right\} \quad \dots \text{(viii)}$$

from which we have $H = 5P/6$; $V = 25P/48$.

The angular movement of B in this situation now comes from (iii) which becomes
$$\frac{P}{EI_0}\int_0^{L/2}\left(\frac{L}{2}-x\right)dx + \frac{H}{EI_0 L}\int_0^L x(L-x)dx - \frac{V}{EI_0}\int_0^L (L-x)dx = \frac{PL^2}{288EI_0}$$

Problems for Solution

7.12.   The cross-section of the parabolic arched rib shown in the diagram varies so that the second moment of area is proportional to the secant of the angle of slope of

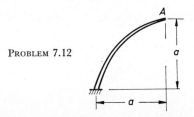

PROBLEM 7.12

the neutral axis at that point. Find the direction in which a point load must be applied at A if A is to move solely in the line of action of the load.

(London, 1957)

7.13. The steel bar ABC of uniform cross-section, with its upper portion bent into a quadrant of radius R, is rigidly fixed at C. Find the ratio of V to H such that the

PROBLEM 7.13

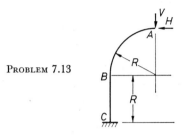

displacement of A shall be entirely vertical. Consider only the strains due to bending.

(London, 1951)

7.14. The two parabolic arches shown are pinned to one another and to a column BC at B, are fixed to the abutments at A and D and have variable second moments of area $I = I_0 \sec \alpha$, where I_0 refers to the crowns of the arches. The column has uniform second moment of area I_0.

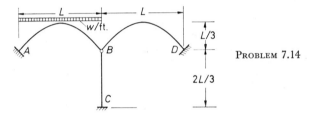

PROBLEM 7.14

Find the value of the horizontal thrust at each abutment when one arch only carries a uniformly distributed load of w per horizontal foot run.

(London, 1954)

PROBLEM 7.15

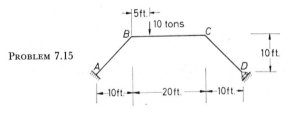

7.15. Find the reaction at D and the movement there; the rib is of uniform flexural rigidity EI_0. The rollers at D are set at $45°$ to the horizontal.

(Birmingham, 1952)

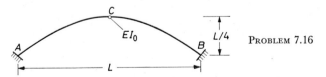

PROBLEM 7.16

7.16. The parabolic arched rib shown has secant variation of flexural rigidity. Find the movement of C and the thrust there caused by a rise of temperature of $t°$.

191

7.17. Show that the rotational stiffness at the end *A* of the frame shown in the

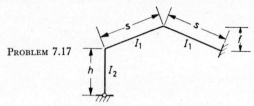

PROBLEM 7.17

diagram is given by

$$m_\phi^{ad} = \frac{3EI_1(8 + 12\phi + 8\phi^2 + 4x_1)}{s(12 + 12\phi + 7\phi^2 + 8x_1)}$$

where $\phi = f/h$, $x_1 = \dfrac{I_1 h}{I_2 s}$ and translation is prevented.

(Leeds, 1956)

7.5. THE TWO-HINGED ARCH [Volume I, Section 7.3]

When the ideas of Section 7.4 are applied to the analysis of the two-arched arch, in which the horizontal component of thrust is usually taken as the redundant, they readily yield the formula for the horizontal thrust

$$H = \frac{\displaystyle\int \frac{M_0 y}{EI}\,ds}{\displaystyle\int \frac{y^2}{EI}\,ds} \qquad \dots \ [7.7]$$

when the hinges are at the same level. The influence line for *H* is obtained by considering a moving unit load and influence lines for bending moment and shear then follow exactly as in the case of the three-hinged arch. (See *Problem 7.6.*)

The treatment must be modified if the hinges are not at the same level, as in *Problem 7.18* below.

Problem 7.18—In the two-pinned parabolic arch shown in the diagram the supports *A* and *B* are at different levels. Find the horizontal thrust at the supports when a

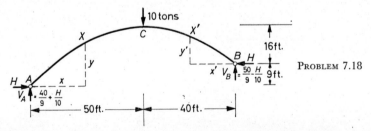

PROBLEM 7.18

point load of 10 tons acts at the crown C. It may be assumed that the second moment of inertia at any point *X* (or *X′*) is $I_x = I_0 \sec \alpha$, where I_0 is the second moment of area at the crown and α is the angle which the tangent at *X* (or *X′*) makes with the horizontal.

192

With origin at A the equation to AC is $\quad y = \dfrac{x(100 - x)}{100}$ $\qquad$ .... (i)

With origin at B the equation to CB is $\quad y' = \dfrac{x'(80 - x')}{100}$ $\qquad$ .... (ii)

From Castigliano's Theorem of Compatibility

$$0 = \frac{dU}{dH} = \frac{d}{dH} \int_A^B \frac{M^2 ds}{2EI} = \int_A^B M \frac{dM}{dH} \frac{ds}{EI}$$

$$= \frac{1}{EI_0} \int_A^B M \frac{dM}{dH} dx \qquad \text{.... (iii)}$$

Taking moments about B,

$$90 V_A = 9H + 400$$

or $\qquad V_A = \dfrac{H}{10} + \dfrac{40}{9}$

Similarly,

$$V_B = -\frac{H}{10} + \frac{50}{9}$$

In AC: $\qquad M = Hy - V_A x$

$$= \frac{Hx(100 - x)}{100} - \frac{Hx}{10} - \frac{40x}{9}$$

$$= \frac{9Hx}{10} - \frac{Hx^2}{100} - \frac{40x}{9}$$

$$\frac{dM}{dH} = \frac{9x}{10} - \frac{x^2}{100}$$

In CB: $\qquad M = Hy' - V_B x'$

$$= \frac{Hx'(80 - x')}{100} - \frac{50x'}{9} + \frac{Hx'}{10}$$

$$= \frac{9Hx'}{10} - \frac{H(x')^2}{100} - \frac{50x'}{9}$$

$$\frac{dM}{dH} = \frac{9x'}{10} - \frac{(x')^2}{100}$$

Hence in (iii)

$$0 = \int_0^{50} \left(\frac{9Hx}{10} - \frac{Hx^2}{100} - \frac{40x}{9} \right) \left(\frac{9x}{10} - \frac{x^2}{100} \right) dx$$

$$+ \int_0^{40} \left(\frac{9Hx'}{10} - \frac{H(x')^2}{100} - \frac{50x'}{9} \right) \left(\frac{9x'}{10} - \frac{(x')^2}{100} \right) dx'$$

from which we eventually obtain $H = 8.55$ tons.

Problems for Solution

7.19. The two hinged arch ACB shown in the figure consists of two identical uniform straight members AC and CB, rigidly connected at C and hinged to immovable foundations at A and B. Find the horizontal thrust and the bending moment at C

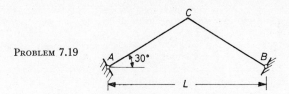

PROBLEM 7.19

(a) when there is a point load P on AC, distant x_1 ft. (horizontal) from A;

(b) when there is a load of w per horizontal foot uniformly distributed over AC;

(c) When the temperature rises by $t°$.

What is the change of level of C in case (c)?

(Manchester)

7.20. The symmetrical two-hinged portal frame shown in the figure is welded on the ground and then lifted into its final vertical position when the pins at A and E are inserted. BC and CD are at an angle of $30°$ to the horizontal.

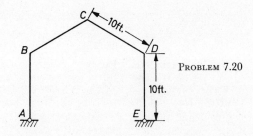

PROBLEM 7.20

Find the horizontal thrust and the maximum bending moment in the frame (a) if there is a vertical load of 4 tons at C, and (b) if A and E have to be sprung apart by a relative amount of 1 in. before the pins can be inserted ($EI = 144 \times 10^7$ lb. in.^{2}).

(Manchester)

7.21. $ABCDE$ is a rigid rib of uniform cross-section, hinged at A and E and loaded as shown. Determine the horizontal thrust and the bending moment at C.

(Melbourne, 1951)

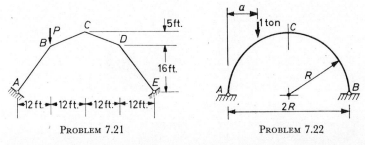

PROBLEM 7.21   PROBLEM 7.22

7.22. ACB is a semi-circular two-hinged arch rib of uniform second moment of area I. Obtain an expression for the influence line for horizontal thrust as a unit vertical load moves across the rib.

(Birmingham)

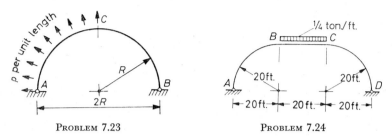

PROBLEM 7.23   PROBLEM 7.24

7.23. Find the reactions at the supports of the two-hinged semi-circular arch rib shown in the diagram when it carries a wind suction of p per unit of perimetral length acting on the left-hand half of the rib. The flexural rigidity is constant.

(St. Andrews, 1954)

7.24. The two-pinned arch form of constant section comprises two quarter-circular arcs AB and CD connected by a straight beam BC. A uniform loading of $\frac{1}{4}$ ton ft. is supported over the whole length of the beam. Determine the horizontal thrust at the constraints and sketch the bending moment diagram indicating critical values.

(Glasgow, 1957)

7.25. The steel segmental rib ACB shown in the diagram is of constant second moment of area I throughout and carries a central load P. The ends A and B are tied together by a steel tie whose cross-sectional area is equal to I/R^2. Calculate the load in the tie.

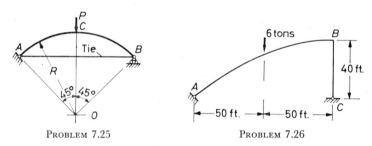

PROBLEM 7.25   PROBLEM 7.26

7.26. Calculate the horizontal thrust at the supports of the two-pinned structure shown in the diagram. The second moment of area of BC is I_0 and of AB is $I_x = I_0 \sec \alpha$, where α is the angle which the tangent to the parabolic portion AB makes with the horizontal.

(St. Andrews, 1956)

7.27. The two-pinned parabolic arch shown in the diagram has secant variation of flexural rigidity. Find the horizontal thrust at B when a load P acts horizontally

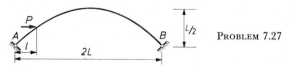

PROBLEM 7.27

as shown. Hence find the horizontal thrust at B when a wind load of p per unit of height acts horizontally on the left-hand half of the span.

(St. Andrews, 1955)

195

7.28. A two-hinged parabolic steel arch, with secant variation of flexural rigidity, has span L and rise h and carries a load P at the crown; derive an expression for the bending moment at the crown assuming that the abutments are perfectly rigid.

If $L = 100$ ft., $h = 10$ ft. and $P = 50$ tons while the mean cross-sectional area of the arch ring is 0.62 ft.^{2} and the second moment of area at the crown is 0.385 ft.^{4} calculate the horizontal thrust due to the 50-ton load

    (a) neglecting the effect of rib shortening,

    (b) allowing for rib shortening, yielding of the abutments of 0.0025 in. ton and a temperature rise of $50°F$.   (Leeds, 1954)

7.29. Two parabolic two-pinned arches are connected as shown in the diagram. If the arch ADB carries the loading indicated, and the pin B is mounted on a roller

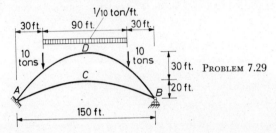

PROBLEM 7.29

bearing, calculate the bending moment at C, the crown of arch ACB. The second moments of area of both arches vary according to the 'secant law' and $I_D = 2I_C$.

        (Glasgow, 1957)

7.30. Find the horizontal thrust in the double parabolic arch shown in the diagram.

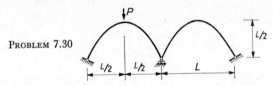

PROBLEM 7.30

The arches are identical and their second moments of area vary according to the 'secant law'.

        (Manchester, 1957)

7.31. A shallow parabolic arch of constant flexural rigidity EI, span L and rise h has its ends tied by a rod of the same material and of constant section α. One end of this tied arch is pinned to a rigid support and the other end rests on rollers. Show that a load P applied vertically at the crown causes a movement of the rollers of approximately $\dfrac{25PLh^2}{E(128ah^2 + 240I)}$

        (Leeds, 1952)

7.32. ACB is a two-hinged steel parabolic arch with secant variation of flexural rigidity.

    (a) Show that $H = \dfrac{5L}{8h}(n - 2n^3 + n^4)$ tons.

    (b) Find the amounts by which the quarter-points rise due to a temperature increase of $50°F$ if $L = 100$ ft., $h = 30$ ft. and $\alpha_t = 7 \times 10^{-6}$ per $°F$.

        (Oxford, 1948)

(c) Calculate the bending moment at the crown if the supports yield horizontally by 0·05 in. per ton of horizontal reaction. $L = 80$ ft., $h = 12$ ft., and I_{crown}

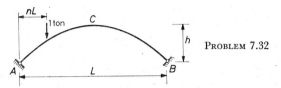

PROBLEM 7.32

$= 0·75$ ft.[4]; there is a uniformly distributed load of 1 ton ft. over the whole span and a concentrated load of 8 tons at the crown.

(London, 1957)

7.6. THE ARCH WITH FIXED ENDS

7.6.1. THE ELASTIC CENTRE METHOD

The elastic centre method described in Volume I, Section 7.4.1, using either the cantilever primary structure or an auxiliary primary structure, is generally the best for the analysis of the fixed arch, although the arithmetic involved is often tedious. It can be used either for arches whose shape is such that the integrals of equations [7.14] to [7.18] can be evaluated algebraically or for arches of irregular shape or cross-section when arithmetical integration is called for: this procedure is illustrated in *Problem 7.33* below. It is to be remembered that fixed-ended portals or beams of any shape can be treated as fixed-ended arches and this is often the best approach for structures having non-uniform members.

The column analogy can, if desired, be used for all the problems quoted.

Problem 7.33—The centre line of an arch with fixed ends A and B is defined by the coordinates given in TABLE 7.33(a). The points 1, 2 etc., are the mid-points of 16

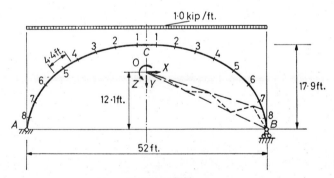

PROBLEM 7.33

segments, each of length 4·4 ft., into which the arch is divided. It is required to find the fixed end moments and the horizontal component of thrust caused by a vertical load of 1 kip per horizontal foot uniformly distributed over the whole arch.[†] The second moment of area is constant and equal to 4·4 ft.[4]

---

† See FOWLER, K. T. 'Slope deflexion equations for curved members.' *Proc. Amer. Soc. Civil Engrs*, Vol. 76, Separate No. 6, March 1950.

TABLE 7.33(a)

COORDINATES OF ARCH (origin A or B) (ft.)

Point	x	y	Point	x	y
1	23·8	17·8	5	7·4	12·6
2	19·5	17·2	6	4·1	9·8
3	15·3	16·3	7	1·6	6·3
4	11·2	14·7	8	0·3	2·1

$\sum y = 96\cdot8$ for the half-arch.

The centroid of elastic weights, or elastic centre, lies on the vertical axis of symmetry; its vertical distance from the line AB is given by

$$\frac{\int_A^B yds/EI}{\int_A^B ds/EI} = \frac{\sum y}{16} = \frac{2 \times 96\cdot8}{16} = 12\cdot1 \text{ ft.} \qquad \dots \text{(i)}$$

since $\qquad ds/I$ for each segment $= 4\cdot4/4\cdot4 = 1\cdot0$ ft.$^{-3}$

The origin is now transferred to O, in TABLE 7.33(b), and the summations [7.15] to [7.18] carried out using the simply supported beam AB as the primary structure.

TABLE 7.33(b)

CALCULATION OF INTEGRALS (origin O)

Point	x	y	x^2	y^2	M_0	$M_0 y$
1	2·2	5·7	4·9	32·5	− 335·6	− 1912·9
2	6·5	5·1	42·2	26·0	− 316·9	− 1616·2
3	10·7	4·2	114·5	17·6	− 280·8	− 1179·4
4	14·8	2·6	219·0	6·8	− 228·5	− 594·1
5	18·6	0·5	346·0	0·3	− 165·0	− 82·5
6	21·9	− 2·3	479·6	5·3	− 98·2	+ 225·9
7	24·4	− 5·8	595·4	33·6	− 40·3	+ 233·7
8	25·7	− 10·0	660·5	100·0	− 7·7	+ 77·0
$\sum$ for half arch			2462·1	222·1	− 1473·0	− 4848·5
$\sum$ for whole arch			4924·2	444·2	− 2946·0	− 9697·0

Thus, putting $E = 1$ (since it will cancel later)

in [7·15] $\qquad W = \int \frac{M_0 ds}{EI} = \sum M_0 = -2946 \qquad \dots \text{(ii)}$

in [7.16] $\qquad Wy_G = \mu_x = \int \frac{M_0 y ds}{EI} = \sum M_0 y = -9697 \qquad \dots \text{(iii)}$

and $\qquad Wx_G = \mu_y = \int \frac{M_0 x ds}{EI} = \sum M_0 x = 0 \qquad \dots \text{(iv)}$

198

in [7.17] $$I_y = \int \frac{x^2 ds}{EI} = \sum x^2 = 4924\cdot2$$ .... (v)

and $$I_x = \int \frac{y^2 ds}{EI} = \sum y^2 = 444\cdot2$$ .... (vi)

and $$I_{xy} = \int \frac{xy ds}{EI} = \sum xy = 0$$ .... (vii)

and in [7.18] $$A = \int \frac{ds}{EI} = \sum ds = 16$$ .... (viii)

These results are now inserted in equations [7.19(a)]

$$\left.\begin{array}{l} X = \dfrac{\mu_x}{I_x} = -\dfrac{9697}{444\cdot2} = -21\cdot83 \text{ kips} \\[2mm] Y = \dfrac{\mu_y}{I_y} = 0; \quad Z = \dfrac{W}{A} = -\dfrac{2946}{16} = -184\cdot12 \text{ kip. ft.} \end{array}\right\} \quad .... \text{ (ix)}$$

The bending moment M at any point is now given by equation [7.12],

$$M = M_0 - Z - Xy - Yx \quad .... [7.12]$$

Thus at A $$M_A = 0 + 184\cdot12 - (21\cdot83)(12\cdot1)$$
$$= -80\cdot02 \text{ kip. ft.}$$
$$= M_B$$

The horizontal component of thrust is everywhere $21\cdot83$ kips.

Problems for Solution

7.34. A symmetrical fixed ended steel frame bridge is illustrated. Calculate the values of the reactions at the left-hand abutment A when the concentrated load

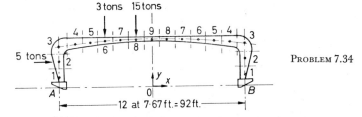

PROBLEM 7.34

Section	x ft.	y ft.	Cross-sectional area of section ft.^{2}	Second moment of area of section ft.^{4}
1	46·0	5·1	0·44	0·51
2	46·0	12·8	0·63	2·20
3	46·0	20·5	0·68	3·74
4	38·35	21·7	0·63	2·35
5	30·68	22·3	0·59	1·27
6	23·01	22·8	0·44	0·49
7	15·34	23·2	0·41	0·25
8	7·67	23·4	0·40	0·17
9	0	23·5	0·40	0·16

system shown is applied. The properties of each of a number of sections of the frame are given in the table. For the purpose of the calculation the equivalent length of each section may be taken as 7·7 ft.

(Birmingham, 1957)

7.35. Find the moments at A and D due to the loads P in the fixed-end beam of variable flexural rigidity shown in the figure.

(Melbourne, 1957)

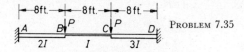

PROBLEM 7.35

7.36. Solve *Problem 6.35* by the arch method.

7.37. A fixed-ended semi-circular arch of constant section carries a vertical point load P at 30° from the centre as shown in the figure. Using the principle of superposition show that the horizontal thrust at the abuments is

$$\frac{24\sqrt{3} - 11\pi}{12(\pi^2 - 8)} P$$

(St. Andrews, 1953)

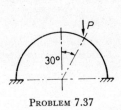

PROBLEM 7.37

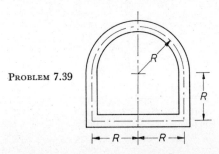

PROBLEM 7.38

7.38. Find the bending moment at the crown of the segmental fixed ended arch of constant section shown in the figure.

7.39. The culvert shown in the diagram is to be constructed of monolithic reinforced concrete of uniform cross-section in porous waterlogged ground and is to be designed

PROBLEM 7.39

to withstand full hydrostatic pressure wH. Obtain the bending moment diagram neglecting axial distortion and the weight of the structure and assuming the hydrostatic pressure to be uniform.

(After Melbourne, 1950)

7.40. The uniform fixed-ended arch shown in the diagram is of unit thickness perpendicular to the paper and of depth t radially. It is subjected to a radial inward

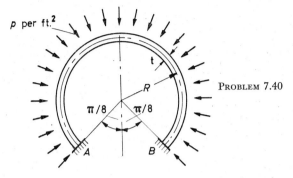

p per ft.^{2}

t

R

$\pi/8$ $\pi/8$

A B

PROBLEM 7.40

pressure of p lb. per sq. ft. Show that if axial shortening is neglected the fixing moments at A and B are zero, and find their value if arch shortening is included.

7.41. The arch shown in the diagram is rigidly attached to its foundations at A

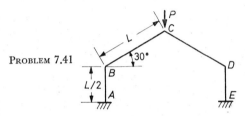

PROBLEM 7.41

P
C
L
$30°$
D
B
$L/2$
A
E

and E. Find the bending moment thrust and shear in BC at B. The flexural rigidity is constant and the effect of rib-shortening may be neglected.

(Melbourne, 1947)

7.42. The rigidly jointed frame shown in the diagram is fixed at A and F; the relative values of the flexural rigidities of the members are indicated in circles.

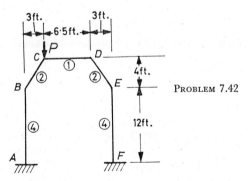

3ft.   3ft.
6·5ft.
P
C D
①
②   ② E 4ft.
B
④   ④   12ft.
A F

PROBLEM 7.42

A vertical load P acts at C. Find, by the elastic centre method:

(a) the bending moments at A, B and C;

(b) the horizontal displacement at B and the vertical component of the displacement at C.

(Melbourne)

7.43. Determine the bending moment at E in the stepped structure shown in the diagram under the loads indicated. The members are uniform, identical and rigidly attached to one another. (Melbourne)

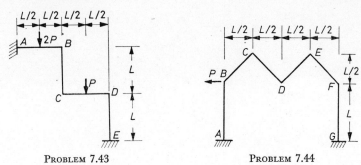

PROBLEM 7.43   PROBLEM 7.44

7.44. The second moments of area of the vertical members are $\sqrt{2}$ times those of the sloping members of the rigid portal frame shown in the diagram. Find the bending moments at B, D and F under the load P.

(Birmingham, 1947)

7.45. A symmetrical parabolic arched rib AB with fixed ends, span L and rise h has secant variation of flexural rigidity. Obtain expressions for the influence lines for H, V_A and M_A in terms of L, h and α, the horizontal distance of the moving unit load from A.

7.46. A symmetrical fixed-ended parabolic steel arch, having secant variation of flexural rigidity, has a span of 60 ft. and a rise of 18 ft. The value of the flexural rigidity at the crown is 50,000 ton. ft.^{2} Calculate the change in the thrust and the bending moment at the crown when the temperature rises through 40°F.

(Leeds, 1957)

7.47. Determine at what horizontal distance from the centre of a symmetrical parabolic arched rib, with secant variation of flexural rigidity, a concentrated vertical load produces zero bending moment at one support.

(Leeds, 1957)

7.6.2. THE EFFECTS OF RELATIVE MOVEMENTS OF THE ARCH ENDS

A useful application of the column analogy which was not discussed in Volume I is in the determination of the forces and moments induced in an arched structure when it is subjected to rotations or displacements at one end. The following problem illustrates the procedure:

Problem 7.48—The end A of the portal frame illustrated at (a) is given (1) an anti-clockwise rotation of θ, and (2) a downward displacement without rotation. Find the bending moments induced in the frame at A and D in each case.

(1) The primary structure can be taken as in (b), and we may assume that the rotation θ occurs over a very short length of the member AB just above A.

In illustrations of the use of the column analogy, in Volume I, Section 7.5, the primary structure was subjected to loads which produced bending moments M_0, and the load which was applied to the analogous column over any length ds was equal to $\dfrac{M_0 ds}{EI}$. This quantity actually denotes the angular rotation over the length

202

ds, so that we were in fact loading the column with the change of angle over each elementary length.

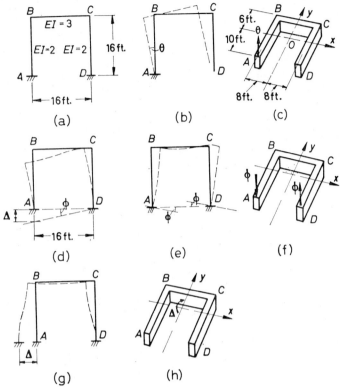

PROBLEM 7.48. (a) Portal frame with fixed feet (see Volume I, Figure 7.25). (b) The effect of a rotation θ at A. (c) Analogous column under load θ at A. (d) The effect of a subsidence Δ at A. (e) The subsidence is seen to be equivalent to rotations ϕ at A and D. (f) Analogous column under loads ϕ at A and D. (g) Lateral displacement Δ at A. (h) Analogous column under couple Δ.

We can now see that in the present problem the load on the analogous column is simply a load θ applied at A. Since the rotation produces tension on the inner face of the column the analogous load is upwards, following the sign convention we have already adopted.

The values of I_x, I_y and A for this frame were worked out in Volume I, Section 7.4.3 and are

$$I_x = 1792/3, \quad I_y = 10{,}240/9, \quad A = 64/3.$$

Then the compressive stress at the end A

$$= -\frac{\theta}{A} - \frac{10\theta \times 10}{I_x} - \frac{10\theta \times 8}{I_y}$$

$$= -\theta\left[\frac{3}{64} + \frac{300}{1792} + \frac{720}{10240}\right] = -0{\cdot}285\theta$$

At D the compressive stress is

$$-\frac{\theta}{A} - \frac{10\theta \times 10}{I_x} + \frac{10\theta \times 8}{I_y} = -0{\cdot}144\theta.$$

The bending moments at A and D are therefore

$$M_A = 0 - (-0.285\theta) = 0.285\theta.$$

$$M_D = 0 - (-0.144\theta) = 0.144\theta.$$

We have here determined two basic properties of this frame, namely its overall stiffness when a moment is applied to the end A, and the carry-over factor from A to D. In this example the stiffness at A is $\dfrac{M}{\theta} = 0.285$; the carry-over factor is

$$\frac{M_D}{M_A} = 0.505. \qquad \text{(Negative in the moment-distribution sign convention)}$$

(2.) The effect of a vertical displacement Δ of A without rotation is shown in (d). A little thought will indicate that the distortion of the frame is identical with that set up if bases A and D are each rotated clockwise through an angle ϕ, where $\phi = \dfrac{\Delta}{16}$ (see diagram (e)).

From the reasoning developed earlier in this solution we can see that the loads on the analogous column are as shown in (f). These two loads form a couple of magnitude $\dfrac{\Delta}{16} \times 16 = \Delta$ about the y-axis.

In this case the compressive stress at A is

$$+\frac{8\Delta}{I_y} = +\frac{72\Delta}{10,240} = +0.00703\Delta,$$

and the moment at A is therefore -0.00703Δ.

The moment at D is $+0.00703\Delta$.

Finally it may be remarked that if we wished to determine the effect of a *horizontal* displacement Δ of A towards the left (diagram (g)) we should have to apply to the analogous column a couple Δ about the x-axis, acting in the direction shown in diagram (h).

The reader will now find it instructive to carry out the above calculations by the elastic centre method and to compare his figures with those just given.

Problems for Solution

7.49. Determine the moments at A and B in the beam shown if the end A is (a) rotated anticlockwise through unit angle, (b) displaced vertically upwards, without rotation, by unit distance.

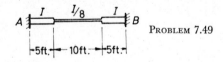

PROBLEM 7.49

7.50. Solve *Problem 6.35* using the column analogy method.

7.51. The symmetrical fixed-ended parabolic arch shown has secant variation of second moment of area; I_c is the value at the crown. The arch is subjected to a rise in temperature $t°$

(a) over the whole arch;

(b) over the right-hand half of the arch.

Determine the bending moments at A, B and C in each case, if α_t is the coefficient of linear expansion of the material of the arch.

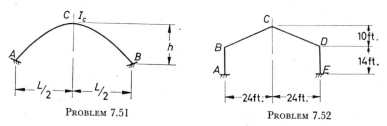

PROBLEM 7.51   PROBLEM 7.52

7.52. The steel gabled frame shown has I-section members of uniform second moment of area equal to 300 in.[4] and section modulus 40 in.[3] After construction is complete, prolonged rain causes a softening of the fixed base at E, and a clockwise rotation of $0\cdot2°$ and a horizontal spread of $0\cdot25$ in. are observed. Calculate the maximum changes of bending stress in the frame caused by the rotation and the spread.

7.7. INTERCONNECTED ARCHES

Volume I, Section 7.6 was devoted to an account of Fowler's[†] modified slope deflexion procedure for dealing with frames having curved members. *Problem 7.53* below is a numerical example based on one of those in Fowler's paper.

Problem 7.53—It is required to analyse the viaduct shown in the diagram at (a);

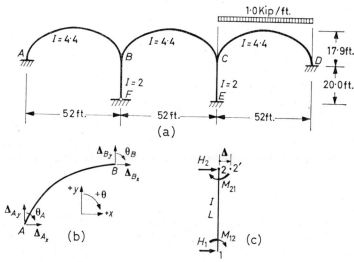

PROBLEM 7.53. (a) Interconnected arch for analysis. (b) Sign convention for displacements and forces. (c) Vertical member under positive forces and moments.

the arches are identical with that of *Problem 7.33* where the elastic constants for the arch were worked out. These are:

$$I_x = 444\cdot2; \qquad I_y = 4924\cdot2; \qquad I_{xy} = 0; \; A = 16.$$

[†] *loc. cit.* p. 197.

The fixed end moments and forces for the end C of the arch CD are also required in the present problem: these were found to be:

$$M_{FCD} = + 80\cdot02 \qquad\qquad M_{FDC} = - 80\cdot02$$

$$V_{FC} = + 26\cdot0 \qquad\qquad V_{FD} = + 26\cdot0$$

$$H_{FC} = + 21\cdot83 \qquad\qquad H_{FD} = - 21\cdot83$$

The procedure is first to find the forces acting at the elastic centre of a curved member produced by relative movements of the ends. The nomenclature and sign convention is shown at (b) and this must be strictly observed; it is particularly to be noticed that the forces and moments, *including X, Y* and *Z*, are all positive when acting in the directions shown. We then have

$$
\left.
\begin{aligned}
X &= \frac{(\varDelta_{2x} - \varDelta_{1x} - y_2\theta_2 + y_1\theta_1)I_y + (\varDelta_{2y} - \varDelta_{1y} + x_2\theta_2 - x_1\theta_1)I_{xy}}{I_xI_y - I_{xy}^2} \\
Y &= \frac{(\varDelta_{2x} - \varDelta_{1x} - y_2\theta_2 + y_1\theta_1)I_{xy} + (\varDelta_{2y} - \varDelta_{1y} + x_2\theta_2 - x_1\theta_1)I_x}{I_xI_y - I_{xy}^2} \\
Z &= \frac{\theta_2 - \theta_1}{A}
\end{aligned}
\right\} \quad \cdots \text{[7.28]}
$$

The corresponding equations at the joints are:

at end 1
$$
\left.
\begin{aligned}
M_{12} &= M_{F12} - Z - Yx_1 + Xy_1 \\
V_{12} &= V_{F12} - Y \\
H_{12} &= H_{F12} - X
\end{aligned}
\right.
$$

and at end 2
$$
\left.
\begin{aligned}
M_{21} &= M_{F21} + Z + Yx_2 - Xy_2 \\
V_{21} &= V_{F21} + Y \\
H_{21} &= H_{F21} + X
\end{aligned}
\right\} \quad \cdots \text{[7.29]}
$$

These correspond to the member equations [6.5] of the slope deflexion equations for straight members and they are similarly combined to give the equilibrium equations for the various joints that are free to rotate or translate. These equations are solved to obtain the various joint movements from which the end forces and moments are eventually found by substitution in equations [7.28] and [7.29]. Thus in arch AB:

$$\varDelta_{A_x} = \varDelta_{A_y} = \varDelta_{B_y}\dagger = \theta_A = 0; \qquad \varDelta_{B_x} \text{ and } \theta_B \text{ are unknown.}$$

Substituting in [7.28]

$$X = \frac{\varDelta_{B_x} - (-12\cdot1)\theta_B}{I_x} = 0\cdot00225\,\varDelta_{B_x} + 0\cdot02723\theta_B$$

$$Y = +\frac{26\theta_B}{I_y} = 0\cdot00528\theta_B$$

$$Z = \frac{\theta_B}{A} = 0\cdot06250\theta_B$$

---

† Assuming no compression of the column BF.

Substituting in [7·29]

$$M_{AB} = -Z - Y(-26) + X(-12\cdot1) = -0\cdot2547\theta_B - 0\cdot02723\Delta_{B_x} \quad \ldots \text{(i(a))}$$

$$M_{BA} = Z + Y(26) - X(-12\cdot1) = 0\cdot52926\theta_B + 0\cdot02723\Delta_{B_x} \quad \ldots \text{(i(b))}$$

$$V_{AB} = -Y = -0\cdot005528\theta_B = -V_{BA} \quad \ldots \text{(i(c))}$$

$$= -V_{BA} \quad \ldots \text{(i(d))}$$

$$H_{AB} = -X = -0\cdot00225\Delta_{B_x} - 0\cdot02723\theta_B \quad \ldots \text{(i(e))}$$

$$= -H_{BA} \quad \ldots \text{(i(f))}$$

in arch BC:

$$\Delta_{B_y} = \Delta_{C_y} = 0; \Delta_{B_x}, \quad \Delta_{C_x}, \theta_B \text{ and } \theta_C \text{ are unknown}$$

Substituting in [7.28]

$$X = \frac{\Delta_{C_x} - \Delta_{B_x} - (-12\cdot1)\theta_C + (-12\cdot1)\theta_B}{I_x}$$

$$= 0\cdot00225\Delta_{C_x} - 0\cdot00225\Delta_{B_x} + 0\cdot02723\theta_C - 0\cdot02723\theta_B$$

$$Y = \frac{26\theta_C - (-26)\theta_B}{I_y} = 0\cdot005528\theta_C + 0\cdot005528\theta_B$$

$$Z = \frac{\theta_C - \theta_B}{A} = 0\cdot0625\theta_C - 0\cdot0625\theta_B$$

Substituting in [7.29]

$$M_{BC} = 0\cdot52926\theta_B - 0\cdot2547\theta_C + 0\cdot02723\Delta_{B_x} - 0\cdot02723\Delta_{C_x} \quad \ldots \text{(ii(a))}$$

$$M_{CB} = 0\cdot52926\theta_C - 0\cdot2547\theta_B + 0\cdot02723\Delta_{C_x} - 0\cdot02723\Delta_{B_x} \quad \ldots \text{(ii(b))}$$

$$V_{BC} = -0\cdot005528\theta_B - 0\cdot005528\theta_C \quad \ldots \text{(ii(c))}$$

$$= -V_{CB} \quad \ldots \text{(ii(d))}$$

$$H_{BC} = -0\cdot00225\Delta_{C_x} + 0\cdot00225\Delta_{B_x} - 0\cdot02723\theta_C + 0\cdot02723\theta_B \quad \ldots \text{(ii(e))}$$

$$= -H_{CB} \quad \ldots \text{(ii(f))}$$

in arch CD:

$$\Delta_{C_y} = \Delta_{D_x} = \Delta_{D_y} = \theta_D = 0; \quad \Delta_{C_x}, \Delta_{C_y} \text{ and } \theta_C \text{ are unknown.}$$

$$X = -0\cdot00225\Delta_{C_x} - 0\cdot02723\theta_C$$

$$Y = 0\cdot005528\theta_C$$

$$Z = -0\cdot0625\theta_C$$

Substituting in [7.29]

$$M_{CD} = 80\cdot02 + 0\cdot52926\theta_C + 0\cdot02723\Delta_{C_x} \quad \ldots \text{(iii(a))}$$

$$M_{DC} = -80\cdot02 - 0\cdot2547\theta_C - 0\cdot02723\Delta_{C_x} \quad \ldots \text{(iii(b))}$$

$$V_{CD} = 26\cdot0 - 0\cdot005528\theta_C \quad \ldots \text{(iii(c))}$$

$$V_{DC} = 26\cdot0 + 0\cdot005528\theta_C \quad \ldots \text{(iii(d))}$$

$$H_{CD} = 21\cdot83 + 0\cdot00225\Delta_{C_x} + 0\cdot02723\theta_C \quad \ldots \text{(iii(e))}$$

$$= -H_{DC} \quad \ldots \text{(iii(f))}$$

The ordinary slope deflexion equations [6.5] hold for the straight members: thus in diagram (c)

$$M_{12} = 2E\frac{I}{L}\left(2\theta_1 + \theta_2 - \frac{3\varDelta}{L}\right)\Bigg|$$

$$M_{21} = 2E\frac{I}{L}\left(\theta_1 + 2\theta_2 - \frac{3\varDelta}{L}\right)\Bigg|$$

also
$$H_1 = \frac{M_{21} + M_{12}}{L}\Bigg|$$

and
$$H_2 = -\frac{M_{21} + M_{12}}{L}\Bigg|$$

If end 1 is pinned, we have

$$\theta_1 = -0\cdot5\theta_2 + 1\cdot5\frac{\varDelta}{L}$$

i.e.
$$M_{21} = 2E\frac{I}{L}\left(1\cdot5\theta_2 - 1\cdot5\frac{\varDelta}{L}\right)$$

In column BF:

$I = 2; L = 20$. θ_F has been eliminated and θ_B and $\varDelta_{B_x}$ are unknown.

$$M_{BF} = 2\frac{2}{20}\left(1\cdot5\theta_B - 1\cdot5\frac{\varDelta_{B_x}}{20}\right) = 0\cdot3\theta_B - 0\cdot015\varDelta_{B_x} \qquad \ldots\ \text{(iv(a))}$$

$$H_{BF} = -0\cdot015\theta_B + 0\cdot00075\varDelta_{B_x} \qquad \ldots\ \text{(iv(e))}$$

$$= -H_{FB} \qquad \ldots\ \text{(iv(f))}$$

In column CE:

$I = 2; L = 20$. $\theta_E = 0$; θ_C and $\varDelta_{C_x}$ are unknown.

$$M_{EC} = 0\cdot2\theta_C - 0\cdot03\varDelta_{C_x} \qquad \ldots\ \text{(v(a))}$$

$$M_{CE} = 0\cdot4\theta_C - 0\cdot03\varDelta_{C_x} \qquad \ldots\ \text{(v(b))}$$

$$H_{CE} = -0\cdot03\theta_C + 0\cdot003\varDelta_{C_x} \qquad \ldots\ \text{(v(e))}$$

$$= -H_{EC} \qquad \ldots\ \text{(v(f))}$$

Equilibrium equations:

at B:

$$\sum M_B = 0, \text{ hence from (i(b)), (ii(a)) and (iv(a))}$$

$$0 = 1\cdot35852\theta_B + 0\cdot039464\varDelta_{B_x} - 0\cdot2547\theta_C + 0\cdot02723\varDelta_{C_x} \qquad \ldots\ \text{(vi)}$$

$$\sum H_B = 0, \text{ hence from (i(f)), (ii(e)) and (iv(e))}$$

$$0 = 0\cdot03926\theta_B + 0\cdot00525\varDelta_{B_x} - 0\cdot02723\theta_C - 0\cdot00225\varDelta_{C_x} \qquad \ldots\ \text{(vii)}$$

at C:

$$\sum M_C = 0, \text{ hence from (ii(b)), (iii(a)) and (v(b))}$$

$$-80\cdot02 = -0\cdot2547\theta_B - 0\cdot02723\varDelta_{B_x} + 1\cdot45852\theta_C + 0\cdot02446\varDelta_{C_x} \qquad \ldots\ \text{(viii)}$$

$$\sum H_C = 0, \text{ hence from (ii(f)), (iii(e)) and (v(e))}$$

$$-21\cdot83 = -0\cdot02723\theta_B - 0\cdot00225\varDelta_{B_x} + 0\cdot02446\theta_C + 0\cdot0075\varDelta_{C_x} \qquad \ldots\ \text{(iv)}$$

The solution to these equations is:

$$\theta_{B} = -33{\cdot}76; \qquad \Delta_{Bx} = -1331$$
$$\theta_{C} = -29{\cdot}67; \qquad \Delta_{Cx} = -3336$$

Finally, substituting in the member equations, we obtain:

in (i(a)) $M_{AB} = 8{\cdot}60 + 36{\cdot}24 = 44{\cdot}84$

in (i(b)) $M_{BA} = -54{\cdot}11$ $\left.\right\}$
in (ii(a)) $M_{BC} = +44{\cdot}29$ $\left.\right\}$ $\sum = +0{\cdot}01$
in (iv(a)) $M_{BF} = +9{\cdot}83$ $\left.\right\}$

in (ii(b)) $M_{CB} = -61{\cdot}70$ $\left.\right\}$
in (iii(a)) $M_{CD} = -26{\cdot}52$ $\left.\right\}$ $\sum = -0{\cdot}01$
in (v(b)) $M_{CE} = +88{\cdot}21$ $\left.\right\}$

in (iii(b)) $M_{DC} = +18{\cdot}38$

in (i(e)) $H_{AB} = +3{\cdot}91$

in (i(f)) $H_{BA} = -3{\cdot}91$ $\left.\right\}$
in (ii(e)) $H_{BC} = +4{\cdot}40$ $\left.\right\}$ $\sum = 0$
in (iv(e)) $H_{BF} = -0{\cdot}49$ $\left.\right\}$

in (ii(f)) $H_{CB} = +4{\cdot}40$ $\left.\right\}$
in (iii(e)) $H_{CD} = +13{\cdot}51$ $\left.\right\}$ $\sum = -0{\cdot}01$
in (v(e)) $H_{CE} = -9{\cdot}12$ $\left.\right\}$

in (i(c)) $V_{AB} = +0{\cdot}18$ $\left.\right\}$ shear in $AB = \dfrac{44{\cdot}84 - 54{\cdot}11}{25} = -0{\cdot}18$
in (i(d)) $V_{BA} = -0{\cdot}18$

in (ii(c)) $V_{BC} = +0{\cdot}34$ $\left.\right\}$ shear in $BC = \dfrac{44{\cdot}29 - 61{\cdot}70}{52} = -0{\cdot}33$
in (ii(d)) $V_{CB} = -0{\cdot}34$

in (iii(c)) $V_{CD} = 26{\cdot}00 + 0{\cdot}16 = +26{\cdot}16$ $\left.\right\}$ shear in $CD = \dfrac{-26{\cdot}52 + 18{\cdot}38}{52}$
in (iii(d)) $V_{DC} = 26{\cdot}00 - 0{\cdot}16 = +25{\cdot}84$
$$= 0{\cdot}16.$$

Problem for Solution

7.54. The symmetrical parabolic arches shown in the diagram have secant variation of flexural rigidity; the flexural rigidity of the column is equal to that at the crowns

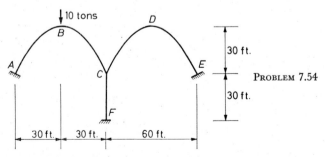

PROBLEM 7.54

of the arches. Find the bending moments caused by the point load of 10 tons acting at the crown D of arch CDE.

209

7.55. Determine the bending moments in the members of the two frames shown†.

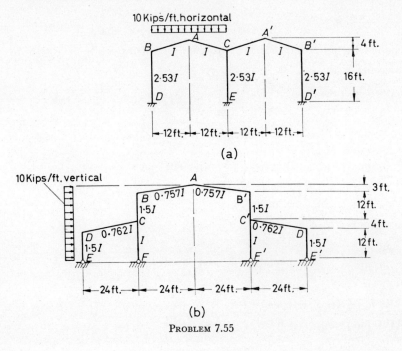

(a)

(b)

Problem 7.55

---

† See Francis, A. J., 'The Analysis of Single-storey, Multi-bay, Gabled Rigid Frames'. *The Structural Engineer*, July 1951, p. 189.

210

CHAPTER 8

STABILITY OF STRUTS AND FRAMEWORKS†

8.1 INTRODUCTION

IN Chapter 8 of Volume I the influence of stability and plastic effects on the behaviour of frameworks with rigid joints was described. The study of stability effects in a particular framework is most easily carried out by using the dimensionless functions s, c and m, which are tabulated in TABLE 8.1 in

TABLE 8.1

Tension				Compression			
F/P_E	s	c	m	F/P_E	s	c	m
0	+ 4·000	+ 0·500	+ 1·000	+ 0	+ 4·000	+ 0·500	+ 1·000
− 0·5	+ 4·619	+ 0·402	+ 0·724	+ 0·1	+ 3·867	+ 0·526	+ 1·091
− 1·0	+ 5·175	+ 0·338	+ 0·584	+ 0·2	+ 3·730	+ 0·550	+ 1·205
− 1·5	+ 5·681	+ 0·293	+ 0·498	+ 0·3	+ 3·589	+ 0·587	+ 1·351
− 2·0	+ 6·147	+ 0·260	+ 0·440	+ 0·4	+ 3·444	+ 0·624	+ 1·545
− 2·5	+ 6·581	+ 0·235	+ 0·397	+ 0·5	+ 3·294	+ 0·666	+ 1·817
− 3·0	+ 6·988	+ 0·214	+ 0·364	+ 0·6	+ 3·140	+ 0·714	+ 2·223
− 3·5	+ 7·372	+ 0·198	+ 0·338	+ 0·7	+ 2·981	+ 0·769	+ 2·900
− 4·0	+ 7·737	+ 0·185	+ 0·317	+ 0·8	+ 2·816	+ 0·833	+ 4·253
				+ 0·9	+ 2·645	+ 0·909	+ 8·307
				+ 1·0	+ 2·467	+ 1·000	∞
				+ 1·1	+ 2·283	+ 1·111	− 7·902
	Compression			+ 1·2	+ 2·090	+ 1·249	− 3·847
				+ 1·3	+ 1·889	+ 1·424	− 2·495
F/P_E	s	c		+ 1·4	+ 1·678	+ 1·656	− 1·818
				+ 1·5	+ 1·457	+ 1·973	− 1·411
+ 2·6	− 2·249	− 2·231		+ 1·6	+ 1·224	+ 2·435	
+ 2·7	− 2·809	− 1·928		+ 1·7	+ 0·978	+ 3·166	
+ 2·8	− 3·445	− 1·708		+ 1·8	+ 0·717	+ 4·497	
+ 2·9	− 4·176	− 1·543		+ 1·9	+ 0·439	+ 7·661	
+ 3·0	− 5·032	− 1·416		+ 2·0	+ 0·143	+ 26·684	
+ 3·1	− 6·052	− 1·316		+ 2·1	− 0·176	− 21·072	
+ 3·2	− 7·297	− 1·236		+ 2·2	− 0·519	− 7·511	
+ 3·3	− 8·863	− 1·173		+ 2·3	− 0·893	− 4·623	
+ 3·4	− 10·908	− 1·122		+ 2·4	− 1·301	− 3·370	
+ 3·5	− 13·719	− 1·082		+ 2·5	− 1·750	− 2·673	

This table is extracted from *Stability Functions for Structural Frameworks*, by courtesy of Manchester University Press.

an abridged form. *Problems 8.1 to 8.3* are intended to help the reader to become familiar with these functions. Stability functions are applicable only to structures which are behaving elastically and *Problems 8.4 to 8.6* show

† This chapter was contributed by Dr. N. W. Murray, Senior Stress Analyst, Simon-Carves, Erith, Kent.

how they can be used to analyse the elastic behaviour of frameworks with rigid joints. It will be seen that the deflexions increase indefinitely but that the applied loads cannot be increased beyond what is called the 'critical load, W_c'. *Problems 8.7 to 8.21* show exact and approximate methods of evaluating this load, again using the stability functions. If the framework is now assumed to be made of a perfectly plastic material (i.e. one in which no strain occurs until the stress reaches the yield stress after which the stress remains constant) its behaviour can be studied and superimposed on its elastic behaviour. *Problems 8.22 to 8.26* illustrate the effects of plasticity in typical structures. In Section 8.5 some examples are given of the conventional method used to calculate the moments and stresses arising from changes in axial length of the members; stability effects are ignored.

8.2. STABILITY FUNCTIONS

The stability functions s, c and m are defined by equations [8.4], [8.5] and [8.9]. The formulae which contain these functions and are most widely used are summarized below in FIGURE 8.1. In these equations moments

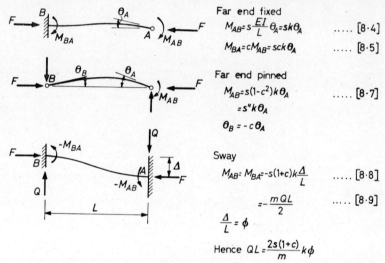

Far end fixed
$$M_{AB} = s\frac{EI}{L}\theta_A = sk\theta_A \qquad \ldots\ldots [8\cdot4]$$
$$M_{BA} = cM_{AB} = sck\theta_A \qquad \ldots\ldots [8\cdot5]$$

Far end pinned
$$M_{AB} = s(1-c^2)k\theta_A \qquad \ldots\ldots [8\cdot7]$$
$$= s''k\theta_A$$
$$\theta_B = -c\theta_A$$

Sway
$$M_{AB} = M_{BA} = -s(1+c)k\frac{\Delta}{L} \qquad \ldots\ldots [8\cdot8]$$
$$= -\frac{mQL}{2} \qquad \ldots\ldots [8\cdot9]$$
$$\frac{\Delta}{L} = \phi$$

Hence $QL = \frac{2s(1+c)}{m}k\phi$

FIGURE 8.1

acting on the ends of the members, rotations and pairs of reactive forces Q are positive when they act in a clockwise sense. Values of s, c and m are tabulated in TABLE 8.1 for values of F/P_E. Only elastic conditions are assumed to exist.

Problem 8.1—Consider the cantilever shown with a moment M_{AB} applied at the free end A. Sideways movement of A is prevented.

PROBLEM 8.1
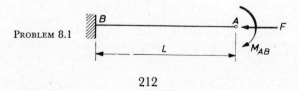

(a) Determine the axial load, in terms of E, I and L, at which the stiffness is halved. The stiffness is defined as

$$\frac{M_{AB}}{\theta_A} = sk = s\frac{EI}{L} \qquad \dots\dots [8.4]$$

When the axial load is zero, $s = 4$ (TABLE 8.1) so the stiffness is $4k$. To halve the stiffness s must be 2 and this occurs when

$$\frac{F}{P_E} \text{ is } 1\cdot24$$

i.e.
$$F = 1\cdot24\,P_E = 1\cdot24\,\frac{\pi^2 EI}{L^2} \text{ (compression)}$$

(b) In a similar way show that the stiffness will be half as much again when $F = 1\cdot83\dfrac{\pi^2 EI}{L^2}$ (tension).

Problem 8.2—Consider the built-in steel stanchion shown with a moment $M_{AB} = 1000$ lb. in. applied at the free end A. Determine the amount of rotation at A and the lateral force Q when $I = 5\cdot20$ in.^{4}, $L = 250$ in. and $F = 20,000$ lb. Sidesway is prevented at A.

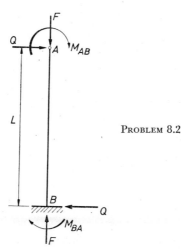

PROBLEM 8.2

$$P_E = \frac{\pi^2 EI}{L^2} = \frac{\pi^2 \times 30 \times 10^6 \times 5\cdot20}{250^2} = 24,700 \text{ lb.}$$

Hence
$$\frac{F}{P_E} = \frac{20,000}{24,700} = 0\cdot810$$

i.e.
$$s = 2\cdot799 \text{ and } c = 0\cdot840\dagger$$

Hence
$$\theta_A = \frac{M_{AB}}{sk} = \frac{1000 \times 250}{2\cdot799 \times 30 \times 10^6 \times 5\cdot20} = 5\cdot72 \times 10^{-4} \text{ radian}$$

$$M_{BA} = cM_{AB} = 0\cdot840 \times 1000 = 840 \text{ lb. in.}$$

† By interpolation in TABLE 8.1 or in the published Table of Stability Functions.

By taking moments about B, for equilibrium

$$QL + M_{AB} + M_{BA} = 0$$

i.e. $\quad Q = -\dfrac{M_{AB} + M_{BA}}{L} = -\dfrac{1840}{250}$ i.e. 7·36 lb. to the left.

It is seen that this load is quite small, indicating that sidesway can be prevented very easily.

Problem 8.3—In the steel stanchion shown (diagram (a)) a lateral force $Q = 50$ lb. and an anticlockwise moment $M_{AB} = 1000$ lb. in. are applied at A. Determine the lateral displacement and rotation of the stanchion at A when the axial load is 8000 lb. and locate the point of contraflexure (i.e. zero moment). $I = 2{\cdot}60$ in.^{4}, $L = 240$ in.

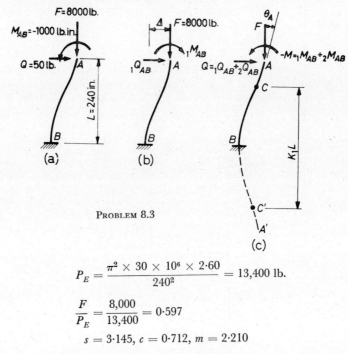

PROBLEM 8.3

$$P_E = \frac{\pi^2 \times 30 \times 10^6 \times 2{\cdot}60}{240^2} = 13{,}400 \text{ lb.}$$

$$\frac{F}{P_E} = \frac{8{,}000}{13{,}400} = 0{\cdot}597$$

$$s = 3{\cdot}145, \ c = 0{\cdot}712, \ m = 2{\cdot}210$$

The final shape of the stanchion can be reached in two stages. First let A move laterally through distance $\varDelta$ in. without rotating, as at (b).

Then $_1M_{AB} = -s(1 + c)\dfrac{k\varDelta}{L}$ .... [8.8]

$$= -3{\cdot}145 \times 1{\cdot}712 \times \frac{30 \times 10^6 \times 2{\cdot}60\varDelta}{240^2} = -7290\varDelta \text{ lb. in.}$$

$_1Q_{AB} = -\dfrac{2M_{AB}}{mL}$ .... [8.9]

$$= \frac{2 \times 7290\varDelta}{2{\cdot}210 \times 240} = 27{\cdot}5\varDelta \text{ lb.}$$

Now apply a clockwise moment at A, which rotates A through angle θ_A.

$$_2M_{AB} = sk\theta_A = 3{\cdot}145 \times \frac{30 \times 10^6 \times 2{\cdot}60}{240}\,\theta_A = 1{\cdot}02 \times 10^6\theta_A$$

$$_2Q_{AB} = -\frac{_2M_{AB}(1+c)}{L} = -\frac{1{\cdot}02 \times 10^6 \times 1{\cdot}712}{240}\,\theta_A = -0{\cdot}730 \times 10^4\theta_A$$

For equilibrium at A

$$1{\cdot}02 \times 10^6\theta_A - 7290\varDelta = -1000$$

$$-0{\cdot}730 \times 10^4\theta_A + 27{\cdot}5\varDelta = 50$$

Solving for θ_A and $\varDelta$

$$\theta_A = -0{\cdot}01339 \text{ radian}, \quad \varDelta = -1{\cdot}736 \text{ in.}$$

i.e. A moves to the left and rotates anticlockwise.

When an axial force is applied to the stanchion a point of contraflexure occurs at some point C in its length. The mirror image of the stanchion is drawn at (c). The part CC' behaves as a pin-ended strut at the point of collapse. Its length is $k_1 L$ and its axial load is the applied load $F = 8000$ lb.

Then
$$F = \frac{\pi^2 EI}{(k_1 L)^2} = \frac{P_E}{(k_1)^2}$$

i.e.
$$k_1 = \sqrt{\frac{1}{\dfrac{F}{P_E}}} = \sqrt{\frac{1}{0{\cdot}597}} = 1{\cdot}294$$

i.e. the point of contraflexure C is 155 in. from B.

If the axial load is increased, C moves towards B.

Problem 8.4—The two storey portal frame shown is subjected to vertical loads of 3000 lb. at C and D and sway loads of 50 lb. at C and B. EI is 120×10^6 lb. in.²

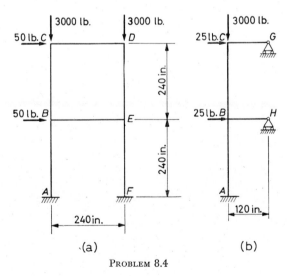

PROBLEM 8.4

for all members. Determine the deflexions and joint rotations at C and B. Assume $s = 4$, $c = \frac{1}{2}$ for the beams.

215

Because of antisymmetry it is only necessary to treat one half of the frame. Points of contraflexure (i.e. no moment) occur at the centres of the beams. The equivalent structure is shown in diagram (b).

For the stanchions

$$\frac{F}{P_E} = \frac{3000 \times 240^2}{\pi^2 \times 120 \times 10^6} = 0.146$$

From stability tables

$s = 3.805 \qquad sc = 2.051$

$c = 0.539 \qquad s(1 + c) = 5.856$ [see equation 8.8, Volume I, p. 391]

$m = 1.140 \qquad \dfrac{2s(1 + c)}{m} = 10.27$ [see equations 8.8 and 8.9, Volume I, p. 391]

$k = \dfrac{EI}{L} = 0.5 \times 10^6$ lb. in.

The values of s and c for the substitute beams CG and BH of diagram (b) are obtained as in Section 8.2.2 of Volume I. As there is no axial load and G and H are pinned

$$\frac{F}{P_E} = 0; \quad s = 4\left\{1 - \left(\frac{1}{2}\right)^2\right\} = 3; \quad c = 0.$$

As the length has been halved

$$(EI/L)_{\text{beam}} = 2k = 10^6 \text{ lb. in.}$$

The effects of independent rotation and sway at B and C can now be written down as in TABLE 8.4.

Here $\quad \phi_C = \dfrac{\varDelta_C}{L} = \dfrac{\text{sway of } C \text{ relative to } B}{\text{storey height}} = \dfrac{\varDelta_C}{240}$. Similarly for ϕ_B.

The conditions of equilibrium required to solve the four unknowns can be written down.

For rotational equilibrium of C
$$2.051\theta_B + 9.805\theta_C - 5.856\phi_C = 0 \qquad \dots (i)$$

For rotational equilibrium of B
$$13.610\theta_B + 2.051\theta_C - 5.856\phi_B - 5.856\phi_C = 0 \qquad \dots (ii)$$

For sway equilibrium of the top storey
$$-5.856\theta_B - 5.856\theta_C + 10.27\phi_C = \frac{25 \times 240}{0.5 \times 10^6} = 0.0120 \qquad \dots (iii)$$

For sway equilibrium of the bottom storey
$$-5.856\theta_B + 10.27\phi_B = \frac{50 \times 240}{0.5 \times 10^6} = 0.0240 \qquad \dots (iv)$$

The solution of these equations is
$$\theta_B = 0.00328$$
$$\theta_C = 0.00171$$
$$\phi_B = 0.00421$$
$$\phi_C = 0.00401$$

TABLE 8.4

ANALYSIS OF SUBSTITUTE FRAME SHOWN AT (b)

Operation	M_{AB}	M_{BA}	M_{BC}	M_{BH}	M_{CB}	M_{CG}	QL top storey	QL bottom storey
Rotate C through θ_C			$2\cdot051k\theta_C$		$3\cdot805k\theta_C$	$6k\theta_C$	$-5\cdot856k\theta_C$	
Rotate B through θ_B	$2\cdot051k\theta_B$	$3\cdot805k\theta_B$	$3\cdot805k\theta_B$	$6k\theta_B$	$2\cdot051k\theta_B$		$-5\cdot856k\theta_B$	$-5\cdot856k\theta_B$
Sway C through ϕ_C			$-5\cdot856k\phi_C$		$-5\cdot856k\phi_C$		$+10\cdot27k\phi_C$	
Sway top and bottom storeys through ϕ_B	$-5\cdot856k\theta_B$	$-5\cdot856k\phi_B$						$+10\cdot27k\phi_B$

Therefore

$$\text{Rotation of } B = 0 \cdot 00328 \text{ radian}$$

$$\text{Rotation of } C = 0 \cdot 00171 \text{ radian}$$

$$\text{Displacement of } B = 0 \cdot 00421 \times 240 = 1 \cdot 01 \text{ in.}$$

$$\text{Displacement of } C = 1 \cdot 01 + 0 \cdot 00401 \times 240 = 1 \cdot 97 \text{ in.}$$

It is obviously now a simple matter to obtain the values of the end moments, if required, by substitution in TABLE 8.4. The above procedure is clearly a modified version of the slope-deflexion and moment distribution methods.

Problems for Solution

Problem 8.5—The stiffness of a strut is defined as the ratio of disturbing force to deflexion at the point of its application, or disturbing moment to rotation at the point of application. Determine the stiffness of the steel struts shown for the disturbing forces and moments indicated by arrows. For all struts $I = 4 \cdot 00$ in.⁴, $L = 200$ in. and $F = 20,000$ lb. Also give the corresponding values when $F = 0$. Comment upon the results.

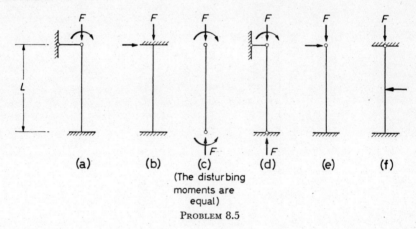

(a)   (b)   (c)   (d)   (e)   (f)

(The disturbing moments are equal)

PROBLEM 8.5

Problem 8.6—The simple portal frame illustrated is subjected to vertical loads at B and C of 3000 lb. each. A sway load of 100 lb. is applied at B. Determine the

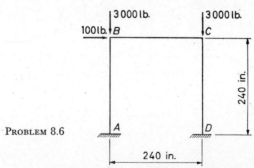

PROBLEM 8.6

displacement and rotation of B. EI is a constant ($= 39 \cdot 6 \times 10^6$ lb. in.²) for all members. Assume $s = 4$ and $c = \frac{1}{2}$ for the beam.

218

8.3. CRITICAL LOADS

The critical load is the load at which the stiffness is zero. Small disturbing forces or moments are applied to the structure to enable stiffness expressions to be obtained. It is not always possible to obtain exact expressions for stiffness especially if the structure contains many members. Approximate methods are used in such structures. It is quite often possible to say that the critical load of a structure lies between two values. This is very helpful when using trial and error methods and it also gives the reader a picture of the behaviour and buckling mode of the structure.

Problem 8.7—A stanchion AB consists of a 6 in. $\times$ 5 in. R.S.J. 25 ft. long. Its lower end B is fixed. Its upper end A is fixed in space but may be considered pinned if bending takes place about the major axis XX of the section. If bending takes place about its minor axis YY, end A is restrained by beams which exert a couple of $1{\cdot}6 \times 10^6$ lb. in. per radian. Determine the lowest critical load of the stanchion. $I_{XX} = 43{\cdot}69$ in.^{4}, $I_{YY} = 9{\cdot}10$ in.^{4}

About XX

$$P_E = \frac{\pi^2 \times 30 \times 10^6 \times 43{\cdot}69}{300 \times 300} = 144,000 \text{ lb.}$$

If bending takes place about XX a disturbing moment M_A will rotate joint A through angle θ_A. From equation [8.4] the stiffness of joint A is

$$\frac{M_A}{\theta_A} = sk$$

i.e. the stiffness is zero when $s = 0$. From TABLE 8.1 $s = 0$ when $\dfrac{F}{P_E}$ is $2{\cdot}046$. Thus the critical load for bending about XX is

$$2{\cdot}046 \times 144,000 \text{ lb.} = 294,600 \text{ lb.}$$

About YY

$$P_E = 30,000 \text{ lb.}$$

$$k = 910,000 \text{ lb. in.}$$

$$\text{Stiffness} = \frac{M}{\theta} = 1,600,000 + 910,000s$$

At the critical load the stiffness is zero

$$\text{i.e.} \quad s = -\frac{1,600,000}{910,000} = -1{\cdot}76$$

From stability tables this occurs when $\dfrac{F}{P_E} = 2{\cdot}50$ approximately

$$\text{i.e.} \quad F = 2{\cdot}50 \times 30,000 = 75,000 \text{ lb.}$$

This is less than the critical load for bending about XX so collapse will occur about YY.

Problem 8.8—(a) The strut illustrated has two springs which offer angular restraints $K_A\theta_A$ and $K_B\theta_B$ to ends A and B respectively. Show that the critical load of the strut

219

occurs when

$$sk(1 - c^2) + K_A + K_B + \frac{K_A K_B}{sk} = 0$$

(b) Use this result to obtain the critical load for a steel column 25 ft. long having $I = 9\cdot10$ in⁴. $K_A = K_B = 1\cdot6 \times 10^6$ lb. in./radian.

(c) Obtain the critical load for the same column if B is fixed (i.e. $K_B = \infty$).

(d) Show that if $K_A = K_B = 0$, the critical load is P_E.

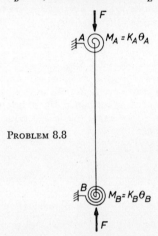

PROBLEM 8.8

(a) As the strut starts to buckle, A and B will rotate through angles which are different. Therefore, we apply unequal disturbing moments M_A and $- M_B$ to rotate A through θ_A and B through $- \theta_B$. The moments acting on the strut are then found by a moment distribution process set out in TABLE 8.8.

TABLE 8.8

Operation	B	A
A rotated through θ_A, B held	$sck\theta_A$	$sk\theta_A$
B rotated through $- \theta_B$, A held	$- sk\theta_B$	$- sck\theta_B$

$$\text{Total moment at end } A = sk\theta_A - sck\theta_B + K_A\theta_A = M_A \quad \dots\text{(i)}$$

and total moment at end $B = - sk\theta_B + sck\theta_A - K_B\theta_B = - M_B \quad \dots\text{(ii)}$

At the critical load the stiffness of each end is zero.

Hence at A, $\qquad \dfrac{M_A}{\theta_A} = 0.$

But since $\theta_A \neq 0$, $\qquad M_A = 0.$

Hence from (i)

$$\theta_B = \frac{sk + K_A}{sck}\theta_A$$

220

Substituting this result in (ii) gives

$$sck - \frac{sk + K_A}{c} - \frac{K_B(sk + K_A)}{sck} = 0$$

i.e.

$$sk(1 - c^2) + K_A + K_B + \frac{K_A K_B}{sk} = 0$$

from which the critical load can be obtained by trial when numerical values are known. Exactly the same result is obtained by considering the end B.

Problem 8.9—A stanchion AB is built-in at end A and restrained against lateral movement by a spring at its other end B. The length of AB is L in. and the spring stiffness is K lb./in. Derive an expression which enables its critical load to be evaluated and discuss the behaviour of the strut for different values of K.

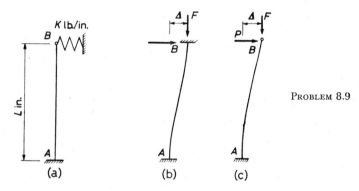

(a)   (b)   (c)

PROBLEM 8.9

When a small lateral force P is applied to B (say to the right) the end of the strut will move through a small distance Δ. To determine the stiffness of the strut without the spring support consider the strut in diagram (b).

$$M_A = M_B = - s(1 + c)k\frac{\Delta}{L} \qquad \cdots \cdot [8.8]$$

On releasing B (diagram (c)) the moment at A becomes

$$M_A = - s(1 - c^2)k\frac{\Delta}{L}$$

Now consider the equilibrium of this strut

$$PL + F\Delta = s(1 - c^2)k\frac{\Delta}{L}$$

The stiffness of the strut is

$$\frac{P}{\Delta} = \frac{s(1 - c^2)k}{L^2} - \left(\frac{F}{P_E}\right)\frac{P_E}{L}$$

(Notice that the calculation can be checked at this point. When $F = 0$, $s = 4$ and $c = \frac{1}{2}$ and the case of the cantilever is obtained.)

Thus the stiffness of the strut supported by a spring is

$$s(1 - c^2)\frac{k}{L^2} - \left(\frac{F}{P_E}\right)\frac{P_E}{L} + K$$

221

The stiffness is zero when

$$s(1 - c^2)\frac{k}{L^2} - \left(\frac{F}{P_E}\right)\frac{P_E}{L} = -K$$

This expression enables the critical load of the strut to be evaluated. When K is zero the critical value of F is found to be $0·25$ and as K increases the critical value of F increases. When K becomes infinite the critical load occurs at $F = 2·046P_E$. At this value of K the mode of failure is that of pure rotation at B (see *Problem 8.7*).

Problem 8.10—This problem is similar to one worked out in Volume I [FIGURE 8.14]. The simple portal frame illustrated is subjected to equal loads W at B and C. Assume that EI is a constant ($= 39·6 \times 10^6$ lb. in.^{2}) for all members and determine the lowest critical load of the framework.

The mode of failure associated with the lowest critical load is that of sidesway. This statement can be explained by considering the extreme cases of failure of this type of framework, viz. when the beam BC is infinitely rigid or of zero rigidity. The two type of failures are illustrated in diagrams (b) and (c); from (b) it is seen that the maximum critical load obtained for this type of failure occurs when beam BC is infinitely rigid. The value of this critical load is $W_c' = \dfrac{\pi^2EI}{L^2}$. The minimum critical load associated with the type of failure illustrated in diagram (c) occurs when beam BC is infinitely flexible, i.e. BC has no rigidity. The value of the critical load is now $W_c'' = 2·04\dfrac{\pi^2EI}{L^2}$. If BC has finite rigidity the sway type failure occurs at a critical load which lies between $\dfrac{\pi^2EI}{4L^2}$ and $\dfrac{\pi^2EI}{L^2}$. However, the joint rotation type of failure occurs at a minimum critical load of $W_c'' = \dfrac{2·04\pi^2EI}{L^2}$ when BC has zero rigidity (see *Problem 8.9(a)*). Thus it is seen that the lowest critical load of this frame is that associated with a sway-type failure. The above method of reasoning can quite often be used to help the designer decide on the mode of failure.

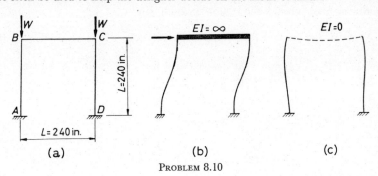

PROBLEM 8.10

The moment distribution process is set out in TABLE 8.10(a). A small disturbing force P has been applied to the right at B. Also because of the antisymmetry of the frame it is known that joints B and C will rotate through equal angles θ. There are two unknowns, θ and lateral deflection, Δ, which can be evaluated from two equilibrium conditions.

Firstly, the total moment at B is zero

i.e.
$$s_1k\theta + 6k\theta - \frac{s_1(1 + c_1)k\Delta}{L} = 0 \qquad \qquad \ldots\ldots \text{(i)}$$

TABLE 8.10(a)

ANALYSIS OF FRAME SHOWN IN DIAGRAM (a)

Operation	A	B	C	D	QL
Rotate B through θ	$s_1c_1k\theta$	$s_1k\theta$ $4k\theta$	$2k\theta$		$-s_1(1+c_1)k\theta$
Rotate C through θ		$2k\theta$	$4k\theta$ $s_1k\theta$	$s_1c_1k\theta$	$-s_1(1+c_1)k\theta$
Sway through $\varDelta$	$-\dfrac{s_1(1+c_1)k\varDelta}{L}$	$-\dfrac{s_1(1+c_1)k\varDelta}{L}$	$-\dfrac{s_1(1+c_1)k\varDelta}{L}$	$s_1c_1k\varDelta$	$\dfrac{4s_1(1+c_1)k\varDelta}{m_1L}$

Note: Suffix 1 refers to stanchions.

and secondly for sway equilibrium

$$PL = -2s_1(1 + c_1)k\theta + \frac{4s_1(1 + c_1)k\Delta}{m_1 L} \qquad \dots (ii)$$

From (i)

$$\theta = \frac{s_1(1 + c_1)\Delta}{(s_1 + 6)L}$$

On substituting in (ii) and noting that at the critical load the sway stiffness $\dfrac{P}{\Delta}$ is

zero it is seen that

$$\frac{s_1(1 + c_1)m_1}{s_1 + 6} = 2 \qquad \dots (iii)$$

Equation (iii) is solved by trial in TABLE 8.10(b). Before starting the solution it is a good idea to decide on the possible range of $\dfrac{F}{P_E}$. If BC were infinitely rigid $\dfrac{F}{P_E}$ would be 1, and if infinitely flexible $\dfrac{F}{P_E}$ would be $\dfrac{1}{4}$. i.e. $\dfrac{1}{4} < \dfrac{F}{P_E} < 1$.

TABLE 8.10(b)

SOLUTION OF EQUATION (iii) BY TRIAL

$\dfrac{F}{P_E}$	s_1	c_1	m_1	$\dfrac{s_1(1 + c_1)m_1}{s_1 + 6}$
0·8	2·816	0·833	4·253	2·490
0·7	2·981	0·769	2·900	1·703
0·76	2·883	0·806	3·577	2·097

These values are sufficient to plot a graph of $\dfrac{F}{P_E}$ against $\dfrac{s_1(1 + c_1)m_1}{s_1 + 6}$ from which it is found that equation (iii) is satisfied when $\dfrac{F}{P_E} = 0.748$. The axial load in the stanchions is then

$$0.748 \frac{\pi^2 \times 39.6 \times 10^6}{240 \times 240} = 5080 \text{ lb.}$$

i.e. the lowest critical load W_c is 5080 lb.

Problem 8.11—A two-bay pitched portal roof is loaded with W at each of its apices B and D. The ends A and E are built-in and the gully C is supported by a pin-ended strut, CF. Show that the critical load occurs when the axial loads in the diagonal members AB, BC, CD and DE are 0·36 times their Euler load. All of the diagonal members have the same values of E, I and L. Assume that CF does not bend.

The moment distribution is carried out in the following manner. Allow the structure to sway to the right as in diagram (b); point C moves through 2Δ while B and D each move through Δ and all joints are prevented from rotating. Joint C is then rotated through $-\theta$ and B and D through ψ. Diagram (b) shows that when B moves Δ to the right it moves a distance Δ cosec α at right angles to AB. The moment distribution is set out in TABLE 8.11(a).

224

TABLE 8.11(a)†

MOMENT DISTRIBUTION

Operation	A	B	C	D	E	QL
C sways 2Δ to the right B and D sway Δ to the right	$-M$	$-M$ $+M$	$+M$ $+M$	$+M$ $-M$	$-M$	$\dfrac{4s(1+c)k\Delta}{mL}$
Rotate C through $-\theta$		$-sck\theta$	$-sk\theta$ $-sk\theta$	$-sck\theta$		$-2s(1+c)k\theta \sin\alpha$
Rotate B and D through ψ	$sck\psi$	$sk\psi$ $sk\psi$	$sck\psi$ $sck\psi$	$sk\psi$ $sk\psi$	$sck\psi$	$+2s(1+c)k\psi \sin\alpha$

† To conserve space in this table $\dfrac{s(1+c)k\Delta \operatorname{cosec}\alpha}{L}$ is written as M.

The column headed QL takes account of the horizontal force to the right at C. The three unknowns Δ, θ and ψ can be found by considering the equilibrium conditions.

For equilibrium at B and D, the total moment there is zero,

i.e. $$2\psi = c\theta \qquad \dots \text{ (i)}$$

and as the total moment at C is zero

$$c\psi - \theta + \frac{(1 + c)\Delta \operatorname{cosec} \alpha}{L} = 0 \qquad \dots \text{ (ii)}$$

Also the sway force Q at C is given by

$$QL = \frac{4s(1 + c)k\Delta}{mL} - 2s(1 + c)k\theta \sin \alpha + 2s(1 + c)k\psi \sin \alpha \qquad \dots \text{ (iii)}$$

Solving for θ and ψ from (i) and (ii) and substituting in (iii),

$$QL = \frac{4s(1 + c)k\Delta}{mL} - \frac{4s(1 + c)^2 k\Delta}{L(2 - c^2)} + \frac{2s(1 + c)^2 ck\Delta}{L(2 - c^2)}$$

At the critical load the stiffness $\dfrac{Q}{\Delta}$ is zero.

$$\frac{2(2 - c^2)}{m} = 2 + c - c^2 \qquad \dots \text{ (iv)}$$

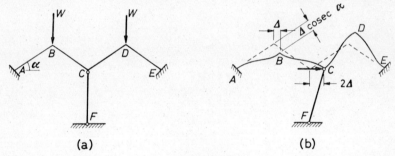

(a)   (b)

PROBLEM 8.11

Equation (iv) is solved by trial in TABLE 8.11(b).

TABLE 8.11(b)

SOLUTION OF EQUATION (IV) BY TRIAL

$\dfrac{F}{P_E}$	m	c	R.H.S.	L.H.S.
0·9	8·31	0·909	2·083	0·282
0·5	1·82	0·666	2·222	1·710
0·4	1·55	0·624	2·234	2·08
0·36	1·46	0·609	2·238	2·23

i.e. the critical load occurs when the axial loads in the diagonal members are 0·36 times their Euler load. It is worth noting that this is an extremely low figure and indicates that this type of structure is not a very desirable one. If other bays are added to it, the position is even worse. Light ties from A to C and E to C will raise the critical load by preventing sway instability. (The figure 0·36 is actually raised to 1·29.)

Problem 8.12—A 50 ft. span footbridge is shown loaded at each of the four left hand joints of the bottom chord by W lb. The bridge is symmetrical about its centre line.

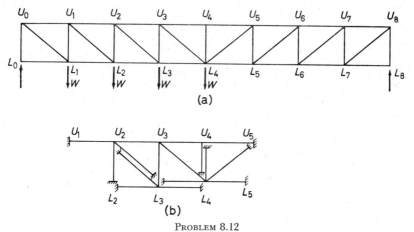

(a)

(b)

PROBLEM 8.12

The properties of the members are given in the first three columns of TABLE 8.12(a). Determine the value of the critical load.

TABLE 8.12(a)

PROPERTIES AND $\dfrac{F}{P_E}$ RATIOS OF MEMBERS (tension is $-$ve)

Member	Length (in.)	I (in.⁴)	P_E lb.	F lb.	$\dfrac{F}{P_E}$
U_0L_0	60·0	3·36	276,500	$+ 2{\cdot}75\ W$	$+ 0{\cdot}994\ W \times 10^{-5}$
U_1L_1	60·0	0·80	65,900	$+ 1{\cdot}75\ W$	$+ 2{\cdot}655\ W \times 10^{-5}$
U_2L_2	60·0	0·80	65,900	$+ 0{\cdot}75\ W$	$+ 1{\cdot}138\ W \times 10^{-5}$
U_3L_3	60·0	0·80	65,900	$- 0{\cdot}25\ W$	$- 0{\cdot}379\ W \times 10^{-5}$
U_4L_4	60·0	0·80	65,900	0	0
U_0U_1	75·0	3·36	177,000	$+ 3{\cdot}44\ W$	$+ 1{\cdot}945\ W \times 10^{-5}$
U_1U_2	75·0	3·36	177,000	$+ 5{\cdot}625\ W$	$+ 3{\cdot}18\ W \times 10^{-5}$
U_2U_3	75·0	3·36	177,000	$+ 6{\cdot}56\ W$	$+ 3{\cdot}71\ W \times 10^{-5}$
U_3U_4	75·0	3·36	177,000	$+ 6{\cdot}25\ W$	$+ 3{\cdot}53\ W \times 10^{-5}$
L_0L_1	75·0	2·94	155,000	0	0
L_1L_2	75·0	2·94	155,000	$- 3{\cdot}44\ W$	$- 2{\cdot}22\ W \times 10^{-5}$
L_2L_3	75·0	2·94	155,000	$- 5{\cdot}625\ W$	$- 3{\cdot}63\ W \times 10^{-5}$
L_3L_4	75·0	2·94	155,000	$- 6{\cdot}56\ W$	$- 4{\cdot}23\ W \times 10^{-5}$
U_0L_1	96·0	2·94	94,500	$- 4{\cdot}40\ W$	$- 4{\cdot}65\ W \times 10^{-5}$
U_1L_2	96·0	0·80	25,700	$- 2{\cdot}80\ W$	$- 10{\cdot}89\ W \times 10^{-5}$
U_2L_3	96·0	0·80	25,700	$- 1{\cdot}20\ W$	$- 4{\cdot}67\ W \times 10^{-5}$
U_3L_4	96·0	0·80	25,700	$+ 0{\cdot}40\ W$	$+ 1{\cdot}56\ W \times 10^{-5}$
U_5L_4	96·0	0·80	25,700	$- 2{\cdot}00\ W$	$- 7{\cdot}78\ W \times 10^{-5}$
L_4L_5	75·0	2·94	155,000	$- 4{\cdot}69\ W$	$- 3{\cdot}03\ W \times 10^{-5}$
U_4U_5	75·0	3·36	177,000	$+ 6{\cdot}25\ W$	$+ 3{\cdot}53\ W \times 10^{-5}$

In this type of problem there are too many members to obtain an exact solution and it is necessary to turn to an approximate method. A model could be constructed and tested using the method described in Volume I. In this example Bolton's

227

approximate method will be used. It is first necessary to simplify the framework and to do this we must find the member with the largest positive $\dfrac{F}{P_E}$ ratio. This is done in TABLE 8.12(a). It is only necessary to consider the left hand half of the frame since the critical member will be there. The last three members are included because the information will be required later on. From TABLE 8.12(a) it is seen that U_2U_3 is the critical member and therefore either U_2 or U_3 is the critical joint. The next step is to guess a value of the critical load and to find the total stiffness of U_2 and U_3 (i.e. $\sum sk$) so that the simplified frame can be sketched. When making the first guess for W it should be realized that $\dfrac{F}{P_E}$ must lie between the limits 1 and 4 for all members. Experience shows that in a well designed truss the value of $\dfrac{F}{P_E}$ for the critical member generally lies between 1·3 and 2·1 approximately. An initial guess in TABLE 8.12(b) of $W = 45,000$ lb. showed that the total stiffness of U_3 (5·54 × 10⁶ lb. in.) was less

TABLE 8.12(b)

DETERMINATION OF CRITICAL LOAD BY TRIAL

Member	$k \times 10^6$ lb. in.	$W = 45,000$ lb.			$W = 44,000$ lb.		
		$\dfrac{F}{P_E}$	$(sk) \times 10^6$	$\dfrac{(sck)^2 \times 10^6}{T_{\text{far}}}$	$\dfrac{F}{P_E}$	$(sk) \times 10^6$	$\dfrac{(sck)^2 \times 10^6}{T_{\text{far}}}$
U_2U_3	1·344	+ 1·67	1·42	2·63	+ 1·63	1·55	2·47
U_1U_2	1·344	+ 1·43	2·17		+ 1·40	2·26	
U_2L_2	0·400	+ 0·51	1·31		+ 0·50	1·32	
U_2L_3	0·250	− 2·10	1·56		− 2·06	1·55	
U_3L_3	0·400	− 0·17	1·69	0·04	− 0·17	1·69	0·04
L_2L_3	1·176	− 1·63	6·82		− 1·60	6·79	
L_3L_4	1·176	− 1·90	7·13		− 1·86	7·08	
U_3L_4	0·250	+ 0·70	0·75	0·02	+ 0·69	0·75	0·02
L_4U_4	0·400	0	1·60		0	1·60	
L_4L_5	1·176	− 1·36	6·51		− 1·33	6·48	
L_4U_5	0·250	− 3·50	1·84		− 3·42	1·83	
U_4U_5	1·344	+ 1·59	1·68		+ 1·55	1·80	
U_3U_4	1·344	+ 1·59	1·68	3·22	+ 1·55	1·80	2·99

Total = 5·91   Total = 5·52

$T_{U_3} = \;\;5·54 \qquad \dfrac{5·91}{5·54} = 1·07 \qquad T_{U_3} = \;\;5·79 \qquad \dfrac{5·52}{5·79} = 0·96$

$T_{U_2} = \;\;6·46 \qquad\qquad\qquad\quad T_{U_2} = \;\;6·68$

$T_{U_4} = \;\;4·96 \qquad\qquad > 1 \qquad\quad T_{U_4} = \;\;5·20 \qquad\qquad < 1$

$T_{L_3} = 17·20 \qquad\quad \therefore\ \text{unstable} \qquad T_{L_3} = 17·11 \qquad\quad \therefore\ \text{stable}$

$T_{L_4} = 17·83 \qquad\qquad\qquad\qquad\quad T_{L_4} = 17·74$

than that of U_2 (6·46 × 10⁶ lb. in.) i.e. U_3 is the critical joint and the simplified frame is as sketched in diagram (b). The notation T for the total stiffness at a joint ($T = \sum sk$) with a suffix which refers to the joint will be used. If a small disturbing moment M is applied to rotate joint U_3 through angle θ, a moment distribution process can be applied to the simplified frame. Consider the moment carried over to L_3, viz. $(sck)_{U_3L_3}\theta$. If U_3 is now held and L_3 released, the moment carried back to

U_3 is $-\dfrac{(sck)^2 U_3 L_3 \theta}{T}$. Thus the total moment carried back to U_3 is $-\theta \sum \dfrac{(sck)^2}{T_{\mathrm{far}}}$

where the summation is for all of the 'far' joints, viz. U_2, L_2, L_4 and U_4. Therefore the total moment at U_3 is

$$M - \theta \sum \frac{(sck)^2}{T_{\mathrm{far}}} = \left[T_{U_3} - \sum \frac{(sck)^2}{T_{\mathrm{Far}}} \right] \theta$$

At the critical load the stiffness of U_3 = total moment/θ is zero. In other words the expression in the square bracket must be zero. A value of W is guessed and this expression is tested to see whether it is zero. If it is positive it means that the critical load is not exceeded but if it is negative (i.e. too much moment is carried back from the 'far' joints) the critical load is exceeded and the frame is unstable. The computation is carried out in TABLE 8.12(b) where it will be seen that the first guess is too large and the second too small; the correct solution evidently lies between the two. It is usually necessary to make about three guesses.

Problem 8.13—To obtain the critical load of a plane framework for buckling within its plane a model has been constructed for testing in its elastic condition only. The Euler loads of the members of the prototype have been scaled down by a factor of 1000. The model was loaded and deflections measured at the centre of the member which deflected most. Results of this test are given in TABLE 8.13. Determine the critical load of the prototype.

TABLE 8.13

Applied load W lb.	Deflexion $\varDelta$ at centre of member, in.	$\dfrac{\varDelta}{W}$ in./lb. $\times 10^{-4}$
0	0	0
100	0·0165	1·65
150	0·0193	1·285
200	0·0233	1·165
250	0·0293	1·17
300	0·0395	1·32
325	0·0480	1·48
350	0·061	1·74
375	0·0825	2·20
400	0·1320	3·30
410	0·1710	4·17
415	0·200	4·82

The critical load of the model can be found by using a Southwell Plot. In this method $\varDelta$ is plotted against the ratio $\dfrac{\varDelta}{W}$. If the graph of W against $\varDelta$ is a hyperbola the graph of $\varDelta$ against $\dfrac{\varDelta}{W}$ is a straight line whose slope is the asymptote, i.e. the critical load W_c. TABLE 8.13 demonstrates the method of treating the results. $\dfrac{\varDelta}{W}$ is tabulated in column 3 of the table and the diagram shows the Southwell Plot. The early points do not lie on the straight line. This is quite often found to be the case with

Q   229

experimental results. The slope of the straight line is 452, i.e. the critical load of the model is 452 lb. At the critical load the $\dfrac{F}{P_E}$ ratios of corresponding members are the same for model and prototype.

Thus the critical load of the prototype is 452,000 lb.

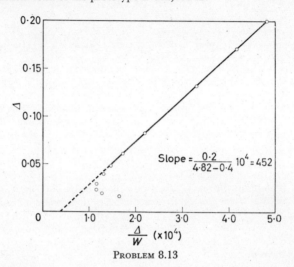

PROBLEM 8.13

Problems for Solution

Problem 8.14—A pin-ended strut of constant cross-section is restrained at mid length against lateral deflexion. If the spring stiffness is λ (i.e. $Q = \lambda\delta$) show that for λ small the critical load of the strut in the plane of restraint is increased to $P_E\left(1 + \dfrac{\lambda L^3}{48EI}\right)$ approximately.

(Manchester College of Science and Technology, 1956)

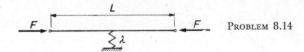

PROBLEM 8.14

Problem 8.15—Two spiral springs each of stiffness $K(M = K\theta)$ are connected to the ends of a simple strut of length L. An axial force F is applied. Derive an expression which will enable the critical load of the strut to be evaluated. Use this solution to determine the critical load of the system of members shown in diagram (b) where length $AB = 240$ in., length $CA = AD = EB = BF = 120$ in. and

$$EI = 39.6 \times 10^6 \text{ lb. in.}^2$$

for all members.

Problem 8.16—The simple portal frame illustrated is identical with that of *Problem 8.10* except that the feet of the stanchions are hinged. Determine the lowest critical load of the framework.

Problem 8.17—Determine the lowest critical load of the framework illustrated.

It is interesting to compare the solutions of *Problems 8.10, 8.16* and *8.17*.

230

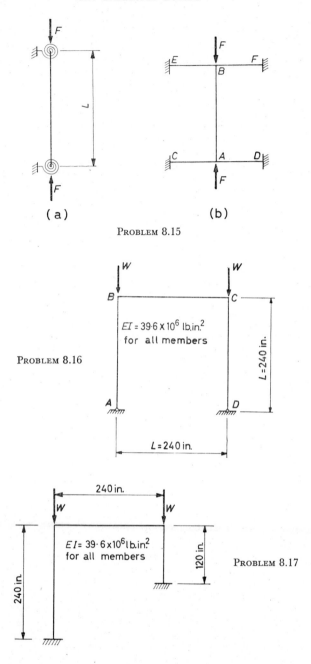

PROBLEM 8.15

PROBLEM 8.16

PROBLEM 8.17

Problem 8.18—Show that the critical loads of the symmetrical single bay rigid frame shown, with sidesway prevented, are given by the equation

$$\left(\frac{2k_2}{sk_1} + 1\right)\left(\frac{k_2}{sk_1} + 1\right) = \frac{c^2}{2}$$

231

where sk_1 is the stiffness of a column allowing for stability effects and c is the corresponding carry-over factor. For no stability effect $s = 4$ and $c = \frac{1}{2}$.

(Manchester College of Science and Technology, 1955)

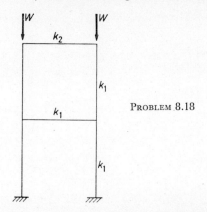

PROBLEM 8.18

Problem 8.19—Show that the lowest critical load of the single storey rigid frame shown occurs when $W = 2\cdot65 \times$ the Euler load of one of the members. Sidesway is prevented and E, I and L are constant for all members.

PROBLEM 8.19

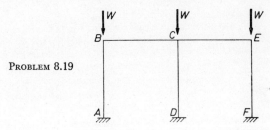

Problem 8.20—The 50 ft. span footbridge described in *Problem 8.12* is loaded vertically downwards by equal loads at each joint of the bottom chord. Determine the critical load.

Problem 8.21—Determine the critical load of the axially loaded strut illustrated. The strut is continuous from A to D and A, B and C are joints which allow free

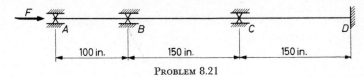

PROBLEM 8.21

rotations and horizontal movements but prevent vertical movements. D is built-in. EI is $39\cdot6 \times 10^6$ lb. in^2 from A to D.

8.4. PLASTIC BEHAVIOUR

Structural steel is normally a ductile material. In this section it is assumed that its stress-strain relation is given by FIGURE 8.2. The first problems deal with the effect of an axial load F on the plastic moment of a section. This $F - M'_P$ relation for a section was demonstrated in Volume I for a member of rectangular section [equation 8.18] and a 3 in. $\times$ 1½ in. R.S.J. [FIGURE 8.21] for a rectangular section

$$M'_P = M_P\left(1 - \frac{F^2}{F_y{}^2}\right) \qquad \dots \ [8.18]$$

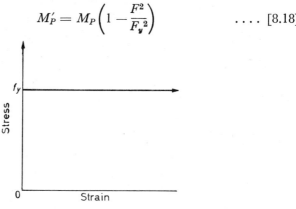

FIGURE 8.2

Problem 8.22—Assuming a yield stress of 40,000 lb. per square inch, draw the graph of plastic moment M'_P against the axial load F for the 6 in. $\times$ 5 in. R.S.J. (simplified as shown in diagram (a)) when it is bent about the axis XX.

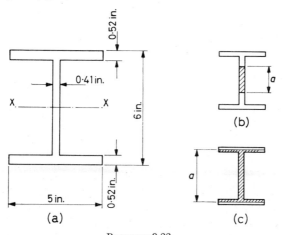

PROBLEM 8.22

There are two cases to consider:

1. When the axial load F can be taken by the web alone,

i.e. $\qquad\qquad F \leqslant$ area of web $\times$ 40,000 lb. = 81,300 lb.

2. When the axial load F is too large to be supported by the web alone,

i.e. $\qquad\qquad F \geqslant$ area of web $\times$ 40,000 lb. = 81,300 lb.

Case 1

$\qquad$ Let a = depth of web which takes the axial load (diagram (b))

i.e. $\qquad F = 40,000 \times 0.41a = 16,400a$ lb. $\qquad\qquad \dots \ (i)$

The plastic moment M'_p can now be considered as being made up of two parts:
(a) the moment arising from the stresses over the remainder of the web

$$= 40,000 \times 0.41 \times \frac{(4.96 - a)}{2} \frac{(4.96 + a)}{2}$$

$$= 4,100(24.6 - a^2)$$

and (b) the moment arising from the stresses over the flange

$$= 40,000 \times 5 \times 0.52 \times (6 - 0.52)$$

$$= 570,000 \text{ lb. in.}$$

i.e. $\qquad M'_p = 570,000 + 4,100 (24.6 - a^2) \qquad \qquad \dots \text{(ii)}$

TABLE 8.22

F AND M'_p VALUES OF 5IN. $\times$ 6 IN. R.S.J.

Assumed a in.	Case	F lb.	M'_p lb. in.
0	1	0	670,800
1	1	16,400	666,800
2	1	32,800	654,500
3	1	49,200	634,000
4	1	65,600	605,300
4·96	1 and 2	81,300	570,000
5	2	90,000	550,000
5·5	2	190,000	287,500
6	2	290,000	0

Case 2

Let a = depth of web and flange which takes axial load (diagram (c))

i.e. $\qquad F = 40,000 \{5a - 4.96(5 - 0.41)\} = (200,000a - 910,000) \text{ lb.}$

$\qquad \qquad \dots \text{(iii)}$

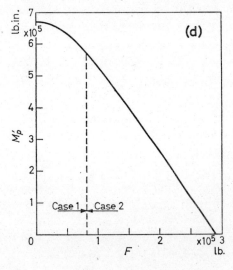

PROBLEM 8.22

234

The plastic moment M'_P can be written as

$$M'_P = 40{,}000 \times 5 \times \frac{(6-a)}{2} \frac{(6+a)}{2}$$

$$= 50{,}000\ (36 - a^2) \qquad\qquad \cdots \text{(iv)}$$

TABLE 8.22 sets out the rest of the computation. Values of a are assumed and F and M'_P then calculated.

The graph of F against $M'^{\cdot}_P$ is plotted in diagram (d).

Problem 8.23—Investigate the plastic behaviour of a mild steel strut of square section, $b \times b$. Derive general expressions which enable the axial load in the strut to be related to its plastic moment (a) for bending about axis XX and (b) for bending about the diagonal axis ZZ (diagram (a)). Plot the plastic collapse lines for these two cases on one graph when the strut is pin-ended, $b = 2 \cdot 0$ in. and $f_y = 40{,}000$ lb./in.²

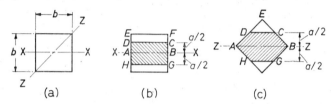

(a)   (b)   (c)

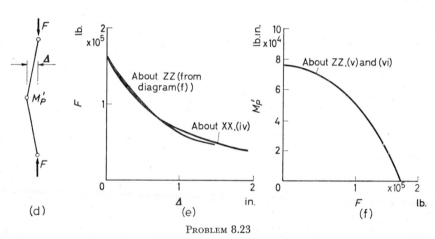

(d)   (e)   (f)

PROBLEM 8.23

(a) Let the part taken by the axial load be $DCGH$ (diagram (b)) of height a.

$$F = f_y \times \text{area of } DCGH = f_y ab \qquad\qquad \cdots \text{(i)}$$

also $\qquad M'_P = 2f_y \times \text{moment of area } CDEF \text{ about } AB = f_y b \frac{(b^2 - a^2)}{4} \qquad \cdots \text{(ii)}$

Hence from (i) and (ii), eliminating a

$$M'_P = \frac{f_y b}{4}\left(b^2 - \frac{F}{f_y^2 b^2}\right) = \frac{b}{4F_y}(F_y^2 - F^2) \qquad\qquad \cdots \text{(iii)}$$

where $\qquad F_y = f_y b^2$.

When $\qquad b = 2 \cdot 0$ and $f_y = 40{,}000$ lb./in.²

235

$$M'_P = 80,000 - \frac{F^2}{320,000}$$

But $\qquad M'_P = F\varDelta$

where $\varDelta$ is the deflexion at the centre of the strut (diagram (d))

i.e. $\qquad\qquad\qquad\qquad \varDelta = \dfrac{80,000}{F} - \dfrac{F}{320,000} \qquad \dots \text{(iv)}$

This curve is plotted in diagram (e).

(b) Let the part taken by the axial load be $DCGH$ (diagram (c))

$$F = f_y \times \text{area of } DCGH = f_y a \left(b\sqrt{2} - \frac{a}{2} \right) \qquad \dots \text{(v)}$$

Also $\qquad\qquad M'_P = 2f_y \times \text{moment of area } DEC \text{ about } AB$

$$= \frac{1}{3}f_y \left(b - \frac{a}{\sqrt{2}} \right)^2 \left(a + \frac{b}{\sqrt{2}} \right) \qquad \dots \text{(vi)}$$

Although a can be eliminated from expressions (v) and (vi), it is easier to assume values of a and plot the resulting values of M'_P against the corresponding values of F:

e.g. $\qquad$ when $\quad a = 2 \cdot 0, F = 146,000 \text{ lb. and } M'_P = 15,600 \text{ lb. in.}$

But $\quad M'_P = F\varDelta$ as before (diagram (d))

i.e. $\qquad\qquad\qquad\qquad \varDelta = \dfrac{M'_P}{F}$

This curve is also plotted in diagram (e) by assuming values of F and determining $\varDelta$:

e.g. $\qquad$ when $F = 100,000 \text{ lb. from diagram (f)}, M'_P = 49,000 \text{ lb. in.}$

i.e. $\qquad\qquad\qquad\qquad \varDelta = 0 \cdot 49 \text{ in.}$

Problem 8.24—The two-storey framework illustrated in diagram (a) is fabricated from 6 in. $\times$ 5 in. R.S.J. Loads W are applied at C and D as shown. Draw a graph of the plastic collapse line for a sidesway failure. Use the $F - M'_P$ graph shown in diagram (d) of *Problem 8.22*.

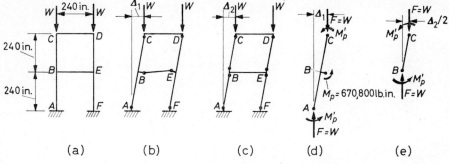

(a) $\qquad\qquad$ (b) $\qquad\qquad$ (c) $\qquad\qquad$ (d) $\qquad\qquad$ (e)

PROBLEM 8.24

There are two possible modes of failure (diagrams (b) and (c)) and it will be necessary to study both modes to decide on the plastic collapse line. It will be noticed that the failure type shown in diagram (c) could equally well be shown as a collapse of the top storey alone or of the bottom storey alone. In an ideal structure these should all occur simultaneously but in an actual structure one storey will always be slightly weaker than the other and it will fail first.

236

For equilibrium of AC (diagram (d))

$$F\Delta_1 = 670{,}800 + 2M_P'$$

i.e.

$$\Delta_1 = \frac{670{,}800}{F} + 2\,\frac{M_P'}{F}$$ 　　.... (i)

For equilibrium of BC (diagram (e))

$$\frac{F\Delta_2}{2} = 2M_P'$$

i.e.

$$\Delta_2 = \frac{4M_P}{F}$$ 　　.... (ii)

Δ can be determined for values of F by reference to diagram (d) of *Problem 8.22* and TABLE 8.24 sets out a few typical values for both types of sway.

TABLE 8.24

SWAY FAILURE

$F = W$ lb.	M_P'	Δ_1	Δ_2
290,000	0	2·31	0
250,000	115,000	3·60	1·84
200,000	260,000	5·95	5·20
175,000	330,000	7·60	7·55
150,000	400,000	9·81	10·66
100,000	528,000	17·27	21·1
75,000	586,000	24·56	31·2
50,000	633,000	38·74	50·6
0	670,800	∞	∞

The resulting plastic collapse lines are shown in diagram (f). The plastic behaviour of an ideal framework can be described with reference to diagram (f). Until deflexion

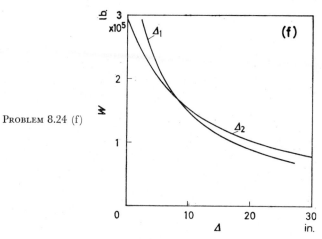

PROBLEM 8.24 (f)

occurs the frame can carry a load of 290,000 lb. when deflexions of the type shown in diagram (c) occur. As the deflexions increase, the load-carrying capacity of the framework falls. When the deflexion is 8·3 in. the framework can carry only 174,000 lb. at each of the top joints. Beyond this deflexion the framework fails in the manner indicated in diagram (b).

Problems for Solution

Problem 8.25—A 10 in. × 8 in. R.S.J. is simplified in the manner shown in diagram (a) for the sake of computation. If the yield stress of the steel is 40,000 lb./in.² and bending takes place about axis XX, what is the full plastic moment M_P and the maximum axial load F_y? If an axial load of 300,000 lb. is applied, what is the plastic moment M'_P? What is M'_P when the axial load is 96,000 lb.?

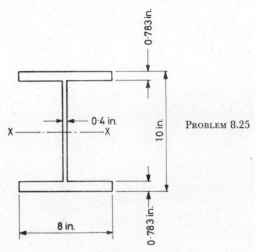

PROBLEM 8.25

Problem 8.26—The portal frame illustrated in diagram (a) is fabricated from a 6 in. × 5 in. R.S.J. Loads W are applied as shown. Draw graphs of the plastic collapse line for

(a) a sway failure,

(b) stanchion failure when sway is prevented and additional plastic hinges form at the centres of the stanchions.

PROBLEM 8.26

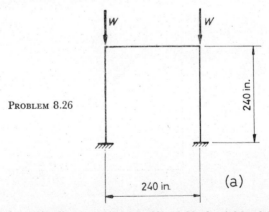

Use the graph shown in diagram (d) of *Problem 8.22* of axial load F against plastic moment M'_P.

238

8.5. CONVENTIONAL SECONDARY STRESS ANALYSIS

In Volume I [Chapter 8, Section 8.3.2], the bending moments induced in the members of a triangular framework because of the rigidity of the joints were calculated. The method used was essentially the same as that described by Hardy Cross modified by the introduction of s- and c-functions because of the high axial stresses.

In the following example the axial stresses are not so high and it is permissible to use the ordinary moment distribution procedure (i.e. $s = 4·0$; $c = 0·5$).

Problem 8.27—The framework shown is rigidly fixed to a wall at A and B and joints C and D are also rigid. The cross-sectional areas of AC and AD are A and that of BD is $2A$. The relevant second moment of area of each member is I. Obtain a first approximation to the moments at the ends of the members and evaluate the magnitudes and directions of the residual restraints at joints C and D.

(Birmingham, 1948)

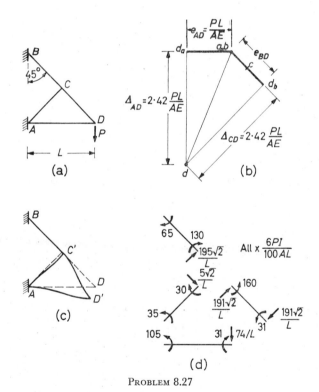

PROBLEM 8.27

On the assumption that the joints are pinned, the primary forces in the members are

$$F_{BC} = F_{CD} = \sqrt{2}P \text{ (tensile)}$$
$$F_{AD} = P \text{ (comp.)}$$

239

TABLE 8.27

DISTRIBUTION OF SECONDARY MOMENTS

	BC	CB	CA	CD	DC	DA	AD	AC	
		1/3	1/3	1/3	0.586	0.414			$K_{DC}=\sqrt{2}\,\dfrac{I}{L}$; $K_{AD}=\dfrac{I}{L}$; $\dfrac{\sqrt{2}}{1+\sqrt{2}}=0\cdot586$
			− 100	− 484	− 484	− 242	− 242	− 100	
		+ 124	+ 124	+ 213	+ 426	+ 300	+ 150		Balance D and C.O.
	+ 62			+ 123	+ 62			+ 62	Balance C and C.O.
				− 18	− 36	− 26	− 13		Balance D and C.O.
	+ 3	+ 6	+ 6	+ 6	+ 3			+ 3	Balance C and C.O.
					− 2	− 1			Balance D
	+ 65	+ 130	+ 30	− 160	− 31	+ 31	− 105	− 35	Final Moments $\Big/ \dfrac{6PI}{100AL}$

240

so that BD elongates by $e_{BD} = \dfrac{\sqrt{2}P \times \sqrt{2}L}{2AE} = \dfrac{PL}{AE}$

and AD shortens by $e_{AD} = \dfrac{PL}{AE}$

The Williot diagram at (b) gives the relative displacement of the joints while at (c) the framework is shown forced into this position with the joints prevented from rotating by imaginary clamps. The fixing moments thus induced in the members are

$$M_{FAD} = M_{FDA} = -\frac{6EI}{L^2}\Delta_{AD} = -\frac{6EI}{L^2}\left(2{\cdot}42\,\frac{PL}{AE}\right) = -\frac{6}{100}\frac{PI}{AL}\times 242$$

$$M_{FCD} = M_{FDC} = -\frac{6EI}{(\sqrt{2}L)^2}\Delta_{CD} = -\frac{6}{100}\frac{PI}{AL}\times 484$$

$$M_{FAC} = M_{FCA} = -\frac{6EI}{(\sqrt{2}L)^2}\Delta_{AC} = -\frac{6}{100}\frac{PI}{AL}\times 100$$

The distribution of moments occurring when the joints are released is worked out in TABLE 8.27 and the residual forces acting on joints C and D are obtained from consideration of diagram (d) which shows the final moments acting on the ends of the members, which have been separated for clarity. The external forces necessary to prevent movement are the resultants of those shown.

Problems for Solution

Problem 8.28—The rigidly jointed framework shown is erected by first fastening A and B to the base. Joint C is then welded. Find the bending moment at C due to the following dimensional errors.
 (a) AC too short by δ_1
 (b) BC too short by δ_2
 (c) Angle ACB too small by θ.

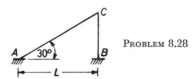

PROBLEM 8.28

The members AC and CB are identical in cross-section; axial and stability effects can be ignored.

(Manchester College of Science and Technology, 1955)

Problem 8.29—The welded steel truss shown is pinned to its support at A and supported on rollers at C. The central load is such as to produce working stresses of 2 and 8 tons per sq. in. in the struts and ties respectively. The relevant second moment

PROBLEM 8.29

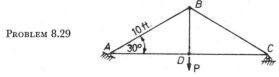

of area of the struts is 20 in.[4] and of the ties 2 in.[4] Find the secondary bending moments at the ends of the members.

(Manchester, 1952)

Problem 8.30—The cross-sectional area of all the members of the symmetrical steel

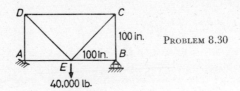

PROBLEM 8.30

truss shown is 3 sq. in., and their radius of gyration is 2 in. Find the bending moments, due to joint rigidity, in the members meeting at *D*.

(Oxford, 1948)

Problem 8.31—The diagram illustrates a steel roof truss of tubular construction which is supported on rollers at *A* and a hinge at *B*. Vertical loads of 100 lb. each

PROBLEM 8.31

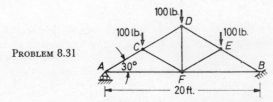

are applied at points *C*, *D* and *E*. The tubular members, whose dimensions are given below, are welded together to give rigid joints.

Norminal O.D.	$1\frac{11}{32}$ in.
Wall thickness	0·128 in.
Cross-sectional area	0·489 in.^{2}
Second moment of area	0·091 in.^{4}
Section modulus	0·136 in.^{3}

Obtain first approximations to the secondary stresses.

(Birmingham, 1957)

242

MATRIX METHODS†

9.1. INTRODUCTION

THE matrix methods presented in Volume I, Chapter 9, are designed to provide a systematic means of setting up the equilibrium equations of a structure in a form suitable for solution on an automatic computer. They are not primarily intended as methods for manual use, although they can be of value if a human computer without structural experience is available to carry out the matrix manipulations.

The rules of matrix algebra are simple, and it is relatively easy to carry out formal manipulations in matrix notation in accordance with these rules. To obtain a true understanding of the processes involved, however, the reader is strongly advised to practise the elementary operations described in Volume I, Section 9.2, on simple numerical examples, using a desk calculating machine if one is available. A few examples are given below, and others will be found in textbooks on numerical analysis, such as those by Crandall‡ and Buckingham§.

Problems for Solution

9.1. Carry out the following matrix operations:

(i) Add
$$\begin{bmatrix} 1 & -2 \\ 3 & -4 \\ 5 & -6 \end{bmatrix} \text{ and } \begin{bmatrix} 4 & -5 \\ 6 & -7 \\ 8 & -9 \end{bmatrix}$$

(ii) Subtract
$$\begin{bmatrix} 1 & -2 \\ 3 & -4 \\ 5 & -6 \end{bmatrix} \text{ from } \begin{bmatrix} 4 & -5 \\ 6 & -7 \\ 8 & -9 \end{bmatrix}$$

(iii) Form
$$\begin{bmatrix} 1 & -2 \\ 3 & -4 \\ 5 & -6 \end{bmatrix} \begin{bmatrix} 4 & 6 & 8 \\ -5 & -7 & -9 \end{bmatrix}$$

---

† This Chapter was contributed by Dr. R. K. Livesley, Engineering Department, Cambridge University.

‡ Crandall, S. H., *Engineering Analysis*. McGraw-Hill. 1956.

§ Buckingham, R. A. *Numerical Methods*. Pitman. 1957.

(iv) Form

$$\begin{bmatrix} 4 & 6 & 8 \\ -5 & -7 & -9 \end{bmatrix} \begin{bmatrix} 1 & -2 \\ 3 & -4 \\ 5 & -6 \end{bmatrix}$$

(v) Solve

$$\begin{bmatrix} 1 & 2 & -3 \\ 4 & 5 & 6 \\ -7 & 8 & 9 \end{bmatrix} \begin{bmatrix} x_1 \\ x_2 \\ x_3 \end{bmatrix} = \begin{bmatrix} 6 \\ 4 \\ 1 \end{bmatrix}$$

(vi) Invert

$$\begin{bmatrix} 1 & 2 & -3 \\ 4 & 5 & 6 \\ -7 & 8 & 9 \end{bmatrix}$$

9.2. STIFFNESS MATRICES FOR VARIOUS TYPES OF STRUCTURAL ELEMENT

The essence of the matrix methods described in Chapter 9 of Volume I is the way in which they divide the process of structural analysis into two parts:
  (a) the calculation of the properties of the individual elements from which the structure is formed.
  (b) the combination of the equations describing these properties into a set of equations describing the behaviour of the connected structure.

The first part of the process is concerned with the physical characteristics of the structural elements; it is normally carried out either by an integration of the equations of bending or by a simple application of Hooke's law, according to the type of element involved. The second part is concerned only with the connections of the elements and is formally the same whether the structure is a pin-jointed plane frame or a rigidly jointed space frame. Indeed, exactly the same methods can be adopted in dealing with electric networks.

Since matrix techniques are normally used in conjunction with automatic computers it is difficult to find examples, suitable for a textbook, which demonstrate the full power of the method. The following problems are designed to give the reader practice in the use of matrix notation, and are not all intended to be carried through to the final computational stages.

Problem 9.2†—Set up the member stiffness matrices for a straight uniform beam forming part of a grillage lying in a horizontal plane. The loading on the grillage consists of concentrated vertical loads acting at the joints, which are assumed to be rigid. There are no loads acting in the plane of the grillage.

This problem has obvious practical significance. Grillages are usually highly redundant structures and are difficult to analyse by conventional means. Using the

---

† This analysis is taken from a paper by Lightfoot and Sawko (*Engineering*, January 2, 1959, p. 18), with changes in notation to agree with Volume I, Section 9.3.

stiffness matrix approach, however, we find that the analysis has many points of similarity with that already derived for a rigidly-jointed plane frame loaded in its plane.

Since the joints are to be treated as rigid, a beam will be able to transmit torsion as well as shear and bending moment. The coordinate system we shall use is shown in the diagram; it will be seen that this is identical with Figure 9.2 in Volume I, except

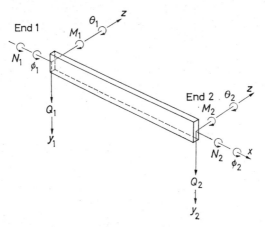

PROBLEM 9.2.   Coordinate system for a grillage beam.

for the addition of twisting moments N_1, N_2 and rotations ϕ_1, ϕ_2 about the x-axis. The end-loads acting on the beam may be written

$$F_1 = \begin{bmatrix} N_1 \\ M_1 \\ Q_1 \end{bmatrix} \qquad F_2 = \begin{bmatrix} N_2 \\ M_2 \\ Q_2 \end{bmatrix}$$

while the associated end-displacements are

$$D_1 = \begin{bmatrix} \phi_1 \\ \theta_1 \\ y_1 \end{bmatrix} \qquad D_2 = \begin{bmatrix} \phi_2 \\ \theta_2 \\ y_2 \end{bmatrix}$$

Since we are considering only simple linear small-deflexion theory, it is apparent that the presence of moments and (small) rotations about the x-axis do not affect the bending of the beam in the x-y plane. The relations between the loads M_1, Q_1; M_2, Q_2 and the displacements θ_1, y_1; θ_2, y_2 are therefore exactly the same as those derived in Volume I, Section 9.3 (note, however, the transposition of the quantities M and Q, θ and y, in the present force and displacement vectors, as compared with those used in Section 9.3). These equations are

$$
\begin{aligned}
\begin{bmatrix} M_1 \\ Q_1 \end{bmatrix} &= \begin{bmatrix} 4EI/L & 6EI/L^2 \\ 6EI/L^2 & 12EI/L^3 \end{bmatrix} \begin{bmatrix} \theta_1 \\ y_1 \end{bmatrix} + \begin{bmatrix} 2EI/L & -6EI/L^2 \\ 6EI/L^2 & -12EI/L^3 \end{bmatrix} \begin{bmatrix} \theta_2 \\ y_2 \end{bmatrix} \\[2mm]
\begin{bmatrix} M_2 \\ Q_2 \end{bmatrix} &= \begin{bmatrix} 2EI/L & 6EI/L^2 \\ -6EI/L^2 & -12EI/L^3 \end{bmatrix} \begin{bmatrix} \theta_1 \\ y_1 \end{bmatrix} + \begin{bmatrix} 4EI/L & -6EI/L^2 \\ -6EI/L^2 & 12EI/L^3 \end{bmatrix} \begin{bmatrix} \theta_2 \\ y_2 \end{bmatrix}
\end{aligned}
\quad \Bigg\} \dots.(9.1)
$$

The reader will note that transposing the quantities M and Q, θ and y, involves transposing both the rows and the columns of the 2×2 matrices (compare with Volume I, equation [9.1]).

The complete behaviour of the member is obtained by adding to equations 9.1 the relation between the couples and the rotations about the x-axis. If the torsional rigidity of the beam is $\dfrac{GJ}{L}$, then these relations are simply

$$
\left.
\begin{aligned}
N_1 &= \frac{GJ}{L}\,(\phi_1 - \phi_2) \\[2mm]
N_2 &= -\frac{GJ}{L}\,(\phi_1 - \phi_2)
\end{aligned}
\right\} \qquad \dots\dots (9.2)
$$

Combining equations 9.1 and 9.2 we obtain

$$
\begin{bmatrix} N_1 \\ M_1 \\ Q_1 \end{bmatrix}
=
\begin{bmatrix}
GJ/L & 0 & 0 \\
0 & 4EI/L & 6EI/L^2 \\
0 & 6EI/L^2 & 12EI/L^3
\end{bmatrix}
\begin{bmatrix} \phi_1 \\ \theta_1 \\ y_1 \end{bmatrix}
+
\begin{bmatrix}
-GJ/L & 0 & 0 \\
0 & 2EI/L & -6EI/L^2 \\
0 & 6EI/L^2 & -12EI/L^3
\end{bmatrix}
\begin{bmatrix} \phi_2 \\ \theta_2 \\ y_2 \end{bmatrix}
$$

$$
\begin{bmatrix} N_2 \\ M_2 \\ Q_2 \end{bmatrix}
=
\begin{bmatrix}
-GJ/L & 0 & 0 \\
0 & 2EI/L & 6EI/L^2 \\
0 & -6EI/L^2 & -12EI/L^3
\end{bmatrix}
\begin{bmatrix} \phi_1 \\ \theta_1 \\ y_1 \end{bmatrix}
+
\begin{bmatrix}
GJ/L & 0 & 0 \\
0 & 4EI/L & -6EI/L^2 \\
0 & -6EI/L^2 & 12EI/L^3
\end{bmatrix}
\begin{bmatrix} \phi_2 \\ \theta_2 \\ y_2 \end{bmatrix}
$$

which may be written symbolically in the normal form

$$
\left.
\begin{aligned}
F_1 &= Y_{11} D_1 + Y_{12} D_2 \\
F_2 &= Y_{21} D_1 + Y_{22} D_2
\end{aligned}
\right\} \qquad \dots\dots (9.3)
$$

Problem for Solution

9.3. As in problems of plane frame analysis, before equations 9.3 for the individual members can be combined they must be converted into a single overall coordinate

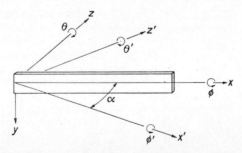

PROBLEM 9.3. Overall system coordinates for a grillage beam.

system. If a member makes a horizontal angle α with the x' axis of this overall coordinate system, as shown in the diagram, show that the transformed equations are

246

$$F_1' = Y_{11}' D_1' + Y_{12}' D_2'$$
$$F_2' = Y_{21}' D_1' + Y_{22}' D_2'$$

where F_1', F_2', D_1', D_2' are the end-loads and end-displacements expressed in the overall coordinate system, and the Y'-matrices are given by

$$Y_{ij}' = T^{-1} Y_{ij} T, \quad (i, j = 1, 2)$$

where

$$T = \begin{bmatrix} \cos\alpha & \sin\alpha & 0 \\ -\sin\alpha & \cos\alpha & 0 \\ 0 & 0 & 1 \end{bmatrix}$$

(The reader will notice that this transformation is identical with that which appears in the analysis of a rigidly jointed plane frame; see Volume I, Section 9.4.2.)

Problem 9.4†—A uniform beam consists of a straight member of length L and flexural rigidity EI, with rigid gusset plates at its ends of length g_1, g_2 respectively, as shown in the diagram. Set up the stiffness matrices for the complete member.

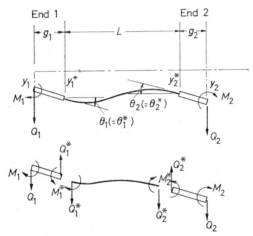

PROBLEM 9.4. Flexible beam with rigid gusset plates.

There are many problems, particularly in reinforced concrete structures, where the finite size of joints must be considered. We use an asterisk to denote quantities at the junctions between the flexible part of the beam and the gusset plates. For the flexible part of the beam the analysis in Volume I, Section 9.3 gives the equations

$$F_1^* = Y_{11} D_1^* + Y_{12} D_2^*$$
$$F_2^* = Y_{21} D_1^* + Y_{22} D_2^*$$

$$\dots\dots (9.4)$$

where the Y-matrices are identical with those given in that section.

We now write geometrical and equilibrium equations which relate the force and displacement variables at the joints to the starred quantities appearing in equation 9.4. The geometrical equations are

$$y_1^* = y_1 + g_1\theta_1$$
$$\theta_1^* = \theta_1$$

† This treatment was developed by S. T. Ariaratnam (Ph.D. Thesis, Cambridge, 1959.)

$$\left.\begin{aligned} y_2^* &= y_2 - g_2\theta_2 \\ \theta_2^* &= \theta_2 \end{aligned}\right\}$$

which may be written in matrix form as

$$D_1^* = G_1 D_1, \quad D_2^* = G_2 D_2 \qquad \dots (9.5)$$

where

$$G_1 = \begin{bmatrix} 1 & g_1 \\ 0 & 1 \end{bmatrix}, \qquad G_2 = \begin{bmatrix} 1 & -g_2 \\ 0 & 1 \end{bmatrix}$$

The equilibrium equations are

$$\left.\begin{aligned} Q_1 &= Q_1^* \\ M_1 &= Q_1^* g_1 + M_1^* \end{aligned}\right\}$$

$$\left.\begin{aligned} Q_2 &= Q_2^* \\ M_2 &= -Q_2^* g_2 + M_2^* \end{aligned}\right\}$$

which may be written in matrix form as

$$F_1 = G_1^t F_1^*, \quad F_2 = G_2^t F_2^* \qquad \dots (9.6)$$

where G_1^t, G_2^t are the transposes of G_1, G_2. The matrices G_1, G_2 are known as transfer matrices, and the transposition of the G-matrices which occurs when changing from equations 9.5 to 9.6 is called contragredience. Combining equations 9.4, 9.5, and 9.6 we obtain

$$F_1 = G_1^t \left(Y_{11} G_1 D_1 + Y_{12} G_2 D_2 \right)$$
$$F_2 = G_2^t \left(Y_{21} G_1 D_1 + Y_{22} G_2 D_2 \right)$$

or

$$\left.\begin{aligned} F_1 &= (G_1^t Y_{11} G_1) D_1 + (G_1^t Y_{12} G_2) D_2 \\ F_2 &= (G_2^t Y_{21} G_1) D_1 + (G_2^t Y_{22} G_2) D_2 \end{aligned}\right\} \qquad \dots (9.7)$$

Thus the modified matrices are the matrix products

$$G_i^t Y_{ij} G_j, \quad (i,j = 1, 2). \qquad \dots (9.8)$$

In view of the simple nature of the G-matrices, it is not necessary to carry out the multiplications implied in expression 9.8 by applying the general rules for multiplying matrices. The reader will find it easy to show that the modification of each matrix Y_{ij} can be achieved by adding g_i times the first row to the second, and then adding g_j times the first column to the second, where i and j take the values 1 and 2, provided that g_2 is treated as a negative quantity during this process.

It is also easy to show that the modified matrices Y_{11} and Y_{22} remain symmetrical, and that the modified matrix Y_{21} is still the transpose of the modified matrix Y_{12}. These are left as exercises for the reader.

Problem for Solution

9.5. Show that the treatment developed in the solution of *Problem 9.4*, which referred to a continuous beam, can be extended to members of a plane framework.

9.3. THE ASSEMBLY OF COMPLETE STIFFNESS MATRICES

The remaining problems are concerned with the assembly of the complete stiffness matrices for a number of different types of structure. Although this may be done by writing down the equations of equilibrium and compatibility for all the joints of a frame, it is simpler to construct the matrix by applying the following rule: If a member has its end 1 at joint i of a structure, and its end 2 at joint j, then the Y'-matrices appear in the complete stiffness matrix in accordance with the following scheme

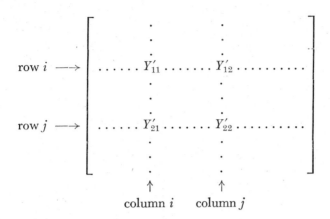

The complete matrix is constructed by applying this process to each member in turn, and adding the results. Since there will normally not be more than one member connecting any two joints, the addition process will only involve the matrices Y'_{11}, Y'_{22}, which lie on the leading diagonal. The final matrix will have for the leading diagonal element in the ith row a summation involving the Y'_{11} or Y'_{22} matrix of each member attached to joint i. The reader will note that if the direction arrows are always chosen to run from a lower to a higher numbered joint, then the Y'_{12} matrices will always appear above the leading diagonal and the Y'_{21} matrices below it.

Problems for Solution

9.6. By applying these rules construct the load-displacement equations for the uniform continuous beam shown. The flexural rigidity is EI.

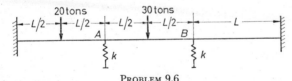

PROBLEM 9.6

9.7. Find the reactions at the two central supports of the beam of *Problem 9.6* when the support springs are very stiff.

Problem 9.8—Find the moments at the ends of the beam in the frame shown in diagram (a). Neglect the effects of axial forces. All members have the same flexural rigidity EI.

In this problem, as in the two previous ones, the first step is to replace the actual loading by equivalent fixed-end forces and moments at the joints, as shown at (b). This figure also shows the coordinate system and the directions of the members.

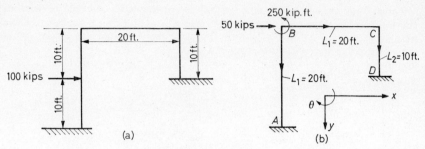

PROBLEM 9.8

The load-displacement equations can be written down immediately in the form

$$\begin{bmatrix} P_B \\ P_C \end{bmatrix} = \begin{bmatrix} (Y'_{11})_{BA} + (Y'_{11})_{BC} & (Y'_{12})_{BC} \\ (Y'_{21})_{BC} & (Y'_{22})_{BC} + (Y'_{11})_{CD} \end{bmatrix} \begin{bmatrix} D_B \\ D_C \end{bmatrix} \quad \dots\dots (9.9)$$

The stiffness matrices for the beam BC are given in Volume I, Section 9.4.2, equation [9.18]. The stiffness matrices for the stanchions can be obtained by putting $\alpha = 90°$ in the general expression on page 441 of Volume I, or by actually carrying out the matrix transformations for change of axes. The general form is

$$Y'_{11} = \begin{bmatrix} 12EI/L^3 & 0 & -6EI/L^2 \\ 0 & EA/L & 0 \\ -6EI/L^2 & 0 & 4EI/L \end{bmatrix}$$

Substituting in 9.9 we obtain the equations

$$\begin{bmatrix} 50 \\ 0 \\ -250 \\ 0 \\ 0 \\ 0 \end{bmatrix} = \begin{bmatrix} 12EI/L_1^3 + EA/L_1 & 0 & -6EI/L_1^2 \cdot \\ 0 & 12EI/L_1^3 + EA/L_1 & 6EI/L_1^2 \cdot \\ -6EI/L_1^2 & 6EI/L_1^2 & 8EI/L_1^2 \cdot \\ \cdots & \cdots & \cdots \\ -EA/L_1 & 0 & 0 \cdot \\ 0 & -12EI/L_1^3 & -6EI/L_1^2 \cdot \\ 0 & 6EI/L_1^2 & 2EI/L_1 \cdot \end{bmatrix}$$

$$\begin{bmatrix} \cdot & -EA/L_1 & 0 & 0 \\ \cdot & 0 & -12EI/L_1^3 & 6EI/L_1^2 \\ \cdot & 0 & -6EI/L_1^2 & 2EI/L_1 \\ \cdots & \cdots & \cdots & \cdots \\ \cdot & 12EI/L_2^3 + EA/L_1 & 0 & -6EI/L_2^2 \\ \cdot & 0 & 12EI/L_1^3 + EA/L_2 & -6EI/L_1^2 \\ \cdot & -6EI/L_2^2 & -6EI/L_1^2 & 4EI/L_2 + 4EI/L_1 \end{bmatrix} \begin{bmatrix} x_B \\ y_B \\ \theta_B \\ \\ x_C \\ y_C \\ \theta_C \end{bmatrix} \qquad (9.10)$$

where $L_1 = 20$ ft., $L_2 = 10$ ft.

These equations are the 'exact' load-displacement equations, and include the effects of axial tensions and compressions. If these axial force effects are to be ignored, we may set $y_B = y_C = 0$. We can thus drop the second and fifth equations (which are equations of vertical equilibrium at the beam ends) and delete terms in y_B, y_C from the other equations, giving

$$\begin{bmatrix} 50 \\ -250 \\ 0 \\ 0 \end{bmatrix} = \begin{bmatrix} 12EI/L_1^3 + EA/L_1 & -6EI/L_1^2 & -EA/L_1 & 0 \\ -6EI/L_1^2 & 8EI/L_1 & 0 & 2EI/L_1 \\ -EA/L_1 & 0 & 12EI/L_2^3 + EA/L_1 & -6EI/L_2^2 \\ 0 & 2EI/L_1 & -6EI/L_2^2 & 4EI/L_2 + 4EI/L_1 \end{bmatrix} \begin{bmatrix} x_B \\ \theta_B \\ x_C \\ \theta_C \end{bmatrix} \quad (9.11)$$

Further, we have $x_B = x_C = x$ (say) so that we may combine the first and third columns of 9.11, giving

$$\begin{bmatrix} 50 \\ -250 \\ 0 \\ 0 \end{bmatrix} = \begin{bmatrix} 12EI/L_1^3 & -6EI/L_1^2 & 0 \\ -6EI/L_1^2 & 8EI/L_1 & 2EI/L_1 \\ 12EI/L_2^3 & 0 & -6EI/L_2^2 \\ -6EI/L_2^2 & 2EI/L_1 & 4EI/L_2 + 4EI/L_1 \end{bmatrix} \begin{bmatrix} x \\ \theta_B \\ \theta_C \end{bmatrix}$$

We now have four equations in three unknowns, so that we must reduce the number of equations by one. The best way of doing this is to add the two equations of horizontal equilibrium (now the first and third) and use this combined equation in place of the other two.

$$\begin{bmatrix} 50 \\ -250 \\ 0 \end{bmatrix} = \begin{bmatrix} 12EI/L_1^3 + 12EI/L_2^3 & -6EI/L_1^2 & -6EI/L_2^2 \\ -6EI/L_1^2 & 8EI/L_1 & 2EI/L_1 \\ -6EI/L_2^2 & 2EI/L_1 & 4EI/L_1 + 4EI/L_2 \end{bmatrix} \begin{bmatrix} x \\ \theta_B \\ \theta_C \end{bmatrix}$$

On substitution for L_1 and L_2, this equation gives

$$\begin{bmatrix} 500 \\ -250 \\ 0 \end{bmatrix} = \left(\frac{EI}{20}\right) \begin{bmatrix} 27 & -3 & -12 \\ -3 & 8 & 2 \\ -12 & 2 & 12 \end{bmatrix} \begin{bmatrix} x/10 \\ \theta_B \\ \theta_C \end{bmatrix}$$

which has the solution

$$x = (200/EI) \times 31\cdot4$$
$$\theta_B = -(20/EI) \times 28\cdot5$$
$$\theta_C = (20/EI) \times 36\cdot2$$

Substituting for θ_B and θ_C in the beam equations (Volume I, equation [9.18]) we obtain the moments at the ends of the beam

$$M_1 = -4 \times 28\cdot5 + 2 \times 36\cdot2 = 41\cdot6 \text{ kip. ft.}$$
$$M_2 = -2 \times 28\cdot5 + 4 \times 36\cdot2 = 87\cdot8 \text{ kip. ft.}$$

Problems for Solution

9.9. Set up the stiffness matrix for the frame shown in the figure for the case when all the joints are rigid.

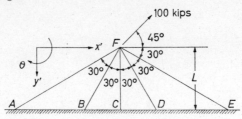

PROBLEM 9.9

9.10. Find the force in member *AF* of the frame of *Problem 9.9*. All the members have the same cross-section but the joints are pinned.

9.11. Set up the load-displacement equations in symbolic form (i.e. using *Y'*-matrices) for the frames shown at (a) and (b).

Arrows indicate directions; end 1 → end 2, in each member.

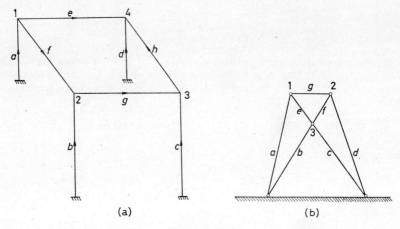

(a)

(b)

PROBLEM 9.11

252

SOLUTIONS TO PROBLEMS

CHAPTER 1

(+ signifies redundants; − signifies deficiencies)

1.5. (a) + 1. (b) 0, but unstable. (c) 0. (d) + 1. (e) + 1.

1.6. (a) + 2. (b) + 2. (c) + 1. (d) + 2. (e) + 2. (f) + 2. (g) + 1. (h) + 1. (j) 0. (k) 0. (l) + 1. (m) 0. (n) 0. (o) − 1. (p) 0, but unstable. (q) + 1. (r) + 6. (s) + 3. (t) − 1. (u) + 1. (v) 0, but unstable. (w) − 5. (x) + 3. (y) + 2. (z) + 6. (a), (b), (c), (d), (e), (f), (g), (h), (n), (r), (s), (u), (x), (y) and (z) are simple structures; (j), (k), (l), (m) and (q) are compound structures; (o), (p) and (t) are complex structures.

1.11. (a) + 1. (b) 0. (c) 0, but unstable. (d) 0. (e) 0. (f) + 2. (g) − 2, but stable because of prestressing. (h) 0. (k) + 9. (j) 0.

1.15. (a) + 3. At each internal hinge we can write $\Sigma M = 0$; the two equations thus obtained reduce the number of redundants by two. (b) + 5. (c) + 4. (d) + 12. (e) + 19. (f) + 18. (g) + 13. (h) + 36. (j) + 6. (k) + 10. (l) + 6.

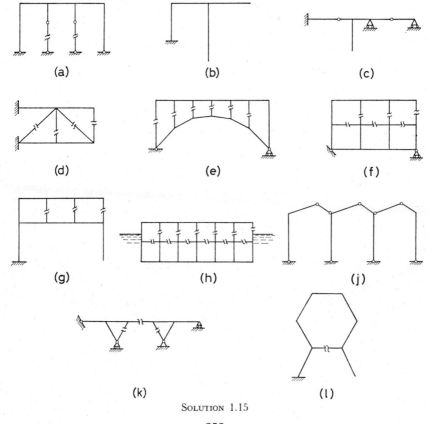

SOLUTION 1.15

1.17.   (a) $+ 3$.   (b) $+ 3$.   (c) $+ 11$.   (d) $+ 8$.   (e) $+ 6$.   (f) $+ 18$.   (g) $+ 6$.

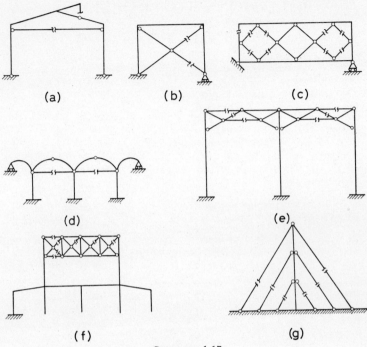

(a)   (b)   (c)

(d)   (e)

(f)   (g)

SOLUTION 1.17

1.22. $F_{AB} = \dfrac{300}{11}$ lb.; $F_{BC} = \dfrac{800}{11}$ lb.

1.23. $F_{AB} = -0.019P$; $F_{CB} = +0.746P$; $F_{DB} = -0.887P$.

1.24. $\dfrac{1.125 \times 10^3}{0.75 + 738/L^2}$ lb. (L in inches).

1.25.   (a) Strain $= 0.0123 \times 10^{-6}F$ (For $F < 4130$ lb. For $F > 4130$ lb., increment of strain $= 1.06 \times 10^{-6}.\delta F$).   (b) 11870 lb./in.^{2} (steel); 23.3 lb./in.^{2} (concrete).

1.26. $\dfrac{wL\left\{\dfrac{5L^2}{24I} + \dfrac{1}{A}\right\}}{\left\{\dfrac{L^2}{6I} + \dfrac{3}{2A}\right\}}$

1.27.   (a) $-0.4P$. (b) $\dfrac{1}{2K}\left\{-\dfrac{L}{AE} \pm \sqrt{\dfrac{L^2}{A^2E^2} + \dfrac{4KPL}{AE}}\right\}$

1.28.   (a) $3P/5$. (b) $5P/9$.

254

1.29. $F_{BD} = \dfrac{P\left(\dfrac{1}{8A} + \dfrac{L^2}{48I}\right)}{\dfrac{1\cdot22}{A} + \dfrac{L^2}{96I}}$

1.30.   Load in rivet 2 $= \dfrac{P\left(\dfrac{L}{t_2 bE} + \rho\right)}{2\rho + \dfrac{L}{bE}\left(\dfrac{1}{t_1} + \dfrac{1}{t_2}\right)}$

1.31. $P\dfrac{(\rho^2 + 4S\rho + 2S^2)}{(5\rho^2 + 10S\rho + 4S^2)}$ when $S = \dfrac{L}{tbE}$

1.32.   Reaction at central pontoon $= \dfrac{3wL(16EI\varDelta + L^3)}{4(9EI\varDelta + L^3)}$

1.33.   1/5 upwards.

CHAPTER 2

2.5. $\dfrac{P\cos\theta_i}{\cos^2\left(\dfrac{2\pi i}{n}\right)}$; $\dfrac{P}{3}$

2.6. x given by $x - \dfrac{(L\alpha_t t - x)^3}{L^2} - \dfrac{2L\alpha_t t(L\alpha_t t - x)}{L} = 0.$

2.7. F_1 given by $\dfrac{a_1 F_1^2}{2} + F_1(4\rho_2 - \rho_3) - 2\rho_2 P = 0.$

2.8. $a = 1\cdot314PL/EI$; $b = -0\cdot0196P/EI$; $c = -0\cdot00645P/EIL$, giving
       $F_1 = 0\cdot0258P$; $F_2 = 0\cdot0996P$; $F_3 = 0\cdot2156P$; $F_4 = 0\cdot363P.$

2.9. $R_A = R_B = 0\cdot84wL$; $R_1 = R_7 = 0\cdot853wL$; $R_2 = R_6 = 0\cdot886wL$;
       $R_3 = R_5 = 0\cdot926wL$; $R_4 = 0\cdot961wL.$

2.12. $R_c = 0$; $M_A = 3L\left(\dfrac{3wL}{2} + W\right)$; $V_A = 3wL + W$;

       $M_D = \dfrac{3L}{2}\left(\dfrac{3wL}{4} + W\right).$

2.13. $V_A = wL$; $V_G = \dfrac{3wL}{2}$; $V_J = \dfrac{25wL}{12} + \dfrac{pL}{3}$; $H_J = \dfrac{pL}{2}$; $M_D = \dfrac{wL^2}{12} + \dfrac{pL^2}{3}$.

2.14. $V_D = 32\cdot0$ tons; $V_F = 4\cdot8$ tons; $M_D = + 96$ ton ft.; $M_F = + 32$ ton ft.;
       $M_J = + 86$ ton ft.; $Q_J = + 7\cdot2$ tons.

2.15. $V_A = 2\cdot1wL$; $V_F = 4\cdot9wL$; $M_C = -2\cdot2wL^2$; $M_J = -1\cdot1wL^2$;
       $Q_J = + 1\cdot4wL.$

2.16. $V_A = 54\ 1/6$ tons; $F_{JK} = -112\cdot5$ tons; $F_{JC} = -19\ 1/6$ tons;
$F_{JD} = +27\cdot1$ tons; $F_{HB} = +15$ tons; $F_{KD} = 0$; $F_{AB} = +54\ 1/6$ tons.

2.17. $V_A = 5\cdot6$ tons; $H_A = 25$ tons; $F_{GH} = -59\cdot7$ tons; $F_{GC} = +6\cdot47$ tons;
$F_{FG} = -53\cdot2$ tons.

2.18. $F_{DE} = -5P/4$; $F_{BD} = -17P/4$; $F_{AD} = +2P$; $F_{AF} = -\sqrt{5}P/2$;
$F_{CD} = -P/2$.

2.19. $F_{DK} = -10/3$ tons.

2.25. -60 tons.

2.26. -10 tons; -40 tons.

2.31. -60 tons.

CHAPTER 3

3.3.   (a) $2\cdot414\ PL/AE$ downwards; (b) $1\cdot148\ P/K$ downwards.

3.4. $8\cdot23\ P/K$; $32\cdot50\ P/K$.

3.5. $6P + 1\cdot69$ units; $0\cdot235$ tons; $2\cdot12$ units.

3.8. $3\cdot328\ P/AE$ clockwise; $\dfrac{PL}{2AE}$ to the left.

3.9. $2\cdot74$ tons.

3.10. $8\cdot27$ tons/ in.^{2}.

3.11. $0\cdot372$ in. to the right; $0\cdot202$ in. downwards.

3.12. $1\cdot55 \times 10^{-3}$ in. downwards and $2\cdot4 \times 10^{-5}$ in. to the left.

3.13. fL/E to the right.

3.14.   (a) $2400\ P/AE$ in.; $519\ P/AE$ in. (b) $-720\ \alpha_t t$ in.; $-72\sqrt{5}\ \alpha_t t$ in.

3.15. $(2\cdot25\ P - 4\cdot33Q)\rho$ downwards; $(11Q - 4\cdot33P)\rho$ inwards.

3.16. $7110/AE$ in. apart.

3.17. $5\cdot0P\rho$ upwards and $22\cdot7P\rho$ to the right.

3.18. $(43\cdot88\ PL/AE + 0\cdot4)$ in.

3.19. $1\tfrac{1}{8}$ in.; $0\cdot124$ in.

3.20. $8\cdot24\ PL/AE$; $-5\cdot27\ PL/AE$.

3.21. $2\cdot356\ WL/aE$.

3.22. $3\cdot80$ in. outwards; $5\cdot71$ in. downwards.

3.23. $1\cdot5P\rho$; $-0\cdot797P\rho$.

3.24. $15\cdot18\ PL/AE$.

3.25. $9 \cdot 26P/AE$.

3.26. $\dfrac{P(a^2 + L^2)^{3/2}}{3a^2AE}$; 0; $\dfrac{M(a^2 + L^2)^{3/2}}{2a^4AE}$

3 31. $-336/EI$ in.; $864/EI$ in.; $27/28$ tons.

3.32. $13wL^3/6EI$; $29wL^4/8EI$.

3.33. $\dfrac{waL}{24EI}\{L^2 - 3aL - a^2\}$

3.34.   (a) $\dfrac{Mab(2a + b)}{6(a + b)EI}$ (b) $\dfrac{Mab(b - a)}{3(a + b)EI}$

3.35. $\dfrac{19wL^4}{48EI}$; $\dfrac{11wL^4}{48EI}$; $\dfrac{-wL^3}{4EI}$; $\dfrac{13wL^3}{16EI}$

3.36. $38,393/EI$ to the left; $63,349/EI$ downwards.

3.37. $-441/EI$; $-14 \cdot 8/EI$.

3.38. $5333w/EI_0$ outwards.

3.39. $PR^3/2EI$ outwards; $0 \cdot 178PR^3/EI$.

3.40. $0 \cdot 722\ PL^3/EI$; $1 \cdot 25\ L^3/EI$; $P/\sqrt{3}$.

3.41.   (a) (i) $0 \cdot 683\ HL^3/EI$;   (ii) $0 \cdot 242\ WL^3/EI$.

       (b) $0 \cdot 204\ W$.

3.42. $2 \cdot 94$ tons.

3.44.   (a), (f) and (h) are correct; the others are incorrect.

3.46. $0 \cdot 04$ in.

3.47. $10 \cdot 5$ lb., $9 \cdot 0$ lb., $0 \cdot 5$ lb.; $+ 0 \cdot 02$ in.; $- 0 \cdot 01$ in.; $+ 0 \cdot 02$ in.; $+ 0 \cdot 19$ in.; $+ 0 \cdot 16$ in.; $+ 0 \cdot 19$ in.

CHAPTER 4

4.3. $5 \cdot 29$ tons; $0 \cdot 35$ tons; $1 \cdot 38$ tons.

4.4. $F_{AB} = + 0 \cdot 15P$; $F_{BC} = - 0 \cdot 30P$; $F_{EF} = - 0 \cdot 18P$; $F_{FG} = + 0 \cdot 36P$; $F_{BF} = - 0 \cdot 29P$.

4.8. $3\sqrt{3}P/32$; $39P\rho/64$ downwards; $3\sqrt{3}P\rho/64$ outwards.

4.9. $- 13P/16$; $28 \cdot 5P\rho$ too long.

4.10. $- 0 \cdot 868$; $5 \cdot 7PL/aE$; $2 \cdot 05PL/aE$.

4.11. $0 \cdot 173P$ (thrust); $- 0 \cdot 191P$.

4.12. $- 5P/14\sqrt{5}$.

4.13.   When the tie is just taught when inserted the tension produced in it by the load is $0 \cdot 204P$ but it has no effect, whether prestressed or not, on the most highly stressed members JD and ND.

4.14. $- 0 \cdot 30P - 0 \cdot 56\dfrac{\Delta AE}{L}$; $- \dfrac{AE\alpha_t}{2 \cdot 53}(t_1 + 4t_2)$.

4.15. $0 \cdot 0178$ in.

4.16. $F_{EF} = + 7200$ lb.; $F_{AE} = + 15,380$ lb.; $F_{EB} = F_{BF} = - 6440$ lb.

4.17. $\dfrac{Ra}{3E}\left(\dfrac{7}{A_1} + \dfrac{6}{A_2}\right)$; $\dfrac{Ra}{E}\left\{\dfrac{\sqrt{3}}{A} + \dfrac{7}{3A_1} + \dfrac{2}{A_2}\right\}$

4.18. $\dfrac{125P}{327}$; $\dfrac{25}{109\rho}\left(\dfrac{5P\rho}{3} - \varDelta\right)$

4.19. $- 0 \cdot 295P$; $+ 3 \cdot 24P/AE$ in.

4.20. $F_{EA} = F_{EB} = - 0 \cdot 99$ tons; $F_{EC} = F_{ED} = - 1 \cdot 31$ tons.

4.21. $F_{AE} = - 6 \cdot 47$ tons; $F_{EF} = - 1 \cdot 40$ tons; $F_{EG} = - 2 \cdot 24$ tons;
$F_{EC} = - 2 \cdot 04$ tons; $F_{GC} = - 5 \cdot 93$ tons; $F_{AF} = - 4 \cdot 32$ tons.

4.22. $A_{AB} = 3P/2f$; $A_{AD} = \sqrt{2}P/f$; $A_{BC} = \sqrt{2}P/f$; $A_{BD} = P/2f$;
$A_{BE} = P/\sqrt{2}f$; $A_{CD} = P/f$; $A_{DE} = 3P/2f$.

4.23. AE: Area $2\sqrt{2}P/3f$; too short by $fL/\sqrt{2}E$.

BD: Area $2\sqrt{2}P/3f$; too short by $5\sqrt{2}fL/6E$.

4.24. $8fL/E$ too long; $\pm 2f/3$.

4.28. $4 \cdot 20$ tons; $74,400/EI$ in. outwards.

4.29. $5 \cdot 42$ tons; $11 \cdot 50$ tons.

4.31. $3 \cdot 40$ tons, upwards; $2 \cdot 21$ tons, to the left.

4.32. $T = \dfrac{0 \cdot 917wL^3/I}{4 \cdot 328/a + 1 \cdot 5/A + 0 \cdot 833L^2/I}$

4.33. (a) $\dfrac{2PaL^2}{8\sqrt{3}I + aL^2}$ (b) $\dfrac{8PL^3}{24EI + \sqrt{3}EaL^2}$ (c) $\dfrac{2aL^3 - 3axL^2 + ax^3}{8\sqrt{3}IL + aL^3}$

4.34. $\dfrac{\sqrt{3}wL^3/2I}{5L^2/4I + 3(1 + \sqrt{3})/a}$

4.35. $0 \cdot 397$ tons; $0 \cdot 795$ tons; $276/EI$ ft.

4.36. $+ \sqrt{6}F/5$; $+ \sqrt{2}F/5$; $- \sqrt{6}F/5$; $- \sqrt{2}F/5$.

4.37. $14 : 13$.

4.38. $F_{DE} = 0 \cdot 0406P$; $F_{AC} = 0 \cdot 4832P$; $\varDelta_B = 131P/E$ ft.

4.39. 1153 lb.; 5000 lb. ft.; $0 \cdot 025$ in.; 1350 lb.; 1710 lb. ft.

4.41. $M_B = 0 \cdot 794M'$ (sagging); $M_D = 0 \cdot 063M'$ (hogging).

4.42. $17wL^2/14$ (hogging); $wL^2/7$; $5wL^2/7$; $5wL^2/14$ (sagging); $2wL^2/7$.

4.43. $0 \cdot 1024 \, wR^2$ (hogging); $0 \cdot 0013 \, wR^2$.

4.44. $V_D = 0 \cdot 784P$; $M_D = 0 \cdot 625PL$; $T_D = 0 \cdot 117PL$.

CHAPTER 5

5.3.   0·21L

5.4.

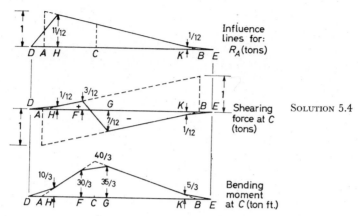

Influence lines for: R_A (tons)

Shearing force at C (tons)   SOLUTION 5.4

Bending moment at C (ton ft.)

Under live load of 2 tons per foot, maximum values are 6·0 tons, 24·92 tons and 800 ton ft. respectively.

5.5.

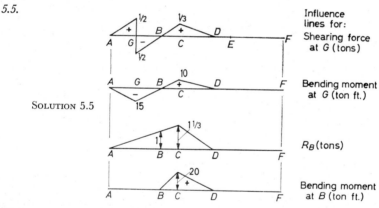

Influence lines for:

Shearing force at G (tons)

Bending moment at G (ton ft.)

SOLUTION 5.5

R_B (tons)

Bending moment at B (ton ft.)

5.6.

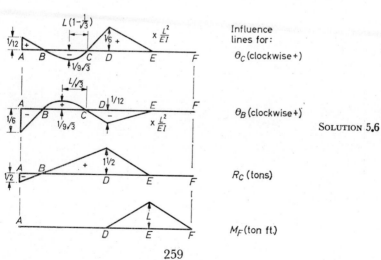

Influence lines for:

θ_C (clockwise +)

θ_B (clockwise +)   SOLUTION 5.6

R_C (tons)

M_F (ton ft.)

259

5.8. Maximum and minimum forces in *FE* are 20 tons and 5 tons (tensile) respectively.

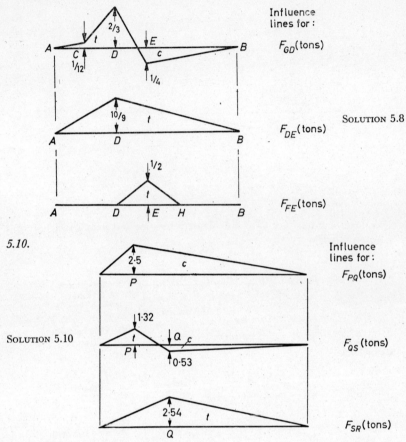

Influence lines for:

F_{GD}(tons)

SOLUTION 5.8

F_{DE}(tons)

F_{FE}(tons)

5.10.

SOLUTION 5.10

Influence lines for:

F_{PQ}(tons)

F_{QS} (tons)

F_{SR}(tons)

5.11. Maximum and minimum forces in *FG* are 76·5 tons and 29·4 tons respectively.

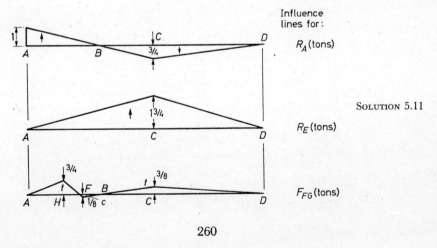

Influence lines for:

R_A(tons)

SOLUTION 5.11

R_E (tons)

F_{FG}(tons)

260

5.12.

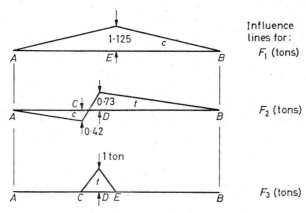

Influence lines for:

F_1 (tons)

F_2 (tons)

F_3 (tons)

SOLUTION 5.12

5.14.

$$R_B = \left(1 - \frac{x}{L}\right)^2 \left(1 + \frac{x}{2L}\right)$$

$$= \frac{3wL}{8} \text{ for uniformly distributed load } w \text{ per foot.}$$

5.15.

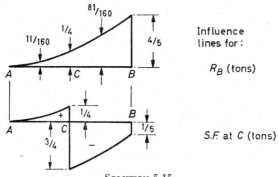

Influence lines for:

R_B (tons)

S.F. at C (tons)

SOLUTION 5.15

5.16.

$$\Delta_B = \frac{(L-x)^2 \, (2L+x)}{6EI + \sqrt{3}\,AEL^2/4}$$

$$F_{\text{tie}} = \frac{A(L-x)^2 \, (2L+x)}{8\sqrt{3}\,IL + AL^3}$$

5.17.

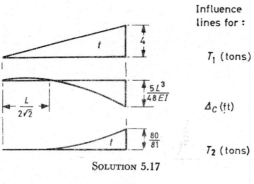

Influence lines for:

T_1 (tons)

Δ_C (ft)

T_2 (tons)

SOLUTION 5.17

S   261

5.18.

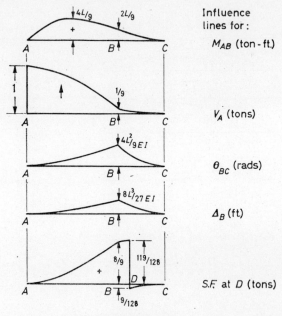

Influence lines for:

M_{AB} (ton-ft.)

V_A (tons)

θ_{BC} (rads)

Δ_B (ft.)

S.F. at D (tons)

SOLUTION 5.18

There is no discontinuity in the influence line for M_{AB}; if this is obtained by imposing unit rotation at A the resulting bending moment diagram is linear and has zero value at B. Hence the hinge at B makes no difference.

5.20.

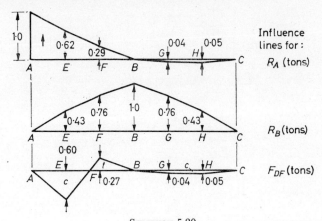

Influence lines for:

R_A (tons)

R_B (tons)

F_{DF} (tons)

SOLUTION 5.20

5.21.

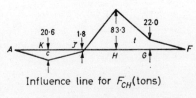

Influence line for F_{CH} (tons)

SOLUTION 5.21

262

5.22.   (a) $R_A = 0.69$ tons; $R_K = 0.32$ tons; $F_{CO} = 2.49$ tons (t)
           (b)   Movement of $K = 136.3\rho$ along AK

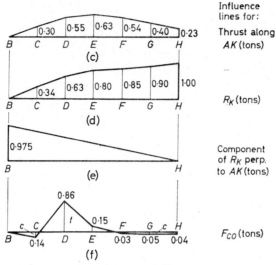

Influence lines for:

Thrust along AK (tons)

(c)

R_K (tons)

(d)

Component of R_K perp. to AK (tons)

(e)

F_{CO} (tons)

(f)

SOLUTION 5.22

(g)   0.035 **tons.**   (h)   1.63 tons.   (i) 40.6ρ.

5.23.   (a)   0.83 tons.

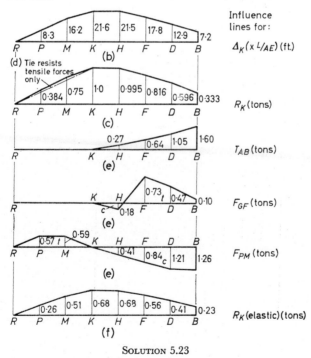

Influence lines for:

$\Delta_K (\times L/_{AE})$ (ft.)

(b)

(d) Tie resists tensile forces only

R_K (tons)

(c)

T_{AB} (tons)

(e)

F_{GF} (tons)

(e)

F_{PM} (tons)

(e)

R_K (elastic) (tons)

(f)

SOLUTION 5.23

5.25.

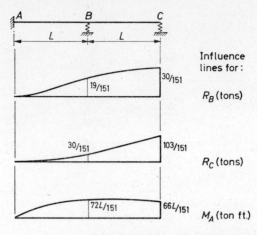

Influence lines for:

R_B (tons)

R_C (tons)

M_A (ton ft.)

SOLUTION 5.25

5.26.

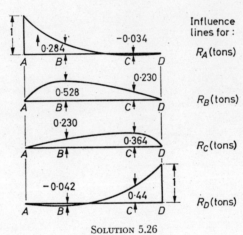

Influence lines for:

R_A (tons)

R_B (tons)

R_C (tons)

R_D (tons)

SOLUTION 5.26

5.27.

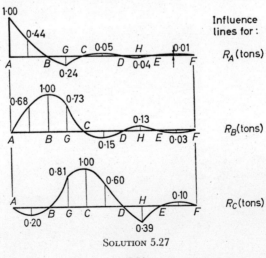

Influence lines for:

R_A (tons)

R_B (tons)

R_C (tons)

SOLUTION 5.27

264

5.28.

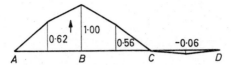

Influence line for R_B (tons) (R_C is mirror image)

SOLUTION 5.28

5.29.   (a) Under given loads deflexion at B is $194 \cdot 5 \, PL/aE$. Force required at E to reduce Δ_B to zero is $27 \cdot 6P$.

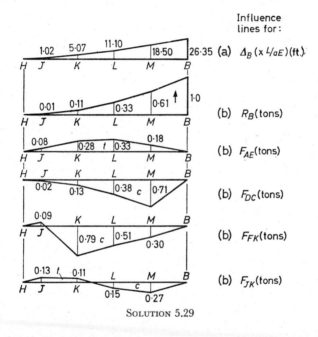

SOLUTION 5.29

(c) The new element is that the deflexion of the part of the structure *GFEKJH* under its own weight implies that the tie *AE* is slightly longer than before; it is in effect too long by an amount which can be calculated. If it then turns out that, for any position of the unit load, the tie appears to be in compression it will, in reality, become inoperative and the structure will then have only the single redundant reaction at B.

5.31.

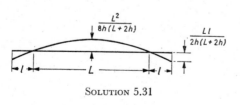

SOLUTION 5.31

5.32. Maximum value of M_{BA} is 9·12 ton ft. occurring when loads are in AB, 11·6 ft. and 5·6 ft. from B respectively.

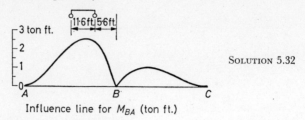

Influence line for M_{BA} (ton ft.)

SOLUTION 5.32

5.36. Spring stiffness $= 0·58L/AE$.

5.38. $M = 54$ ton in. anticlockwise.

$H = 0·5$ ton inwards.

$V = 0·2$ ton upwards.

The influence lines would have been given directly if, while a displacement corresponding to a certain redundant was being imposed, no displacement had been permitted corresponding to the other two redundants.

5.39. 1513 ton ft. (anticlockwise).

5.40. 51/8 ton ft.; 45/16 ton ft.

5.41. 7·33 tons.

5.42. $R_A = 3·55$ tons; $R_B = 8·68$ tons; $R_C = 1·77$ tons.

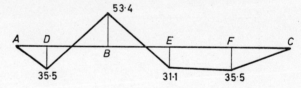

SOLUTION 5.42 Bending moment diagram (ton ft.) under given loads

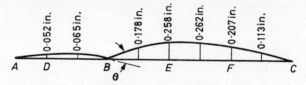

Shape of model if $\theta = 5°$ is imposed at B

CHAPTER 6

6.3. $M_{FAB} = \dfrac{P}{L^2}(ab^2 - 2abd + b^2d)$

$M_{FBA} = \dfrac{P}{L^2}(a^2b + 2abd - a^2d).$

6.4. $\theta = \dfrac{wL^3}{12(2EI + \alpha L)}$; $\alpha = 6EI/L.$

6.5. $\theta = \dfrac{PL^2}{8(2EI + \alpha L)}$; $\alpha = \infty.$

6.6. $M_{FAB} = \dfrac{11wL^2}{192}$; $M_{FBA} = \dfrac{5wL^2}{192}$; $\dfrac{wL^4}{768EI}$; $\dfrac{wL}{4}$

6.7. $\dfrac{wL^4}{384EI}$;   (a) $\dfrac{wL}{2}$;   (b) $\dfrac{wL}{4}$; $\dfrac{kwL^4}{4(kL^3 + 192EI)}$

6.9. $wL^3/6L_1L_2$.

6.10. $wL^2/10$.

6.11.   70 tons.

6.12. $M_B = 24 \cdot 02$ ton ft.; $M_C = -0 \cdot 58$ ton ft.
       $R_A = 0 \cdot 10$ tons; $R_B = 15 \cdot 45$ tons; $R_C = 3 \cdot 00$ tons; $R_D = 22 \cdot 45$ tons.

6.13.   (a) $M_A = + 18 \cdot 16$ ton ft.; $M_B = + 36 \cdot 32$ ton ft.; $M_C + 45 \cdot 50$ ton ft.
         $M_D = + 27 \cdot 25$ ton ft.; $R_A = -1 \cdot 82$ tons.

      (b) $M_A = + 17 \cdot 13$ ton ft.; $M_B = + 34 \cdot 27$ ton ft.; $M_C = 51 \cdot 92$ ton ft.
         $R_A = -1 \cdot 71$ tons.

      (c) $M_A = -3 \cdot 36$ ton ft.; $M_B = -6 \cdot 72$ ton ft.; $M_C = + 180$ ton ft.
         $R_A = + 0 \cdot 34$ tons.

These solutions enable the bending moment diagrams to be drawn.

6.14. $wL^3/168EI$.

6.15. $22 \cdot 4 \times 10^{-4}$ in. downwards.

6.16.   (a) $M_A = -5 \cdot 41$ ton ft.; $M_B = 13 \cdot 70$ ton ft.
         $R_A = 2 \cdot 91$ tons; $R_B = 9 \cdot 37$ tons; $R_C = 7 \cdot 72$ tons.

      (b) $M_A = + 21 \cdot 79$ ton ft.; $M_B = -11 \cdot 1$ ton ft.
         $R_A = 6 \cdot 62$ tons; $R_B = 5 \cdot 42$ tons; $R_C = 8 \cdot 96$ tons.

6.17. $R_A = 8 \cdot 38$ tons; $R_B = 32 \cdot 11$ tons; $R_C = 30 \cdot 46$ tons; $R_D = 9 \cdot 03$ tons.
      $M_B = 86 \cdot 97$ ton ft.; $M_C = 71 \cdot 34$ ton ft.

6.18.   Due to loads: $M_B = 411 \cdot 27$ ton ft.; $M_C = 736 \cdot 62$ ton ft.
                 $R_A = -10 \cdot 56$ tons; $R_B = 85 \cdot 14$ tons;
                 $R_C = 163 \cdot 83$ tons; $R_D = 61 \cdot 59$ tons.
      Due to settlement: $M_B = -21 \cdot 34$ ton ft.; $M_C = 9 \cdot 46$ ton ft.
                      $R_A = 1 \cdot 07$ tons; $R_B = -1 \cdot 58$ tons;
                      $R_C = 0 \cdot 75$ tons; $R_D = -0 \cdot 24$ tons.

6.20.   4·76 lb.

6.21. $R_B = 9 \cdot 18$ tons; $R_C = 15 \cdot 01$ tons.
      $M_B = 9 \cdot 52$ ton ft.; $M_C = 22 \cdot 42$ ton ft.

6.23. $R_A = 0 \cdot 208P$; $R_B = 0 \cdot 542P$; $R_C = 0 \cdot 292P$; $R_D = -0 \cdot 042P$.

6.24. $k = 0 \cdot 01116$.

6.25. $M_A = 0 \cdot 932$ ton ft.; $M_B = -0 \cdot 1094$ ton ft.; $M_C = -1 \cdot 555$ ton ft.

6.26.   (a) $R_B = \dfrac{wL(\varDelta + 5L^3/24EI)}{(3\varDelta/2 + L^3/6EI)}$

      (b) $M_B = -wL^2/20$.

      (c) $\varDelta = L^3/12EI$.

6.28.

x (×L)	6.28(a) M_B (×L)	6.28(a) R_A	6.28(a) R_B	6.28(b) M_A (×L)	6.28(b) M_B (×L)	6.28(b) R_A	6.28(b) R_B	6.28(b) R_C	6.28(c) M_A (×L)	6.28(c) M_B (×L)	6.28(c) R_A	6.28(c) R_B
0·0	0	1·0	0	0	0	1·0	0	0	0	0	1·0	0
0·2	0·048	0·752	0·296	0·137	0·014	0·923	0·091	—0·014	0·136	0·016	0·920	0·104
0·4	0·084	0·516	0·568	0·170	0·041	0·729	0·312	—0·041	0·168	0·048	0·720	0·352
0·6	0·096	0·304	0·792	0·137	0·062	0·475	0·587	—0·062	0·132	0·072	0·460	0·648
0·8	0·072	0·128	0·944	0·069	0·055	0·214	0·841	—0·055	0·064	0·064	0·200	0·896
1·0	0	0	1·0	0	0	0	1·0	0	0	0	0	1·0
1·2	0·072	—0·072	0·944	—0·042	0·082	—0·124	1·006	0·118	—0·032	0·064	—0·096	0·896
1·4	0·096	—0·096	0·792	—0·055	0·110	—0·165	0·875	0·290	—0·036	0·072	—0·108	0·648
1·6	0·084	—0·084	0·568	—0·048	0·096	—0·144	0·640	0·504	—0·024	0·048	—0·072	0·352
1·8	0·048	—0·048	0·296	—0·027	0·055	—0·082	0·337	0·745	—0·008	0·016	—0·024	0·104
2·0	0	0	0	0	0	0	0	1·0	0	0	0	0

Problem 6.28(a)

Problem 6.28 (b)

Problem 6.28(c)

Problem 6.28(d) and **Problem 6.28(e)**

x $(\times L)$	6.28(d) M_B $(\times L)$	6.28(d) R_A	6.28(d) R_B	6.28(e) M_A $(\times L)$	6.28(e) M_B $(\times L)$	6.28(e) M_C $(\times L)$	6.28(e) R_A	6.28(e) R_B	6.28(e) R_C	6.28(e) R_D
0·0	0	1·0	0	0	0	0	1·0	0	0	0
0·2	0·051	0·749	0·315	0·137	0·015	−0·004	0·922	0·097	−0·023	0·004
0·4	0·090	0·510	0·602	0·170	0·044	−0·011	0·726	0·329	−0·066	0·011
0·6	0·102	0·298	0·830	0·135	0·066	−0·017	0·469	0·614	−0·100	0·017
0·8	0·077	0·123	0·973	0·066	0·059	−0·015	0·207	0·867	−0·089	0·015
1·0	0	0	1·0	0	0	0	0	1·0	0	0
1·2	0·064	−0·064	0·896	−0·037	0·074	0·030	−0·111	0·955	0·186	−0·030
1·4	0·080	−0·080	0·696	−0·046	0·092	0·061	−0·138	0·769	0·430	−0·061
1·6	0·064	−0·064	0·448	−0·037	0·074	0·078	−0·111	0·507	0·682	−0·078
1·8	0·032	−0·032	0·200	−0·019	0·037	0·063	−0·056	0·230	0·889	−0·063
2·0	0	0	0	0	0	0	0	0	1·0	0
2·2	−0·019	0·019	−0·115	0·011	−0·022	0·077	0·033	−0·132	0·976	0·123
2·4	−0·026	0·026	−0·154	0·015	−0·029	0·103	0·044	−0·176	0·835	0·297
2·6	−0·022	0·022	−0·134	0·013	−0·026	0·090	0·039	−0·155	0·606	0·510
2·8	−0·013	0·013	−0·077	0·007	−0·015	0·052	0·022	−0·089	0·319	0·748
3·0	0	0	0	0	0	0	0	0	0	1·0

Problem 6.28(f)

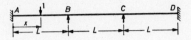

x ($\times L$)	M_A ($\times L$)	M_B ($\times L$)	M_C ($\times L$)	M_D ($\times L$)	R_A	R_B	R_C	R_D
0·0	0	0	0	0	1·0	0	0	0
0·2	0·136	0·015	− 0·004	0·002	0·922	0·096	− 0·024	0·006
0·4	0·170	0·045	− 0·013	0·006	0·725	0·333	− 0·077	0·019
0·6	0·134	0·067	− 0·019	0·010	0·467	0·619	− 0·115	0·029
0·8	0·066	0·060	− 0·017	0·008	0·206	0·871	− 0·102	0·025
1·0	0	0	0	0	0	1·0	0	0
1·2	− 0·036	0·072	0·034	− 0·017	− 0·108	0·946	0·213	− 0·051
1·4	− 0·045	0·090	0·070	− 0·035	− 0·135	0·755	0·485	− 0·105
1·6	− 0·035	0·070	0·090	− 0·045	− 0·105	0·485	0·755	− 0·135
1·8	− 0·017	0·034	0·072	− 0·036	− 0·051	0·213	0·946	− 0·108
2·0	0	0	0	0	0	0	1·0	0

Problem 6.28 (g)

x (ft.)	M_A (ton ft.)	M_B (ton ft.)	R_A (tons)	R_B (tons)	R_C (tons)
0	0	0	1·0	0	0
2·8	1·89	0·25	0·917	0·095	− 0·012
5·6	2·31	0·76	0·711	0·327	− 0·038
8·4	1·78	1·15	0·445	0·612	− 0·057
11·2	0·84	1·02	0·182	0·869	− 0·051
14·0	0	0	0	1·0	0
18·0	− 0·57	1·15	− 0·123	0·981	0·142
22·0	− 0·76	1·53	− 0·164	0·840	0·324
26·0	− 0·67	1·34	− 0·143	0·610	0·533
30·0	− 0·38	0·76	− 0·081	0·319	0·762
34·0	0	0	0	0	1·0
38·0	0·43	− 0·86	0·092	− 0·335	1·243

6.29.   Load in AB: $M_A = \dfrac{19}{41}\left(M_{FAB} + \dfrac{5}{19} M_{FBA} \right)$

$$M_B = \dfrac{21}{41}\left(M_{FBA} + \dfrac{2}{7} M_{FAB} \right) = - 3M_C$$

Load in BC: $M_B = \dfrac{20}{41}\left(M_{FBC} + \dfrac{1}{5} M_{FCB} \right) = - 4M_A$

270

$$M_C = \frac{26}{41}\left(M_{FCB} + \frac{7}{26} M_{FBC}\right)$$

Load in CD: $M_C = \frac{15}{41}\left(M_{FCD} + \frac{1}{2} M_{FDC}\right) = -\frac{15}{4} M_B = 15M_C$

6.30. Influence line for M_A: $\theta_A = \pm 1$; $\theta_B = \mp 0.268$; $\theta_C = \pm 0.072$;

$$\theta_D = \pm 0.019;\ \theta_E = \pm 0.006;\ \theta_F = \mp 0.003.$$

Influence line for M_C: $\theta_A = 0$; $\theta_B = \mp 0.124$; $\theta_{CB} = \pm 0.497$;

$$\theta_{CD} = \pm 0.503;\ \theta_D = \mp 0.135;\ \theta_E = \pm 0.039;$$

$$\theta_F = \mp 0.019.$$

6.31. $M_A = M_C = 500$ lb. in.; $M_B = 1,500$ lb. in.

6.32. $M_A = 1,734$ lb. ft.; $M_B = 1,460$ lb. ft.

6.33. $M_A = 360Ed/71L_2$; $M_B = 252Ed/71L_2$.

6.34. $\theta = 5M/72EK$.

6.35. $M_{AB} = 2EK\left(\dfrac{20}{11}\theta_{AB} + \dfrac{8}{11}\theta_{BA} - \dfrac{28}{11}\dfrac{\delta}{L}\right)$

$$M_{BA} = 2EK\left(\frac{12}{11}\theta_{BA} + \frac{8}{11}\theta_{AB} - \frac{20}{11}\frac{\delta}{L}\right)$$

6.36. $M_A = 6,770$ lb. ft.; $M_B = 830$ lb. ft.; $M_C = 1,660$ lb. ft.

6.37. $M_B = \dfrac{2nL}{7}(1 - n^2)$; $M_C = \dfrac{1}{2}M_B$.

6.38. $M_B = 33.75$ ton ft.; $M_{CB} = 15$ ton ft.; $M_E = 3.75$ ton ft.; $M_F = 33.1$ ton ft.

6.39. $M_{BA} = +272$ lb. ft.; $M_{BE} = -75$ lb. ft.; $M_{BC} = -197$ lb. ft.;
$M_{CB} = 53$ lb. ft.

6.40. $M_{BA} = +61$ kip. ft.; $M_{BE} = +123$ kip. ft., $M_{BC} = -184$ kip. ft.
$M_{CB} = +153$ kip. ft.; $H_A = 3.1$ kips.; $V_A = 4.5$ kips.

6.41. $M_{BA'} = +30.0L$ kip. ft.; $M_{BE} = +26.1L$ kip. ft.; $M_{BC} = -56.1L$ kip. ft.;
$M_{CB} = +35.4L$ kip. ft.; $M_{CF} = -16.5L$ kip. ft.; $M_{CD'} = -18.9L$ kip. ft.
Tension in $AB = 9.6$ kips.

6.42. $M_{BE} = -21$ ton ft.; $M_{BC} = -14$ ton ft.; $H_E = 2.1$ tons.

6.43. $M_{BA} = -399$ lb. ft.; $M_{BC} = -4549$ lb. ft.; $M_{FB} = +2240$ lb. ft.
$M_D = 4,354$ lb. ft.; $M_E = 1,772$ lb. ft.

6.44. $M_{AB} = -3.16$ ton ft.; $M_{CA} = -2.91$ ton ft.; $M_{CE} = -1.77$ ton ft.

6.45. $M_{AB} = -55.3$ ton ft.; $M_{CA} = +42.3$ ton ft.; $M_{CD} = -57.1$ ton ft.
$M_{DC} = +86.5$ ton ft.

6.46. $M_{EF} = -239$ ton ft.; $M_{FB} = -157$ ton ft.; $M_{FE} = +362$ ton ft.;
$M_{FJ} = -26$ ton ft. $M_{JF} = +262$ ton ft.

6.48. (a) $M_{AB} + M_{BA} + M_{CD} + M_{DC} = 75$ ton ft.

(b) $M_{AB} + M_{BA} + M_{CD} + M_{DC} = 0$

(c) $M_{AB} + M_{BC} + M_{CD} = -375$ kip. ft.

(d) $M_{AB} + M_{CB} + M_{DE} + M_{ED} = -Pa$

(e) $M_{AE} + M_{CD} + M_{DC} = -QL/2.$

(f) $\left.\begin{array}{l} M_{BC} + M_{CB} + M_{DE} + M_{ED} - M_{AB} - M_{BA} = PL \\ M_{BE} + M_{EB} + M_{CD} + M_{DC} - M_{DF} - M_{FD} = 0 \end{array}\right\}$

(g) $\left.\begin{array}{l} M_{AB} + M_{BA} + M_{FG} + M_{GF} = 0 \\ M_{BC} + M_{CB} + M_{DE} + M_{ED} = 0 \\ \dfrac{2}{3}(M_{CD} + M_{DC}) + 2(M_{EF} + M_{FE}) = -PL \end{array}\right\}$

(h) $M_{AD} + M_{DA} + M_{BC} + M_{CB} = -Pb$

(i) $\left.\begin{array}{l} M_{AF} + M_{FA} + M_{BE} + M_{EB} + M_{CD} + M_{DC} = 0 \\ M_{BC} + M_{CB} + M_{DE} + M_{ED} - (M_{AB} + M_{BA} + M_{EF} + M_{FE}) \\ \hspace{8cm} = 1{,}200 \text{ lb. ft.} \end{array}\right\}$

(j) $\left.\begin{array}{l} M_{BE} + M_{EB} + M_{CF} + M_{FC} = -P_1 h_1 \\[2mm] M_{AB} + M_{BA} + M_{CD} + M_{DC} - \dfrac{2h_2}{L\tan\theta}(M_{BC} + M_{CB} + M_{EF} + M_{FE}) \\ \hspace{8cm} = -(P_1 + P_2)h_2 \end{array}\right\}$

(k) $1{\cdot}732 M_{AB} + 2{\cdot}732 M_{BA} + 2M_{CD} = PL$

(l) $\left.\begin{array}{l} \dfrac{1}{4}(M_{AG} + M_{GA} + M_{FM} + M_{MF}) + \dfrac{1}{8}(M_{BH} + M_{HB} + M_{EL} + M_{LE}) \\[2mm] \hspace{2cm} + \dfrac{1}{10}(M_{CJ} + M_{JC} + M_{DK} + M_{KD}) = 0 \\[3mm] M_{AB} + M_{GH} + \dfrac{1}{2}(M_{BA} + M_{HG}) = -3{,}000 \text{ kip. ft.} \\[3mm] M_{BC} + M_{HJ} + \dfrac{8}{10}(M_{CB} + M_{JH}) = -3{,}600 \text{ kip. ft.} \\[3mm] M_{ED} + M_{LK} + \dfrac{8}{10}(M_{DE} + M_{KL}) = 2{,}400 \text{ kip. ft.} \\[3mm] M_{FE} + M_{ML} + \dfrac{1}{2}(M_{EF} + M_{LM}) = 2{,}000 \text{ kip. ft.} \end{array}\right\}$

6.49. $M_{AB} = 16{\cdot}6$ ton ft.; $M_{BA} = 27{\cdot}8$ ton ft.; $M_{BC} = 22{\cdot}2$ ton ft.; $M_{CB} = 0.$

6.50. $M_{AB} = -44$ ton ft.; $M_{BA} = -23$ ton ft.; $M_{CD} = -13$ ton ft.; $M_{DC} = -38$ ton ft.

6.51. $M_{AB} = -0{\cdot}9\,\dfrac{EI\Delta}{L^2}$; $\quad M_{BA} = +0{\cdot}4\,\dfrac{EI\Delta}{L^2}$; $\quad M_{CB} = -0{\cdot}65\,\dfrac{EI\Delta}{L^2}.$

6.52. $M_{AB} = -4{\cdot}5P = -M_{DC}$; $\quad M_{BA} = -1{\cdot}5P = -M_{CD}.$

6.53. $M_{AB} = -31 \cdot 6$ ton ft.; $M_{BA} = +1 \cdot 7$ ton ft.; $M_{CB} = +40 \cdot 1$ ton ft.
$M_{CD} = -33 \cdot 8$ ton ft.

6.54. $M_{AC} = +0 \cdot 0525PL$; $M_{CA} = +0 \cdot 1125PL$; $M_{BD} = -0 \cdot 0575PL$
$M_{DB} = -0 \cdot 108PL$.

6.55.   (a) $M_{\text{torsion}} : M_{\text{bending}} = C : 4EK/N$ (where $C = J/L$)
(b) -1
(c) $M_{AB} = 416$ lb. ft.; $M_{BA} = 833$ lb. ft.; $M_{BC} = 167$ lb. ft.
$M_{CB} = 167$ lb. ft. (M_{BC} and M_{CB} are torsional moments)
(d) $M_{y\,BC} + M_{y\,CB} = M_{z\,BA} + M_{z\,AB}$.

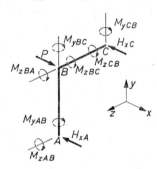

SOLUTION 6.55

6.56. $M_{AB} = -334 \cdot 9$ lb. ft. $M_{BA} = +119 \cdot 7$ lb. ft. $M_{CD} = -33 \cdot 4$ lb. ft.
$M_{DC} = -95 \cdot 6$ lb. ft.

6.57. $M_{AB} = +65 \cdot 8$ kip. ft. $M_{BA} = +131 \cdot 5$ kip. ft. $M_{CD} = -1 \cdot 9$ kip. ft.
$M_{DC} = +1 \cdot 0$ kip. ft.

6.58. $M_{DA} = +2 \cdot 7$ ton ft.; $M_{ED} = +17 \cdot 6$ ton ft.; $M_{EF} = -17 \cdot 8$ ton ft.
$M_{FE} = +2 \cdot 4$ ton ft.; $M_{CF} = -1 \cdot 3$ ton ft.; $M_{BE} = -0 \cdot 1$ ton ft.

6.59. $M_{AD} = +0 \cdot 057PL$; $M_{DA} = +0 \cdot 262PL$; $M_{DE} = +0 \cdot 738PL$
$M_{ED} = +0 \cdot 237PL$; $M_{EB} = -0 \cdot 140PL$; $M_{FE} = +0 \cdot 070PL$
$M_{CF} = -0 \cdot 110PL$.

6.60. $2aM_{AB} + (2a + b)M_{BA} + 2bM_{CD} + bM_{DC} + 2Pab - wbc/2 = 0$ I
$bM_{BC} + 2bM_{CB} + (2a + b)M_{DE} + 2aM_{ED} + wbc/2 = 0$ II
$M_{AB} = 0 \cdot 38Pa$; $M_{BA} = -0 \cdot 24Pa$; $M_{CB} = +0 \cdot 06Pa$; $M_{DE} = -0 \cdot 12Pa$
$M_{ED} = -0 \cdot 25Pa$.

6.61.   Effective stiffness $7K/8$; carry-over factor $-1/7$.
$M_{AB} = -116 \cdot 5 = M_{HG}$; $M_{BA} = -71 \cdot 5 = M_{GH}$
$M_{CB} = +5 \cdot 8 = M_{FD}$; $M_{ED} = -129 \cdot 0$; $M_{DE} = -96 \cdot 0$
$M_{DC} = +48 \cdot 0 = M_{DF}$. (all kip. ft.)

6.62. $M_{BA} = +1{,}037$ lb. ft. $M_{CD} = -123$ lb. ft. $M_{DC} = +206$ lb. ft.

6.63. $M_{AB} = +7$; $M_{BA} = +27$; $M_{BE} = -56$; $M_{CB} = +47$; $M_{DC} = +42$
$M_{ED} = -35$; $M_{EB} = +47$; $M_{FE} = -21$ (all ton ft.)

6.64. $M_{AD} = -130$; $M_{DA} = -106$; $M_{DE} = -60$; $M_{ED} = -57$;
$M_{EH} = -28$; $M_{HE} = -37$; $M_{BC} = -199$; $M_{CB} = -141$;
$M_{CF} = -47$; $M_{FC} = -53$; $M_{FG} = -36$; $M_{GF} = -43$ (all ton ft.)

6.65. $M_{AC} = M_{BD} = -0.13PL$; $M_{CA} = -0.11PL$; $M_{CE} = -0.40PL$;
$M_{EC} = -0.34PL$; $M_{EG} = -0.65PL$; $M_{GE} = -0.59PL$;
$M_{GJ} = -0.76PL$; $M_{JG} = -0.99PL$.

6.66. $M_{AB} = -10.6$; $M_{BA} = -5.9$; $M_{BC} = -8.2$; $M_{CB} = -14.4$
$M_{DE} = -14.7$; $M_{ED} = -6.1$; $M_{EF} = -7.2$; $M_{FE} = -10.6$ (all ton ft.)

6.67. $PL/4\sqrt{2}$; $PL^3/24EI$

6.68. $B = 0.732L$

6.69. $M_{AB} = -44$; $M_{BA} = -74$; $M_{BC} = +70$; $M_{CB} = +49$;
$M_{DA} = +37$; $M_{EB} = +3$; $M_{ED} = -46$; $M_{FE} = +39$. (all ton ft.)

6.70. $M_{A'B'} = -M_{E'D'} = -57.5$; $M_{B'A'} = -55.8$; $M_{B'C'} = -2.4$;
$M_{C'B'} = -32.0$; $M_{AB} = -61.9$; $M_{BA} = -41.0$; $M_{BC} = -16.6$;
$M_{CB} = -21.0$. (all ton ft.)

6.71.† (a) $M_{AB} = \dfrac{5}{14}\left(M_{FAB} + \dfrac{1}{5} M_{FBA}\right)$; $M_{BA} = \dfrac{9}{14}\left(M_{FBA} + \dfrac{1}{3} M_{FAB}\right)$

$M_{BC} = \dfrac{2}{3} M_{BA}$; $M_{CB} = -\dfrac{1}{3} M_{BA}$

(b) $M_{AB} = \dfrac{29}{79}\left(M_{FAB} + \dfrac{8}{29} M_{FBA}\right)$; $M_{BA} = \dfrac{39}{79}\left(M_{FBA} + \dfrac{1}{2} M_{FAB}\right)$

$M_{BC} = \dfrac{5}{13} M_{BA}$; $M_{CB} = -\dfrac{1}{13} M_{BA}$.

6.72.† (a) $M_{BC} = \dfrac{6}{13}\left(M_{FBC} + \dfrac{1}{4} M_{FCB}\right)$; $M_{CB} = \dfrac{7}{13}\left(M_{FCB} + \dfrac{2}{7} M_{FBC}\right)$

$M_{DC} = -\dfrac{1}{2} M_{CB}$

(b) $M_{BC} = \dfrac{9}{17}\left(M_{FBC} + \dfrac{2}{9} M_{FCB}\right)$; $M_{CB} = \dfrac{10}{17}\left(M_{FCB} + \dfrac{1}{4} M_{FBC}\right)$

$M_{CD} = \dfrac{4}{5} M_{CB}$; $M_{DC} = -\dfrac{2}{5} M_{CB}$

(c) $M_{BC} = \dfrac{84}{305}\left(M_{FBC} + \dfrac{8}{21} M_{FCB}\right)$; $M_{CB} = \dfrac{85}{305}\left(M_{FCB} + \dfrac{13}{34} M_{FBC}\right)$

$M_{CD} = \dfrac{2}{5} M_{CB}$; $M_{DC} = -\dfrac{1}{5} M_{CB}$.

6.73.† (a) $M_{AC} = 0.0483PL$; $M_{CA} = 0.0383PL$.
(b) $M_B = 0.045PL$.
(c) Change in $M_B = +0.043PL$.

---

† The solutions to *Problems 6.71–73* inclusive are quoted in the beam-line sign convention.

6.75.   (a) $M_Y = 488$ ton in.; $M_p = 732$ ton in.

      (b) $M_Y = 592$ ton in.; $M_p = 677$ ton in.

6.76.   (a) $6M_p/L$. (b) $4M_p/L$. (c) $5\frac{1}{3} M_p/L$.

6.77. $16/2\pi$; $P = 8M_p/L$.

6.78. $P = 11M_p/3L$.

6.79. $P = 8M_p/3L$.

6.80.   2·94.

CHAPTER 7

7.2.

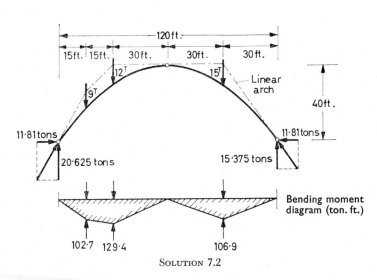

SOLUTION 7.2

7.3.   6·0 ton ft.

7.4.   (a) 88·5 ton ft. (b) 79·5 ton ft.

7.5.   30 tons each.

7.7.

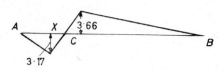

Influence line for bending moment at X (ton, ft.)

SOLUTION 7.7

Maximum positive B.M. at $X = 166$ ton ft.
Maximum negative B.M. at $X = 46$ ton ft.

7.8. + 44 ft. ton ft.
 − 54·5 ft. ton ft.

7.9. Maximum B.M. at $D = 298\frac{3}{4}$ ton ft.
 Corresponding thrust in arch $= 42\frac{1}{12}$ tons.

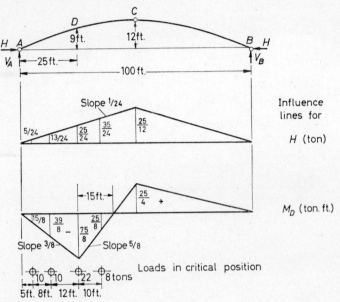

Influence lines for

H (ton)

M_D (ton. ft.)

Loads in critical position

SOLUTION 7.9

7.10.

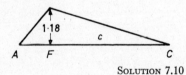

Influence line for F_{DE} (tons)

SOLUTION 7.10

7.12. $\theta = 37°30'$ clockwise from vertical.

7.13. 1·34.

7.14. $H_A = 0·207wL$; $H_D = 0·169wL$.

7.15. 4·2 tons; $6228/EI$ ft.

7.16. $T = \dfrac{80EI_0\alpha_t t}{L^2}$; $\Delta = \dfrac{5\alpha_t tL}{4}$ (upwards).

7.19. (a) $H = \dfrac{12\sqrt{3}Px_1}{L^3}\left(\dfrac{L^2}{8} - \dfrac{x_1^2}{6}\right)$; $M = Px_1\left(\dfrac{1}{4} - \dfrac{x_1^2}{L^2}\right)$

(b) $H = \dfrac{5\sqrt{3}wL}{32}$; $M = \dfrac{wL^2}{64}$

(c) $H = \dfrac{18\sqrt{3}EI\alpha_t t}{L^2}$; $M = \dfrac{9EI\alpha_t t}{L}$

C rises $2\alpha_t tL/\sqrt{3}$ in case (c).

276

7.20.   (a) 0·6024 tons;   − 8·28 ton ft.
       (b) 218 lb;   − 1·46 ton ft.

7.21. $H = 0·338P$; $M_C = 1·1P$.

7.22. $H = \dfrac{a(2R - a)}{\pi R^2}$ tons.

7.23. $\dfrac{pR}{2}$ outwards at B.

7.24.   2·11 tons.

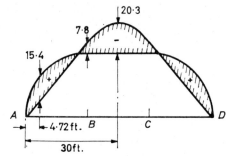

Bending moment
diagram (ton.ft.)

SOLUTION 7.24

7.25.   0·0431P.

7.26.   2·00 tons.

7.27. $H = 5l/2L − 5l^2/2L^2 − 5l^3/L^3 + 10l^4/L^4 − 4l^5/L^5$; $35pL/192$.

7.28. $25PL/128h$;   (a) 97·7 tons.   (b) 97·9 tons.

7.29.   + 181 ton ft.

7.30. $H = 25P/128$.

7.32.   (b) 0·024 ft.   (c) 492 ton ft.

7.34. $H_A = 8·16$ tons, inwards; $V_A = 10·3$ tons, upwards.

7.35. $M_{AB} = 5·47P$ ton ft. $M_{DC} = 6·96P$ ton ft.

7.38.   0·105wR.

7.39.

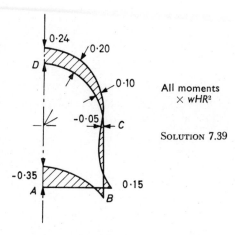

All moments
× wHR²

SOLUTION 7.39

7.40. $\dfrac{1\cdot414pR^2t^2/12}{1\cdot424R^2 + 1\cdot844t^2/12}$

7.41. $M_B = 0\cdot104PL$; $T_B = 0\cdot660P$; $Q_B = 0\cdot197P$.

7.42. (a) $M_A = 0\cdot39P$; $M_B = 1\cdot01P$; $M_C = 0\cdot92P$.
(b) $\varDelta_B = 1\cdot38P/EI_{CD}$ to the right; $\varDelta_C = 4\cdot16P/EI_{CD}$; downwards.

7.43. $M_E = 9PL/128$.

7.44. $M_B = 7PL/30$; $M_D = PL/12$; $M_F = - PL/15$.

7.45. $H = \dfrac{15a^2(L - a)^2}{4hL^3}$; $V_A = \dfrac{(L - a)^2(L + 2a)}{L^3}$

$M_A = \dfrac{a(L - a)^2(2L - 5a)}{2L^3}$

7.46. $5/12$ ton; $2\frac{1}{2}$ ton ft.

7.47. $L/10$.

7.49. (a) $+ 0\cdot091EI$; $- 0\cdot069EI$ (b) $+ 0\cdot008EI$; $- 0\cdot008E$.

7.51. (a) $M_A = M_B = - \dfrac{15\alpha_t tEI_c}{2h}$; $M_c = \dfrac{15\alpha_t tEI_c}{4h}$

(b) $M_A = - \dfrac{3\alpha_t tEI_c}{4hL^2} (5L^2 + 8h^2)$; $M_B = - \dfrac{3\alpha_t tEI_c}{4hL^2} (5L^2 - 8h^2)$

$M_C = 15\alpha_t tEI_C/8h$.

7.52. Due to rotation, 6350 lb./in.^{2} at E.
Due to spread, 1645 lb./in.^{2} at A and E.

7.54. $M_{AB} = - 4\cdot875$; $M_{CA} = 7\cdot125$; $M_{CE} = 25\cdot875$;
$M_{CF} = - 33\cdot000$; $M_{EC} = - 23\cdot625$; $M_{FC} = - 34\cdot500$. (All in ton ft.)

7.55. (a) $M_{DB} = + 279$. $M_{EC} = - 257$.
$M_{BD} = + 371$. $M_{D'B'} = - 51$.
$M_{CA} = + 376$.
$M_{CE} = - 349$.
(b) $M_{CD} = + 919$. $M_{C'B'} = - 687$.
$M_{CF} = - 1100$. $M_{C'F'} = - 147$.
$M_{CB} = + 182$. $M_{C'D'} = + 835$.

(All moments in Kip. ft.)

CHAPTER 8

8.5. (a) $1\cdot813 \times 10^6$ lb. in./radian.   (b) $59\cdot0$ lb./in.
(c) 446,000 lb. in./radian.   (d) 782,000 lb. in./radian.
(e) $- 80\cdot3$ lb./in.   (f) 2410 lb./in.

The critical load has not been exceeded except in case (e) where the minus sign shows that if the deflexion is to the right a force must be applied towards the left to prevent failure.

(a) $2\cdot4 \times 10^6$ lb./in. radian.   (b) 180 lb./in.
(c) $1\cdot2 \times 10^6$ lb. in./radian.   (d) $1\cdot8 \times 10^6$ lb. in./radian.
(e) 45 lb./in.   (f) 2880 lb./in.

278

8.6. $\Delta = 5 \cdot 04$ in., $\theta = 0 \cdot 0124$ radian.

8.8.   (b) 48,000 lb.   (c) 75,000 lb.

8.14.   Deflexion at centre of strut when $F = 0$ is $\dfrac{QL^3}{48EI}$. When F is applied the deflexion is magnified by the factor $\left(\dfrac{1}{1 - \dfrac{F}{P_E}}\right)$ [see equation 8.15, Volume I].

8.15. $sk(1 - c) + K = 0$;   21,650 lb.

8.16.   1230 lb.

8.17.   10,450 lb.

8.20.   28,000 lb.

8.21.   27,000 lb.

8.25. $M_P = 2{,}590{,}000$ lb. in., $F_y = 636{,}000$ lb., $M'_P = 1{,}590{,}000$ lb. in.
$M'_P = 2{,}450{,}000$ lb. in.

8.26.   Both solutions coincide and are shown in the figure.

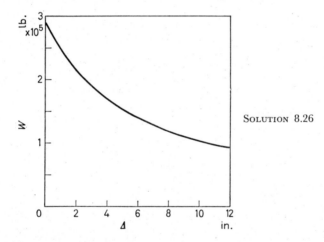

SOLUTION 8.26

8.28.   (a) $3\sqrt{3}EI\delta_1/L^2$. (b) 0. (c) $4EI\theta/\sqrt{3}L$.

8.29. $M_{AB} = - M_{AD} = 0 \cdot 60$ ton in. $M_{DA} = - M_{DC} = - 1 \cdot 65$ ton in.
$M_{BA} = - M_{BC} = - 8 \cdot 42$ ton in. $M_{BD} = M_{DB} = 0$.

8.30. $M_{AE} = - 10{,}000$ lb. in. $M_{DA} = + 5100$ lb. in.
$M_{DE} = - 5900$ lb. in. $M_{DC} = + 800$ lb. in.
$M_{ED} = - 7000$ lb. in. $M_{EA} = - 16{,}600$ lb. in.

8.31. $f_{AF} = f_{AC} = 22 \cdot 6$ lb./sq. in. $f_{CF} = 23 \cdot 3$ lb./sq. in.
$f_{FA} = 26 \cdot 0$ lb./sq. in. $f_{FC} = 2 \cdot 4$ lb./sq. in.
$f_{CA} = 81 \cdot 0$ lb./sq. in. $f_{DC} = 32 \cdot 0$ lb./sq. in.
$f_{CD} = 57 \cdot 7$ lb./sq. in.

279

CHAPTER 9

9.1.

(i)

$$\begin{bmatrix} 5 & -7 \\ 9 & -11 \\ 13 & -15 \end{bmatrix}$$

(ii)

$$\begin{bmatrix} 3 & -3 \\ 3 & -3 \\ 3 & -3 \end{bmatrix}$$

(iii)

$$\begin{bmatrix} 14 & 20 & 26 \\ 32 & 46 & 60 \\ 50 & 72 & 94 \end{bmatrix}$$

(iv)

$$\begin{bmatrix} 62 & -80 \\ -71 & 92 \end{bmatrix}$$

(v)

$$x_1 = 0 \cdot 44167$$
$$x_2 = 1 \cdot 48333$$
$$x_3 = -0 \cdot 86389$$

(vi)

$$\begin{bmatrix} 3 & 42 & -27 \\ 78 & 12 & 18 \\ -67 & 22 & 3 \end{bmatrix} /360$$

9.5. If moments due to axial forces are ignored, equations 9.7 still hold for a general member of a frame, where the symbols F, D and Y now indicate the normal 3-vectors and 3×3 matrices associated with such a member, and where

$$G_1 = \begin{bmatrix} 1 & 0 & 0 \\ 0 & 1 & g_1 \\ 0 & 0 & 1 \end{bmatrix} \qquad G_2 = \begin{bmatrix} 1 & 0 & 0 \\ 0 & 1 & -g_2 \\ 0 & 0 & 1 \end{bmatrix}$$

The rule

$$Y'_{ij} = T^{-1} Y_{ij} T$$

applies unchanged to the modified matrices.

9.6.   If the concentrated loads on the beams are replaced by equivalent forces and moments at A and B, the equations of equilibrium for these joints are

$$
\begin{bmatrix} 25 \\ 10L/8 \\ \cdots \\ 15 \\ -30L/8 \end{bmatrix} = \begin{bmatrix} (24EI/L^3 + k) & 0 & \cdot & -12EI/L^3 & 6EI/L^2 \\ 0 & 8EI/L & \cdot & -6EI/L^2 & 2EI/L \\ \cdots & \cdots & \cdot & \cdots & \cdots \\ -12EI/L^3 & -6EI/L^2 & \cdot & (24EI/L^3 + k) & 0 \\ 6EI/L^2 & 2EI/L & \cdot & 0 & 8EI/L \end{bmatrix} \begin{bmatrix} y_A \\ \theta_A \\ \cdots \\ y_B \\ \theta_B \end{bmatrix}
\qquad (9.12)
$$

9.7.   If k is very large, y_A and y_B will be very small, and may be ignored except when multiplied by k. (Note that ky_A, ky_B are in fact the reactions at the supports). Thus the second and fourth equations of 9.12 become

$$
\begin{bmatrix} 10L/8 \\ -30L/8 \end{bmatrix} = \begin{bmatrix} 8EI/L & 2EI/L \\ 2EI/L & 8EI/L \end{bmatrix} \begin{bmatrix} \theta_A \\ \theta_B \end{bmatrix}
$$

with the solution

$$
\theta_A = \frac{7L^2}{24EI}; \quad \theta_B = -\frac{13L^2}{24EI}
$$

The first and third equations become

$$
25 = ky_A + (6EI/L^2)\theta_B
$$
$$
15 = -(6EI/L^2)\theta_A + ky_B
$$

Thus the reactions are

$$
R_A = ky_A = 25 + \frac{6EI}{L^2} \times \frac{13L^2}{24EI} = 28{\cdot}25 \text{ tons.}
$$

$$
R_B = ky_B = 15 + \frac{6EI}{L^2} \times \frac{7L^2}{24EI} = 16{\cdot}75 \text{ tons.}
$$

9.9.   The complete stiffness matrix is

$$
\begin{bmatrix} \frac{(3+\sqrt{3})}{4} \times \frac{EA}{L} + \frac{(17+9\sqrt{3})}{16} \times \frac{12EI}{L^3} & 0 & -\frac{(5+3\sqrt{3})}{4} \times \frac{6EI}{L^2} \\ 0 & \frac{(5+3\sqrt{3})}{4} \times \frac{EA}{L} + \frac{(3+3\sqrt{3})}{16} \times \frac{12EI}{L^3} & 0 \\ -\frac{(5+3\sqrt{3})}{4} \times \frac{6EI}{L^2} & 0 & (2+\sqrt{3}) \times \frac{4EI}{L} \end{bmatrix}
$$

9.10.   If the members are pinned at their ends, we have $I = 0$ effectively. Substituting this in the solution to *Problem 9.9* we obtain the load-displacement equations

$$
\begin{bmatrix} 100/\sqrt{2} \\ -100/\sqrt{2} \end{bmatrix} = \frac{EA}{L} \begin{bmatrix} \frac{3+\sqrt{3}}{4} & 0 \\ 0 & \frac{5+3\sqrt{3}}{4} \end{bmatrix} \begin{bmatrix} x' \\ y' \end{bmatrix}
$$

whence

$$x' = \frac{400}{\sqrt{2}(3 + \sqrt{3})} \times \frac{L}{EA}; \quad y' = \frac{-400}{\sqrt{2}(5 + 3\sqrt{3})} \times \frac{L}{EA}$$

If we set up a new coordinate system, x, y, with x-axis along FA, our displacements x, y in this system are given by

$$\begin{bmatrix} x \\ y \end{bmatrix} = \begin{bmatrix} \cos 150° & \sin 150° \\ -\sin 150° & \cos 150° \end{bmatrix} \begin{bmatrix} x' \\ y' \end{bmatrix}$$

whence $\qquad x = \dfrac{\sqrt{3}}{2} x' + \dfrac{1}{2} y'$

$$= -\frac{400L}{2EA} \left[\frac{3}{\sqrt{2}(3 + \sqrt{3})} + \frac{1}{\sqrt{2}(5 + 3\sqrt{3})} \right]$$

Hence the tensile force is

$$\frac{200}{\sqrt{2}} \left[\frac{1}{1 + \sqrt{3}} + \frac{1}{5 + 3\sqrt{3}} \right] = 65 \cdot 6 \text{ Kips.}$$

9.11

(a) The load-displacement equations are

$$\begin{bmatrix} P_1 \\ P_2 \\ P_3 \\ P_4 \end{bmatrix} = \begin{bmatrix} (Y'_{22})_a + (Y'_{11})_e + (Y'_{11})_f & (Y'_{12})_f & 0 & (Y'_{12})_e \\ (Y'_{21})_f & (Y'_{22})_b + (Y'_{22})_f + (Y'_{11})_g & (Y'_{12})_g & 0 \\ 0 & (Y'_{21})_g & (Y'_{22})_c + (Y'_{22})_g + (Y'_{11})_h & (Y'_{12})_h \\ (Y'_{21})_e & 0 & (Y'_{21})_h & (Y'_{22})_d + (Y'_{22})_e + (Y'_{22})_h \end{bmatrix} \begin{bmatrix} \Delta_1 \\ \Delta_2 \\ \Delta_3 \\ \Delta_4 \end{bmatrix}$$

(Note that since the frame is a 3-dimensional one, each symbol represents a 6-vector or a 6×6 matrix.)

(b) The load displacement equations are

$$\begin{bmatrix} P_1 \\ P_2 \\ P_3 \end{bmatrix} = \begin{bmatrix} Y'_a + Y'_e + Y'_g & -Y'_g & -Y'_e \\ -Y'_g & Y'_d + Y'_f + Y'_g & -Y'_f \\ -Y'_e & -Y'_f & Y'_b + Y'_c + Y'_e + Y'_f \end{bmatrix} \begin{bmatrix} \Delta_1 \\ \Delta_2 \\ \Delta_3 \end{bmatrix}$$